Protein

The Practical Approach Series

SERIES EDITORS

D. RICKWOOD
Department of Biology, University of Essex
Wivenhoe Park, Colchester, Essex CO4 3SQ, UK

B. D. HAMES
Department of Biochemistry and Molecular Biology
University of Leeds, Leeds LS2 9JT, UK

Affinity Chromatography

Anaerobic Microbiology

Animal Cell Culture
(2nd Edition)

Animal Virus
Pathogenesis

Antibodies I and II

Behavioural Neuroscience

Biochemical Toxicology

Biological Data Analysis

Biological Membranes

Biomechanics—Materials

Biomechanics—Structures
and Systems

Biosensors

Carbohydrate Analysis

Cell–Cell Interactions

The Cell Cycle

Cell Growth and
Division

Cellular Calcium

Cellular Interactions in
Development

Cellular Neurobiology

Centrifugation (2nd Edition)

Clinical Immunology

Computers in Microbiology

Crystallization of Nucleic
Acids and Proteins

Cytokines

The Cytoskeleton

Diagnostic Molecular
Pathology I and II

Directed Mutagenesis

DNA Cloning I, II, and III

Drosophila

Electron Microscopy in
Biology

Electron Microscopy in
Molecular Biology

Protein Blotting

A Practical Approach

Edited by
BONNIE S. DUNBAR
*Department of Cell Biology, Baylor
College of Medicine, Houston*

OXFORD UNIVERSITY PRESS
Oxford New York Tokyo

Oxford University Press, Walton Street, Oxford OX2 6DP
Oxford   New York   Toronto
Delhi   Bombay   Calcutta   Madras   Karachi
Kuala Lumpur   Singapore   Hong Kong   Tokyo
Nairobi   Dar es Salaam   Cape Town
Melbourne   Auckland   Madrid
and associated companies in
Berlin   Ibadan

Oxford is a trade mark of Oxford University Press

A Practical Approach 🔵 is a registered trade mark
of the Chancellor, Masters, and Scholars of the University of Oxford
trading as Oxford University Press

Published in the United States
by Oxford University Press Inc., New York

© Oxford University Press, 1994

A catalogue record for this book is available from the British Library

Library of Congress Cataloging-in-Publication Data
Protein blotting: a practical approach / edited by Bonnie S. Dunbar.
(The Practical approach series; 140)
Includes bibliographical references and index.
1. Western immunoblotting—Laboratory manuals.   I. Dunbar, Bonnie S.
II. Series.
[DNLM: 1. Blotting, Western.   2. Proteins—analysis.   QU P9654 1994]
QP519.9W47P765   1994   574.19'245—dc20   93–42043
ISBN 0 19 963438 6 (Hbk)
ISBN 0 19 963437 8 (Pbk)

Typeset by Cambrian Typesetters, Frimley, Surrey
Printed in Great Britain by
Information Press Ltd, Eynsham, Oxford

Preface

Protein blotting techniques have become common laboratory procedures in the past few years. The versatility of the methods utilizing these procedures has brought about the development of different solid support matrices as well as a wide variety of protein detection methods. While the most commonly used method in protein blotting is the use of antibodies to detect protein antigens, this technology has been expanded to examine a number of different interactions between proteins and other proteins as well as other molecules such as carbohydrates and DNA. These methods have further been adapted for amino acid sequencing and purification of proteins for use as immunogens. Because of the heterogeneity of different proteins, the optimization of these methods for individual uses may vary markedly. The purpose of this text is to outline protocols and procedures which should help investigators design methods which will be optimal for their specific use.

Houston   B.S.D.
March 1994

Contents

Contents

5. Protein blotting using semi-dry electrophoretic transfer equipment

Gunilla Jacobson

Contents

Contents

Contents

SECTION 3. DETECTION METHODS AND USES IN IMMUNOBLOTTING

Contents

SECTION 4. APPLICATIONS OF PROTEIN BLOTTING

Contents

16. Amino acid sequence analysis of blotted proteins   207

Richard G. Cook

17. Renaturative catalytic blotting of enzyme proteins   221

Jia-Shi Zhu and Gary M. Gray

Contents

Contributors

MICHEL BINOUX
Institut National de la Santé et de la Recherche Médicale, Unité 142, Hôpital Saint Antoine, Paris, France.

RICHARD G. COOK
Department of Microbiology and Immunology, Baylor College of Medicine, Houston, TX 77030, USA.

ANTONIO DE MAIO
Division of Pediatric Surgery, Johns Hopkins University, School of Medicine, 600 North Wolfe Street, CMSC 7–116, Baltimore, MD 21287–3716, USA.

BONNIE S. DUNBAR
Department of Cell Biology, Baylor College of Medicine, Houston, TX 77030, USA.

IAN DURRANT
Research and Development, Amersham International plc, Amersham, Buckinghamshire, UK.

CONSTANTIN N. FLYTZANIS
Department of Cell Biology, Baylor College of Medicine, Houston, TX 77030, USA.

SUE FOWLER
Research and Development, Amersham International plc, Amersham, Buckinghamshire, UK.

REINHARD ERICH GEIGER
Universität München, Abteilung für Klinische Chemie und Klinische Biochemie, Chirurgische Klinik, Innenstadt, Germany.

J. M. GERSHONI
Department of Cell Research and Immunology, Tel Aviv University, Ramat-Aviv, Israel.

GARY M. GRAY
The Digestive Disease Center (MSLS, P304), Stanford University School of Medicine, Stanford, CA 94305–5487, USA.

DAVID R. HARPER
Department of Virology, Medical College of Bartholomew's Hospital, 51–53 Bartholomew Close, London EC1A 7BE, UK.

PAUL HOSSENLOPP
Institut National de la Santé et de la Recherche Médicale, Unité 142, Hôpital Saint Antoine, Paris, France.

Contributors

TATSURO IRIMURA
Division of Chemical Toxicology and Immunochemistry, Faculty of Pharmaceutical Sciences, University of Tokyo, Bunkyo-ku, Tokyo 113, Japan.

GUNILLA JACOBSON
Pharmacia LKB Biotechnology, Uppsala, Sweden.

HIROTO KAWASHIMA
Division of Chemical Toxicology and Immunochemistry, Faculty of Pharmaceutical Sciences, University of Tokyo, Bunkyo-ku, Tokyo 113, Japan.

R. A. LASKEY
Wellcome/CRC Institute, Tennis Court Road, Cambridge CB2 1QR, UK and Department of Zoology, University of Cambridge, UK.

VAUGHAN H. LEE
Department of Cell Biology, Baylor College of Medicine, Houston, TX 77030, USA.

MICHAEL A. MANSFIELD
Millipore Corporation, 80 Ashby Road, Bedford, MA 01730, USA.

DAVID W. SAMMONS
Veterinary Science Department, University of Arizona, Tucson, AZ, USA.

BOGUSLAW SZEWCZYK
Department of Biochemistry, University of Gdansk, Kladki 24, PL–80–822 Gdansk, Poland.

A. VAN DAM
Department of Medical Microbiology, University of Amsterdam, Meibergdreef 15, 1105 A2 Amsterdam, The Netherlands.

JIA-SHI ZHU
The Digestive Disease Center (MSLS, P304), Stanford University School of Medicine, Stanford, CA 94305–5487, USA.

Abbreviations

BCIP	bromochloroindoyl phosphate disodium salt
BSA	bovine serum albumin
CFA	complete Freund's adjuvant
CHAPS	(3-(3-chloramidopropyl)dimethyl ammonio)-1-propane sulphonate
ConA	conconavalin A agglutinin
DAB	diaminobenzidine
DNA	deoxyribonucleic acid
DONS	dioytylsulphosuccinate
DTT	dithiothreitol
ECA	erythrina cristagalli agglutinin
EDTA	ethylenediamine tetra-acetate
EGF	epidermal growth factor
ELISA	enzyme linked immunoabsorbent assay
LPA	limulus polyphemus agglutinin
HPLC	high pressure liquid chromatography
HRP	horseradish peroxidase
IEF	isoelectric focusing
IFA	incomplete Freund's adjuvant
IgG	immunoglobulin
NBT	Nitroblue tetrazolium
NC	nitrocellulose
PBS	phosphate buffered saline
PVDF	polyvinylidene fluoride
PAGE	polyacrylamide gel electrophoresis
PNA	peanut agglutinin
PVP	polyvinyl pyrrolidone
PPO	2,5-diphenyloxazole
RCA	ricinus communis
SDS	sodium dodecyl sulphate
TMB	tetramethylbenzidine
TCA	trichloroacetic acid
TMPTMA	2-ethyl-2(hydroxymethyl)-1,3 propanediol
TNF	tumour necrosis factor
2D-PAGE	two-dimensional polyacrylamide gel electrophoresis
WGA	wheat germ agglutinin

1

Historical introduction

J. M. GERSHONI

In 1975 Southern published his method for the identification of specific DNA fragments which had been resolved by gel electrophoresis *via* transfer of the band pattern to nitrocellulose membrane filters (1). This technique immediately gained recognition, proving to be a milestone in molecular biology, and has since been referred to as Southern blotting. It was not long thereafter that a new technique was developed in which the macromolecule to be analysed was RNA, also immobilized to a filter matrix; this technique was coined Northern blotting (2). The geographical fever continued and in 1979 blotting technology turned west, and protein blotting (since known as Western blotting) evolved. During the years 1979–80 seven articles appeared, all of which illustrated that electrophoresed proteins can be transferred to nitrocellulose or other filter media and analysed using various probes such as lectins and antibodies (3–9). In this manner specific glycoproteins or antigens could be identified, greatly enhancing the use and importance of protein gel electrophoresis.

Witness to the huge success of protein blotting as a cardinal analytical tool is the fact that Towbin's original article (3) is still routinely cited thousands of times a year and since our first review in 1983 (10) tens of reviews have appeared to be followed by numerous books devoted to this technology. In some respects blotting has afforded to the protein biologist a 'third' dimension to gel electrophoresis.

Whereas undoubtedly the 'classical' use of protein blotting is immunodetection of antigen-containing polypeptides, the diversity of other applications is nothing less than exciting. Blotted proteins have been probed with almost anything that can selectively bind peptide motifs. Thus ligands ranging from nucleotides such as GTP and calcium ions to snake-derived toxins, hormones, viruses, and even whole cells, have all been found to be amenable to blot analyses (11)! The concept of ligand overlay of protein blots has opened up new avenues, not only to the discovery of receptors but also to dissect out their functional domains.

Moreover, new concepts for solid-phase methods in protein chemistry have employed protein blotting, and the direct sequencing of blotted peptides and analyses of their enzymatic activities have all broadened the field of this methodology. The direct result of these innovations has been the development of substantial commercial interest, and no respectable supplier of chemicals and tools for modern biologists can escape the need to provide an elaborate range of reagents and devices to cater for both the amateur and professional blottologist alike.

This book will undoubtedly be an extremely useful addition to the blot literature providing the latest advances and tricks of the trade. In doing so it will surely continue to inspire innovations not yet conceived.

References

1. Southern, E. M. (1975). *J. Mol. Biol.*, **98**, 503.
2. Alwine, J. C., Kemp, D. J., and Stark, G. R. (1977). *Proc. Natl. Acad. Sci., USA*, **74**, 5350.
3. Towbin, H., Staehelin, T., and Gordin, J. (1979). *Proc. Natl. Acad. Sci., USA*, **76**, 4350.
4. Erlich, H. A., Levinson, J. R., Cohen, S. N., and McDevitt, H. O. (1979). *J. Biol. Chem.*, **245**, 12240.
5. Renart, J., Reiser, J., and Stark, G. R. (1979). *Proc. Natl. Acad. Sci., USA*, **76**, 116.
6. Bittner, M., Kupferer, P., and Morris, C. F. (1980). *Anal. Biochem.*, **102**, 459.
7. Bowen, B., Steinberg, J., Laemmli, U. K., and Weintraub, H. (1980). *Nucleic Acids Res.*, **8**, 1.
8. Schaltman, K. and Pongs, O. (1980). *Hoppe-Seylers Z. Physiol. Chem.*, **361**, 207.
9. Stellwag, E. J. and Dahlberg, A. E. (1980). *Nucleic Acids Res.*, **8**, 299.
10. Gershoni, J. M. and Palade, G. E. (1983). *Anal. Biochem.*, **131**, 1.
11. Gershoni, J. M. (1988). *Meth. Biochem. Anal.*, **33**, 1.

SECTION 1

Basic Equipment and Methods for Protein Blotting

Introduction and basic set-up for protein transfer

BONNIE S. DUNBAR

1. Introduction

Since the first studies on the electrophoretic transfer of proteins from acrylamide or other gels to paper or membrane 'matrices', there have been numerous modifications to the types of equipment used for these purposes. Detailed studies have also been carried out which include the development of methods for sample preparation and the electrophoretic separation of complex protein samples and for the transfer techniques and renaturation of molecules. The modifications of methods for specific techniques illustrate the need for an in-depth understanding of the basic principles of protein transfer techniques. The fact that no single method will be suitable for every experimental need is emphasized throughout this text. It will also become apparent that different investigators have had markedly different success in the use of different techniques, depending on their specific proteins and experimental design.

2. Equipment

2.1 Basic equipment for one- and two-dimensional polyacrylamide gel electrophoresis (PAGE) prior to protein transfer

The basic equipment for separation of proteins by PAGE is commercially available from a variety of sources. Descriptions of this equipment and sources of supply have been given in great detail elsewhere (1–3). Numerous commercial sources of equipment are now available, but there are limitations as well as advantages to the design of different types of equipment. There are some basic guidelines that greatly affect the quality of protein separation and subsequent electrophoretic transfer of proteins.

2.1.1 Equipment for one-dimensional PAGE

Extensive studies into the separation of proteins using electrophoresis methods led to the development of sodium dodecyl sulphate (SDS) polyacrylamide gel electrophoresis (see review by Dunbar (1)). The methods outlined by Laemmli (4) increased the popularity of SDS-PAGE, which has now become a routine laboratory procedure. One of the greatest advances of PAGE for protein transfer in one-dimensional (1D) PAGE (but *not* two-dimensional (2D) PAGE) has been the optimization of the 'mini-gel' apparatus now available from many commercial suppliers. The major advantage of the mini-gel equipment is the reduced time for protein separation by electrophoresis and the efficiency of electrophoretic transfer of proteins from the 'thinner' acrylamide gel matrix. One potential drawback to the use of mini-gels is that the sample volume is limited, therefore inadequate solubilization prior to electrophoresis is common. (Guidelines for optimizing solubilization conditions are given in Chapter 7.)

2.1.2 Equipment for two-dimensional PAGE

The use of high-resolution two-dimensional polyacrylamide gel electro-phoresis (separation in the first dimension by isoelectric focusing (IEF) and in the second dimension by SDS-PAGE) has greatly improved the separation and characterization of proteins by electrophoresis. The lack of general knowledge about protein solubilization for IEF has greatly limited the general use of new techniques, therefore limiting the use of this powerful technique. The 2D-PAGE system first described by O'Farrell (5) was optimized and standardized due to the extensive work of N. and L. Anderson and their colleagues (2, 3). These standardized techniques include the simultaneous casting of multiple isoelectric focusing gels and slab acrylamide gels; they are outlined in great detail elsewhere and will not be covered in this text (1, 2, 3, 6). Although there are a number of commercially available 2D-PAGE systems, only a few meet the standardized criteria outlined by these methods (for example, Integrated Separation Systems, Hyde Park, MA, USA). Other systems have been optimized for maximum separation of proteins using the large gel format (Millipore Inc., Bedford, MA, USA). While these gel systems may give excellent resolution of proteins and precast gels are available, these procedures are generally expensive and are not practical for routine laboratory procedures. The 'large gel' format has been optimized for resolution of proteins, but the improved resolution does not give substantially better resolution of proteins to justify the increased time and cost of using the large format on a routine basis.

While the mini-gel system is excellent for 1D-PAGE analyses, it is frequently inadequate for resolution of proteins by 2D-PAGE. It is generally not possible to concentrate a complex protein sample for optimal solubiliza-tion in a volume that is compatible with the quantity of ampholines in the IEF

6

gel matrix. Many artifacts are obtained using the mini-2D-PAGE systems which are never observed using the standardized gel systems.

2.2 Protein equipment for the electrophoretic transfer of proteins

To date, numerous companies provide equipment for the electrophoretic transfer of proteins from acrylamide gels to solid matrices such as nitro-cellulose and polyvinylfluoride membranes. There are two basic types of electrophoretic transfer systems: the 'tank' buffer apparatus and the semi-dry blotting apparatus. These types of equipment have slightly different uses and it is advisable to maintain both types for optimization of different experiments.

2.2.1 The 'tank' buffer system (see *Figure 1*)

These set-ups have been designed from the first reports which demonstrated the successful transfer of proteins to membranes and their subsequent detection by antibodies (see reviews by Towbin *et al.* (7), Gershoni and Palade (8), Dunbar (1, 9), and Bers and Garfin (10). This type of electrophoresis apparatus is basically simple, in that an electrophoretic field is generated to transfer proteins and other macromolecules from a matrix such as agarose or acrylamide to a more stable and permanent matrix such as nitrocellulose paper or nylon membrane. The transfer cassette is submerged in a 'tank' of buffer for electrophoretic transfer of proteins.

Generally, it is necessary to use this apparatus with an efficient cooling system since some transfer conditions require this. For example, the transfer in the absence of methanol which is required for some procedures results in

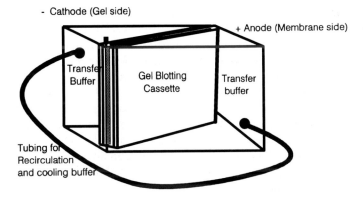

Figure 1. Diagram of standard 'tank' buffer system for protein transfer. The acrylamide gel is placed on the membrane and is tightly compressed in the cassette. Filter paper and sponge material may be used to ensure close contact of the gel on the membrane. If long transfer periods are used, it is recommended that the buffer be recirculated and cooled.

the swelling of the acrylamide gel during transfer. This problem can easily be overcome if adequate cooling and buffer recirculation is used. This type of apparatus is commercially available from numerous vendors including E-C Apparatus Corporation, St Petersburg, FL, USA, Hoeffer Scientific Instruments, San Francisco, CA, USA, BioRad Laboratories, Richmond, CA, USA, or Integrated Separation Systems, Hyde Park, MA, USA. It is sometimes beneficial to add additional quantities of platinum wire to the electrodes of some of these instruments for optimal performance in the electrophoretic transfer of proteins.

2.2.2 The 'semi-dry blotting' system

The semi-dry blotting system and its transfer efficiency are described in detail in Chapter 5 of this text. These systems utilize two graphic plate electrodes instead of the wire electrodes. Because these systems require small quantities of buffer, they are generally more inexpensive. We have found that this system is reproducibly excellent for the mini-acrylamide polyacrylamide gels but is much less efficient for the large-scale polyacrylamide gels (especially the 10–20% acrylamide gradient gels). For the latter, we routinely use the tank buffer system with cooling.

3. Buffers and detergents used for the electrophoretic transfer of proteins

As is emphasized by different authors throughout this text, buffer conditions for transfer of proteins may vary with different protocols and are dependent upon the nature of the experiment (for example, amino acid sequencing of peptides versus antigen detection). The choice of buffers as well as the use of methanol will depend on numerous factors including:

(a) the type of gel matrix (i.e. mini- versus large-scale acrylamide gel, percentage acrylamide) used for transfer

(b) the nature of the proteins to be transferred (i.e. relative molecular weight and charge of protein and degree of post-translational modification such as glycosylation and sulphation)

(c) the type of paper or membrane used in the transfer (see discussions in Chapters 3 and 4) and

(d) the need for special buffers to eliminate modifications of proteins such as is required for amino acid sequencing (see discussion in Chapter 16)

In general, we have found that the transfer of large glycoproteins in thick acrylamide gels of 10–20% acrylamide is most efficient in the tank buffer system with buffer recirculation and cooling in the absence of methanol. It is important to note that methanol may rapidly remove SDS from some proteins. Because SDS is a charged detergent, it aids in the electrophoretic

8

transfer of large proteins, especially if they have a basic charge. On the contrary, many small peptides may transfer optimally in the presence of methanol and binding of proteins to some types of membranes may be enchanced by methanol. It is, therefore, usually necessary to try different transfer conditions when you are testing your protein, antibody, etc. (see discussions in other chapters of this text).

4. Types of immobilizing matrices

Numerous types of papers and membranes have been utilized for protein blotting. Again, as discussed in this text, different matrices may be used for different purposes. Nitrocellulose paper (film of nitric acid esterified cellulose) has historically been the most frequently used membrane (see detailed discussions in (1, 10, 11) and Chapter 3). The recent improvements of different types of polyvinylidene fluoride (PVDF) membranes for different purposes have made these more popular (see detailed discussion in Chapter 4). It is important that all investigators take into account the differences of the chemistry of these membranes to ensure that they are using the optimal matrix for their studies.

5. Summary

In summary, this text is designed to provide a collection of comprehensive methodologies for optimal use of protein blotting techniques and to emphasize the need for understanding the basic principles necessary for utilizing these different protocols.

References

1. Dunbar, B. S. (1987). *Two-dimensional electrophoresis and immunological techniques.* Plenum, New York.
2. Anderson, N. G. and Anderson, N. L. (1978). *Anal. Biochem.*, **85**, 331–40.
3. Anderson, N. L. and Anderson, N. G. (1978). *Anal. Biochem.*, **85**, 341–54.
4. Laemmli, U. K. (1970). *Nature*, **277**, 680–8.
5. O'Farrell, P. (1975). *J. Biol. Chem.*, **250**, 4007–21.
6. Dunbar, B. S., Kimura, H., and Timmons, T. M. (1990). *Methods in Enzymology*, Vol. 28, (ed. Deutcher), pp. 441–58. Academic, New York.
7. Towbin, H., Staehelin, T., and Gordon, J. (1979). *Proc. Natl. Acad. Sci., USA*, **76**, 4350–4.
8. Gershoni, J. M. and Palade, G. E. (1982). *Anal. Biochem.*, **124**, 396–405.
9. Timmons, T. and Dunbar, B. S. (1990). *Meth. Enzymol.*, **128**, (ed. M. Deutcher), pp. 679–87. Academic, New York.
10. Bers, G. and Garfin, D. (1985). *BioTechniques*, **3**, 276–88.
11. Burnette, W. N. (1981). *Anal. Biochem.*, **112**, 195–203.

3

Protein blotting and immunoblotting using nitrocellulose membranes

ANTONIO DE MAIO

1. Scope and introduction

During the last decade protein blotting has emerged as a powerful technique for the study of proteins or glycoproteins immobilized on a membrane filter, without the necessity for painful protein purification procedures. The detection of antibody epitopes in total cell homogenates has been without any doubt the preferred application. However, the use of protein blotting has been expanded to other applications such as the detection of receptors through the binding of their respective ligands, physical chemical analysis of protein–protein interactions, and the study of glycoconjugates (see Chapters 12–14 of this text).

Recently I have had the opportunity to introduce protein blotting to many young investigators (students, technicians, physicians, etc.), and to teach them different protocols and applications. Based on this experience I have written this chapter with those unexperienced researchers in mind, who sooner or later will hear their mentors saying 'I think that we should do a Western blot'. This chapter contains protocols for a few applications of protein blotting. The protocols should be seen as a starting point for your own needs, so please feel free to improve them. The major emphasis has been made to key points of the respective procedure that usually make the difference between a successful blot and a 'blotch', the latter defined as an unsuccessful blot (1).

2. Transfer of proteins onto nitrocellulose filters

Since other chapters in this book deal with the theories and practice of electrotransfer, I will simply provide a few comments about the transfer of proteins from gels onto nitrocellulose (NC) membrane filters, including some helpful hints.

2.1 Type of gel to be blotted

The migration of proteins in polyacrylamide gels in the presence of sodium dodecylsulphate (SDS) is a function of their molecular weight depending on the pore size of the gel matrix. The pore size is a function of the degree of crosslinking between the acrylamide molecules which is proportional to the acrylamide and bis-acrylamide concentrations. The size of the pore is also important at the time of eluting the proteins from the gel. In essence, the larger the protein, the slower the transfer; the larger the pore size, the faster the transfer.

The ideal is to make the polyacrylamide gel of a concentration that will match with the characteristics of the protein to be analysed, if that information is known. Alternatively a polyacrylamide gradient gel (between 5 and 15% of polyacrylamide) is usually a good starting point; this will provide superior resolution of the different bands in the gel, and it will render a better correlation between pore size and molecular weight of the proteins to facilitate the even transfer of the protein pattern.

2.2 Preparation of the samples

Detailed methods for sample preparation are outlined in Chapter 7. However, the following observations have been made with respect to the transfer onto NC membranes. One of the most critical parameters that differentiates between a successful blot and a 'blotch' is the quality of the sample whose constituent components are to be separated by electrophoresis prior to blotting. Partial protein degradation by proteolysis is normally reflected by the appearance of a large smear or a band of erroneous molecular weight. Total degradation will give the false impression that the protein is not present in the sample. To avoid these problems, it is important to homogenize the cells or tissues at low temperatures, add protease inhibitors, and avoid cycles of freezing and thawing. It is sometimes advantageous to lyse the cells in a buffer containing non-ionic detergents such as Nonidet P-40 (NP-40) or Triton X-100 (TX-100), rather than buffers containing SDS. SDS will disrupt the cell nucleus resulting in a very viscous lysate which is difficult to manipulate. In addition, non-ionic detergents do not interfere with further analysis of the sample (for example, affinity chromatography or immunoprecipitations). Tissue samples may also be homogenized in buffers containig non-ionic detergents with help of a polytron homogenizer. In some cases, the relative abundance of the target protein is very low, falling below the detection limit of the method. To increase the amount of the target protein in the sample, a crude step of purification (such as subcellular fractionation) is a good solution.

The sample should be mixed with sample buffers for one or two-dimensional electrophoresis as described in Chapter 5. Addition of SDS denatures proteins, making them better substrates for proteases (normally present in the sample). Consequently, incubation at temperatures above 4 °C may result in the loss of the target protein. Boiling the sample accomplishes a better solubilization and denaturation of the proteins, including proteases. However, boiling may impair the renaturation of the protein during the transfer which may be necessary for its subsequent detection.

A set of molecular weight standards should be included among the samples to be electrophoresed and blotted. One suggestion is to use prestained or radiolabelled molecular weight markers, which are commercially available. You also can use non-stained markers and mark them on the blot after staining with Ponceau S reagent (see protein staining procedure).

The edges of the gel as well as the space between samples can be marked by running a dye such as Pyronine Y on the gel. Pyronine Y is dissolved in 10% (v/v) glycerol in water. This pink dye migrates faster than bromophenol blue during electrophoresis, is retained on NC membrane filters after transfer, and is not washed off the blot during probing.

If the same sample will be probed with different reagents, a preparative gel can be made (the sample is loaded in one big well along the top of the gel), and transferred onto a NC filter. Later, the blot is cut into vertical strips. Each strip can then be probed with a different reagent. This technique is excellent for screening monoclonal antibodies. An alternative is to run the samples separated by Pyronine Y. The gel can either be transferred as a unit and the NC cut later; or the gel can be cut first, and each piece of gel transferred onto an individual strip of NC. In either case, the blot or the gel are cut guided by the presence of the pink dye.

Protocol 1. Electrotransfer of proteins from SDS gels onto NC filters (see Appendix 1 for solutions)

1. About 15 min prior to finishing the electrophoresis, fill up the blotting chamber (Hoefer Scientific Instruments or equivalent as described in Chapter 2) with cold blotting buffer (overnight at 4 °C is fine) to a level just above the electrode grid. In addition, fill two trays up to about ½ inch (about 1 cm) with blotting buffer (one of the trays must be large enough to fit the gel support or cassette of the blotting apparatus).

2. Wearing gloves, cut six pieces of Whatman paper just large enough to completely cover the gel, and one piece of NC filter (0.45 Schleicher and Schull, BA 85) of exactly the same size as the gel. Remember to label one corner of the NC filter with a waterproof marker to orientate the samples. It is also convenient to mark the NC with the date of the experiment, type of samples, etc.

3. Remove gels from the glass plates, trim the portions of unused gel as well as the stacking gel. Gels can easily be cut with a gel spacer or firm plastic ruler. Place the blotting gel support (cassette) in the tray

Protocol 1. *Continued*

  containing blotting buffer, centre the sponge pad support (Scotch-brite) and rub it to remove any air bubbles trapped in the sponge.

4. Place three pieces of Whatman paper (wet with transfer buffer) on the sponge, press gently to remove air bubbles (do not rub), and carefully pick up the gel and place it on the pile of filter papers.

5. Wet the NC membrane with transfer buffer by gently floating the membrane on transfer buffer contained in the second tray. Once the NC is completely wet it can be submerged. *This manipulation prevents air trapping inside the NC.* The wet NC filter is placed onto the gel (label toward gel), and lined up (top of the gel with the top of NC filter). From this point on, maintain gentle pressure on the set-up to prevent slippage of the NC; remove any air bubbles trapped between the gel and the NC by rubbing the membrane gently.

6. Place three more pieces of wet Whatman paper on top of the NC membrane, and another sponge pad support. Rub to remove bubbles that may have been trapped in the set-up and snap the other side of the cassette (use rubber bands for extra support). Place the gel sandwich into the blotting chamber.

7. Fill up the chamber with more transfer buffer and proceed with the transfer at 200 mA (constant current) or 40 V (constant voltage). If the former is chosen, the voltage will start around 40 V, and it will gradually decrease to about 25 V by 4 h of transfer. *We did not find any difference in using either constant current or constant voltage during transfer.* Make sure that the NC membrane is on the side of the positive electrode (red). *Proteins are negatively charged due to the SDS. They will migrate toward the positive electrode (anode).*

8. After transfer is completed, turn off the power supply and remove the gel sandwich. The gel can be fixed and stained to check the efficiency of transfer or otherwise discarded. Place NC (blot) on a piece of clean, dry Whatman paper and allow it to air dry if the blot will be stored (usually at room temperature). Otherwise the blot can immediately be stained with Ponceau S reagent to visualize the total protein pattern, or quenched.

2.3 Electrotransfer of proteins onto nitrocellulose filters

A major concern in transferring proteins onto NC is the composition of the transfer buffer. The original protocol by Towbin *et al.* (2), uses a transfer buffer containing methanol, which was added to counteract swelling of the gel. Methanol also decreases gel pore size, removes SDS from proteins, and may precipitate the protein within the gel (3); however, it increases the capacity and the affinity of NC for proteins (1, 4). We have been highly successful using Gershoni's transfer buffer (1, 4) which does not contain methanol (*Figure 1*).

The duration of the transfer is a more complicated issue. It depends upon the concentration of acrylamide in the gel (see gel type) and the electroblotting chamber employed. Using the prototype design by Gershoni (1, 5) which utilizes a gradient electric field, nearly 100% of transfer can be achieved in a period of 2 h (see *Figure 1*). Using a commercially available apparatus, the conditions must be worked out for each type of gel (generally between 2 and 4 h). The best way to achieve that objective is to run several radiolabelled proteins on a gel of the concentration to be used (the proteins can be radiolabelled molecular weight markers or a total cell lysate of metabolically labelled cells). Transfer the gels and remove a strip of NC every hour. At the end of the experiment, dry the transferred gel, as well as an identical gel that was not transferred, and expose the dried gels and the NC strips to X-ray films. This procedure should provide an estimate of the time necessary for a complete transfer of the proteins onto the NC filter.

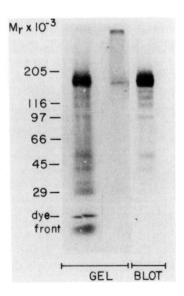

Figure 1. Efficiency in the transfer of proteins from gels onto NC filters using a gradient electric field. Two identical samples of plasma membrane proteins isolated from ^{125}I-surface-labelled mouse thymocytes were subjected to SDS-PAGE (5–15% polyacrylamide gradient slab gel). One lane was dried immediately after electrophoresis (left); the second lane was blotted onto NC filters in an apparatus that generates a gradient electric field between 5 to 40 V, in Gershoni's transfer buffer. Afterwards the blotted gel was dried (centre). The two dried gels and the NC filter were autoradiographed for the same time. Notice the similarity in the electrophoretic pattern between the NC filter and the untransferred gel, and the low radioactivity that remains in the gel after transfer.

The efficiency of transfer is a very important parameter. First, a lack of signal may be due to a deficiency in the transfer of that particular protein. Second, if quantitation of the results is expected (statistical analysis), a reproducible and homogeneous transfer must be obtained. By using the procedure described in the preceding paragraph, an estimation of the efficiency of transfer can be obtained.

3. Staining of blots for total protein pattern

Staining of the blot for the total protein pattern is of interest when the efficiency of transfer is to be evaluated, or when the signal is to be located with respect to other proteins on the gel such as the molecular weight standards.

Several procedures for staining of proteins on NC filters are available. The most recommended is to stain the blots with Ponceau S reagent (6). This procedure gives a clean pattern and, more importantly, the staining is reversible. The latter characteristic is highly valuable when the signal is to be located with respect to the molecular weight markers in order to calculate its relative mobility. The major disadvantage of Ponceau S staining is its low sensitivity.

An application of Ponceau S staining is the preparation of proteins for microsequencing. In this case the blot is stained with Ponceau S, the band of interest is marked, the blot is destained, the piece of NC containing the immobilized protein is excised, and *in situ* digested with a protease. The released peptides are separated by HPLC and sequenced. This methodology described by Aebersold *et al.* (7) has suffered slight modifications depending on the expert in charge. The major advantage of this technique in the United States is that there are several Core Microsequencing Facilities in the country that can perform the analysis, if the piece of NC filter containing the immobilized protein is provided.

If sensitivity is the goal for blot staining, a methodology based on colloidal gold solution is probably the method of choice since this technique is capable of detecting down to 100 pg of protein (8). This reagent is easy to use and commercially available. The total pattern of proteins can also be obtained by staining the blots with Amido Black (2), Coomassie Blue R-250 (9), and India ink (10).

Protocol 2. Staining of proteins with Ponceau S

1. Add enough Ponceau S staining solution (0.1% Ponceau S dye in 7% trichloroacetic acid (TCA) in water) in a plastic container or Pyrex dish, place the blot onto the surface of the solution and slowly allow the blot to absorb the reagent uniformly, then submerge the blot into the staining solution, and incubate for 1 to 5 additional minutes.

---

2. Pour off the staining reagent, and rinse the blot extensively with water until a clear contrast between the bands (pink) and background (white) is observed. Be careful! If the blot is washed with water for too long the colour on the bands will also disappear. If the blot is to be totally destained, just rinse the blot extensively with more water until the colour of the bands disappears. If the blot was stained to visualize the molecular weight markers or any other protein, the bands of interest can be marked with a pencil on the blot before destaining. If the protein pattern is to be permanent, the blot should be washed with 25% isopropyl alcohol: 10% acetic acid. The last consideration: if you plan to stain the blot, do so before quenching.

4. Immunostaining of blots

Protein blotting, as any other art, does not have standard rules to produce a masterpiece (in our case: a blot instead of a blotch). This is especially true when an antibody is used as a probe. Nevertheless, general advice can be given to any particular part of the procedure. A basic protocol using ^{125}I-labelled secondary antibody is provided (*Protocol 3*); an example of an immunostained blot with this procedure is shown in *Figure 2*. *Protocol 3* can

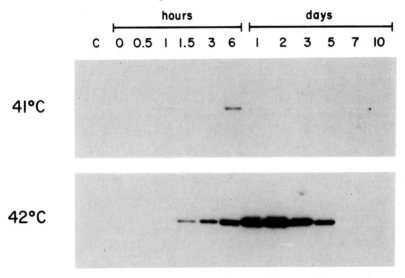

Figure 2. Kinetics of the expression of the major inducible form of heat shock proteins in the liver of thermally stressed rats. Samples of liver (200 μg of protein) isolated from non-stressed rats (C) or rats stressed at 41 °C or 42 °C, and recovered for different times, were electrophoresed (10% polyacrylamide slab gel), transferred onto NC filters, probed with monoclonal antibody C92 (Stressgen), and visualized with ^{125}I-labelled goat anti-mouse antibody. The blots were exposed to X-ray films using intensifying screens. (Courtesy of S. C. Beck.)

be modified for enzyme conjugates probes. A discussion of each step follows the protocol.

Protocol 3. Immunostaining of proteins using iodinated secondary antibodies (see Appendix 1 for solutions)

1. In a covered plastic dish, add enough quenching buffer (3% BSA in Tris buffer) to completely cover the bottom of the dish. Carefully place the dried blot on the surface of the quenching buffer allowing the filter to wet uniformly, then submerge the filter into the quenching buffer. Incubate with agitation on a rocker or shaker for at least 30 min (it can be left overnight). The temperature at which this step is carried out is not critical, it can be done at room temperature or 4 °C.

2. Pour off the quenching buffer, and add the first antibody solution in probing buffer. Incubate for 16 h (overnight) at 4 °C with continuous agitation on a rocker or shaker.

3. Pour off and save the antibody solution (stored at 4 °C, it can be used many more times). Without letting the blot dry, rinse the blot twice with 50 ml of Wash I (5 min each), and two rinses with 50 ml of Wash II (5 min each). Remove the final rinse and pour the secondary antibody solution on the blot.

4. Incubate with the second antibody in probing buffer for 2 to 4 h at 4 °C with agitation. If the second antibody to be used is radiolabelled, dilute the antibody to obtain a concentration of 2×10^5 d.p.m./ml in probing buffer.

5. Discard the secondary antibody solution (be careful!, this is a radioactive solution, and consequently should be handled following the general rules for working with radioactivity). Rince the blot with 50 ml of Wash III (three times, 5 min each) and with 50 ml of Wash IV (two times, 5 min each).

6. Place the blot on Whatman paper and allow it to air dry. Expose the blot to X-ray film (Kodak XAR-5 X-ray film) mounted between two layers of plastic wrap (e.g. 'Saran-Wrap'). To mount the blot between two sheets of plastic wrap, first cover a used X-ray film (from any previous blotch) with a sheet of Saran-Wrap which should be pulled taut over the used film, using masking tape to secure the borders of the plastic wrap. Place the blot on that support and cover the blot with another piece of plastic wrap in the same way as before. Such a procedure helps to provide a flat surface (the presence of wrinkles may affect the final autoradiogram). Expose the blot using intensifying screens at −70 °C.

4.1 Comments about the immunostaining protocol

4.1.1 Quenching

NC membrane filters possess a high binding capacity for proteins (approximately 80–100 μg/cm^2). Such a high adsorbing capacity is important at the moment of transferring the protein from the gel onto the filter, but it is inconvenient at the time of probing (for example, addition of the antibody). This problem is overcome by quenching the filter before probing; in other words, blocking all unoccupied binding sites on the filter. The quenching agent must also be used during probing to avoid non-specific interactions of the ligand with other proteins or with the filter. The most commonly used quenching reagent is an 'inert' protein. The choice of the 'inert' protein is mostly based on its availability (see *Table 1*). Bovine serum albumin (BSA) has been the common selection because of quality (similarity between batches), quantity, and price. Haemoglobin, in spite of being more expensive than BSA, has also been used. Diluted non-fat dry milk (straight from the supermarket) has been very popular primarily due to its cost (11). Although all of these protein quenchers work well, there is no truly 'inert' protein. Consequently, the most important property that should be considered at the time of selecting a 'quencher' is its possible interaction with the ligand, immobilized proteins, and detection system to be employed. For example, haemoglobin has an intrinsic peroxidase activity that will mask the detection of horseradish peroxidase (HRP) conjugated ligands (1). Milk is not recommended with lectins or with antibodies that recognize carbohydrate moieties since milk contains large amounts of sugar that may block binding. Other non-protein quenchers have been used such as polyvinylpyrrolidone (PVP) which works well in lectin overlays (12).

The second option for the quenching of filters is non-ionic detergents such as Tween-20 (13). The rationale behind the use of non-ionic detergents is that they interfere with the binding of proteins to the NC filters reducing the background. The major drawback is that they may interfere with protein–

Table 1. Nitrocellulose quenching reagents

Quencher	Concentration (%)	Probe
Bovine serum albumin	2–5	Antibodies, lectins
Haemoglobin	0.1–1	Lectins, toxin
Gelatin	0.25–3	Antibodies, lectins
Low-fat milk	5	Antibodies
Ovalbumin	1	Cells
PVP	2	Lectins
Tween-20	0.05	Antibodies

ligand interactions, and they may remove proteins from the filter, especially if they are used at high concentrations (over 0.5%).

4.1.2 First antibody solution

As I said before, protein blotting is an art. Nothing is a better example than the use of an antibody for the detection of a protein band (antigen) on a blot. Each antibody will perform differently from every other antibody. Polyclonal antibodies have been used much more extensively for blot immunostaining than monoclonals; however, every polyclonal antibody is not necessarily suitable for Western blots.

When a new antibody is used for Western blots, first determine its titre. A 'good' rabbit polyclonal antibody requires a dilution of just 1:10 000; however, dilutions between 1:1000 and even 1:10 can be used too. An estimation of the titre of a particular antibody can be done by probing identical blots with different dilutions of the antibody; dot or slot blots can also be employed.

The antibody is incubated with the blot in the presence of probing buffer (see Appendix 1). A safe practice to reduced non-specific interactions is to filter the probing buffer containing the antibody through a 0.45 or 0.8 μm filter unit. The incubation time of the blot with the antibody is variable, between 1 and 16 h. Most protocols suggest an overnight incubation. However, increasing the time of incubation increases the background level, decreasing the signal/background ratio.

After incubation with the first antibody, and prior to the addition of the secondary antibody, the blot must be washed with buffers containing detergent (see Section 4.1.4). Keep in mind that the interaction between the antibody and its corresponding epitope follows the equilibrium laws: the more you rinse the blot, the more antibody will come off from the target.

Monoclonal antibodies require special attention when they are used for blot immunostaining. The major reason is that sometimes the epitope recognized by the antibody is lost during the preparation of the sample for electrophoresis due to denaturation of the protein. The best way to test this possibility is to perform a dot blot analysis in which the antigen is spotted on NC filters in its native form as well as after preparation for electrophoresis (addition of SDS, BME, boiling, etc.). The performance of this simple experiment may save time and frustration.

The second consideration that should be made when a monoclonal antibody is used for blot immunostaining is what type of antibody (IgG, IgM) is being used. The choice of the secondary antibody will depend on this parameter. There are many protocols for the typing of the monoclonal antibody (see any book of immunological methods). Another consideration is whether to use hybridoma cell supernatants or ascites fluids. Again that will depend on the antibody itself. Generally ascites fluids are better than supernatants because they have higher titres. The best advice for using monoclonal antibodies for blot immunostainings is to determine the best conditions by using dot or multiple-blot systems.

Before using the antibody, affinity purification is highly recommended. The purification procedure will depend upon the antigen. For example, if the antigen is easily obtained (commercially or by purification), it can be used to make an affinity column to purify the antibody. If this kind of purification cannot be done, a partial purification, for example with an anti-IgG affinity column is very convenient. Such purifications will yield a great deal of improvement in the immunostaining procedure.

4.1.3 Secondary antibody solution

The choice of the secondary antibody depends on the nature of the first antibody. If a rabbit or goat polyclonal antibody is used, Protein A (obtained from *Staphylococcus aureus*) is the most popular option. It binds to the Fc fragment of IgG with high affinity, making the reagent of great sensitivity. However, there are other alternatives to Protein A such as anti-IgG antibody generated from a different species. In the case of monoclonal antibodies, the latter is the most appropriate approach. Several companies sell modified secondary antibodies of high quality.

Obviously the second most important consideration is the type of detection system used to visualize the secondary antibody. A discussion about the use of radiolabelled versus enzyme congjugated probes is provided later.

An interesting approach that has been used to improve the sensitivity of detection is amplification of the signal system. In this case a biotin-labelled or fluorescein-conjugated secondary antibody is employed; the secondary antibody is then detected by avidin (or streptavidin) or with an antibody against fluorescein residues. In both cases, the secondary antibody is conjugated to an enzyme such as alkaline phosphatase or HRP. Such a system provides a large number of enzyme molecules bound per antigen on the blot, generating a stronger signal. This approach may be useful when the relative abundance of the antigen is low in the sample. The major inconvenience of this procedure is that every reagent will contribute to an increase in the final background.

4.1.4 Rinses or washes

The key to a successful Western blot is to obtain an adequate signal/background ratio. While all previous considerations are important, the removal of non-specifically bound ligand is the most critical. Insufficient rinses will result in an intolerable background (blotch), whereas excessive washes will produce a loss of the signal.

As in every step for a successful Western blot protocol, the only way to obtain the best conditions for washing the blots is by trial and error. The most important piece of advice is to include a non-ionic detergent in the washing buffer. Washing buffers are generally based on phosphate or Tris buffers, the pH is normally between 7 to 8; but the pH can be modified to improve the results.

The first detergent to try is Tween-20 (0.1 to 0.5%), this is a weaker detergent which removes less specifically bound ligand. If Tween-20 is not strong enough to achieve a tolerable background, the second choice is NP-40 or TX-100 (0.1 to 0.5%). A mixture of Tween-20 and TX-100 or NP-40 is very convenient. Do not waste time making blends of TX-100 and NP-40, since these two detergents are almost identical. The final alternative is to use SDS (0.1%). Since SDS disrupts protein–protein interactions and dissociates subunits of multimeric molecules special precautions should be taken when using it. The addition of a large excess of SDS and an increase in incubation time frequently results in a very clean blot with no background, but no signal either!

4.1.5 Detection system

There are now numerous detection systems that are generally employed in protein blotting (see Chapters 4–5 and 8–15). The most commonly used are the radioactive and enzyme-linked probes. In both cases the ligand is modified by the addition of a radioactive isotope (commonly ^{125}I), or by coupling of an enzyme such as horseradish peroxidase (HRP), alkaline phosphatase, or β-galactosidase.

i. Radiolabelled probes

Iodination of proteins (Protein A, lectins) is the most common modification used. There are two general procedures for the iodination of proteins. The first is based on the covalent addition of ^{125}I atoms to tyrosine residues of proteins by a chemically (chloramine T (14), iodogen (15)) or enzymatically (lactoperoxidase (16)) catalysed reaction. The second option is based on the reaction between iodinated N-succinimidyl 3-(4-hydroxyphenyl)propionate with free amino terminal groups of proteins, known as Bolton and Hunter reagent (17). The advantages of using iodinated ligands is the high specific activity that can be obtained. In addition, the introduction of a small atom such as iodine does not generally interfere with the biological activity of the probe (if precautions are taken during the iodination). Finally the detection of the signal by autoradiography is highly reproducible and easy to quantitate (densitometry), with control on the linearity of the signal (the blot can be exposed for different time periods). The major disadvantage in the use of iodinated probes is the manipulation of radioactive materials and the short half-life of the isotopes. A protocol for the iodination of proteins is provided (see *Protocol 4*). Iodinated ligands (especially antibodies) of high specific activity and quality can be obtained from several companies at a very reasonable price.

ii. Enzyme conjugated probes

The ligand is modified by a reaction with another protein which possesses an intrinsic enzymatic activity. Generally, the modification occurs via generation of aldehyde groups in one of the molecules (oxidation of carbohydrates) and reaction with amino groups on the other protein (Schiff-base reaction). Also reaction of aldehydes with hydrazide derived proteins has been employed (18, 19).

Binding of the enzyme-conjugated ligand to the target on the blot is detected by a chromogenic reaction, in which the substrate after the reaction changes colour and precipitates in the vicinity of the enzyme-conjugated ligand, producing a colour band. The greatest advantage of this methodology is that it is less hazardous than radioactivity and the probe can be stored for long periods of time without losing activity. The major disadvantage of this technique is that it is difficult to quantitate. The quality of the final product (the blot to be photographed) depends on the expertise of the user. Furthermore, modification of the ligand may affect its biological activity, increasing non-specific interactions. Commercial enzyme-coupled ligands are of excellent quality and are probably the smart choice since the coupling reaction may be discouraging in some circumstances.

Protocols for the detection of HRP and alkaline phosphatase are included (see Appendix 2). An interesting alternative to chromogenic substrates are luminescent substrates (20). In this case the enzymatic activity of HRP or alkaline phosphatase is developed by a chemiluminescent reaction which is detected on a film. This method is faster than chromogenic or radioisotopic procedures and does not possess the hazards of radioactivity, but it may give a higher background with NC filters.

4.1.6 Controls for immunostaining

There are several alternatives for controls (positive or negative) in the immunostaining of blots. The simplest is the addition of two extra samples in the gel, one that is known to contain the antigen and the other which lacks the epitope. Another possibility is to probe an identical blot with an unrelated antibody (both of the same type and species, for example mouse IgGs), followed by the same secondary antibody. A less adequate but still valid control is the omission of the first antibody incubation.

Protocol 4. Iodination of proteins

The following protocol is based on the original procedure by Hunter and Greenwood (14) for the iodination of proteins using chloramine T.

A. *Iodination of antibodies*

1. Dissolve the antibody or Protein A at a concentration of 1 mg/ml in PBS.

Protocol 4. *Continued*

2. Mix 10 to 50 μg of the protein (in 250 μl) with 0.5 mCi of Na^{125}I (13–17 mCi/μg I) and 10 μl of freshly made chloramine T solution (2 mg/ml in PBS) and incubate for 1 min at room temperature.

3. Stop the reaction by addition of 100 μl of a solution of saturated tyrosine (10%) in water, and 1.5 μl of sodium metabisulphate (2 mg/ml, freshly made). Later add 50 μl of non-radioactive KI (10 mg/ml solution), and 50 μl of 1% haemoglobin–PBS solution to give some colour contrast to the mixture and avoid non-specific loss of the antibody.

4. Pass the reaction mixture through a Sephadex G-25 (coarse) column made in a 5 ml disposable pipette (Sephadex is easily retained in the pipette by adding a boiling glass bead before pouring the resin). The separation of the radiolabelled antibody from the free radioactivity can be monitored by using a gamma monitor. Since the antibody will be eluted in the void volume with the haemoglobin, collecting the brownish fraction will recover all the ^{125}I-labelled protein.

5. Count an aliquot of the radiolabelled antibody using a gamma counter, or by counting with scintillation cocktail in the tritium channel.

B. *Iodination of lectins*

1. Dissolve the lectin at a concentration of 1 mg/ml in PBS containing a final concentration of 0.1–0.2 M of the hapten inhibitor sugar corresponding to the lectin to be used (see *Table 2*).

2. Incubate the lectin (50–250 μg) in the presence of the hapten sugar solution (250 μl) with 0.5 mCi of Na^{125}I (13–17 mCi/μg I) and add 10 μl of freshly made chloramine T solution (2 mg/ml in PBS). Incubate for 5 min at room temperature.

3. Stop the reaction by addition of 15 μl of sodium metabisulphite (2 mg/ml in PBS, freshly made), 50 μl of non-radioactive KI (10 mg/ml solution), and 50 μl of 1% haemoglobin–PBS solution to give some colour contrast to the mixture and avoid non-specific loss of the lectin.

4. Pass the reaction mixture through a Sephadex G-25 (coarse) column as indicated in A above.

5. Count an aliquot of the radiolabelled lectin using a gamma counter, or by counting with scintillation cocktail in the tritium channel. A specific activity of 0.5×10^6 c.p.m./μg of lectin is expected using 250 μg of protein.

Table 2. Lectins used in protein overlays

Lectin	Specificity	Hapten sugar	Glycoprotein
Concanavalin A (Con A)	Mannose	αmethylmannoside (0.5 M)	HRP, ovalbumin
Peanut (PNA)	Galβ3GalNAc	Lactose (0.2 M)	Asialofetuin
Erythrina cristagalli (ECA)	Galβ4GlcNAc	Lactose (0.2 M)	Asialofetuin, asialoorosomucoide
Ricinus communis (RCA I)	Gal	Lactose (0.2 M)	Asialofetuin, asialoorosomucoide
Wheat germ (WGA)	GlcNAc, Neu5Ac	GlcNAc (0.2 M)	Fetuin, orosomucoide, ovalbumin
Limulus polyphemus (LPA)	Neu5Ac	Sialic acid	Fetuin, orosomucoide
Lentil (LCA)	Mannose	αmethylmannoside (0.5 M)	
Helix pomatia (HPA)	GalNAc	GalNAc (0.1 M)	
Griffonia simplicifolia (GSA)	GalNAc	GalNAc (0.1 M)	
Soybean (SBA)	GalNAc	GalNAc (0.1 M)	

5. Lectin overlays

A very important and valuable application of protein blotting is the analysis of glycoproteins. Since part of this application is reviewed in Chapter 12, I will just mention the analysis of glycoproteins by lectin overlays.

Lectins (also called agglutinins) are polyvalent sugar binding proteins that interact with complex oligosaccharides (21). Whereas the lectins are better known for their recognition of monosaccharides, they possess a greater specificity for oligosaccharides. Such specificity has been exploited in obtaining information about the sugar structure of glycoproteins immobilized on NC filters. For example, three galactose-specific lectins, peanut agglutinin (PNA), *Erythrina cristagalli* agglutinin (ECA), and *Ricinus communis* lectin (RCA), possess very different oligosaccharide specificity. PNA interacts only with Galβ3GalNAc moieties (a unique component of O-linked sugar side chains), ECA is specific for Galβ4GlcNac (present in both O- and N-linked oligosaccharide), and RCA is capable of interacting with all galactose-containing glycoproteins, even when some of the galactose residues are covered by sialic acid (see *Figure 3a*).

By choosing the appropriate battery of lectins (many of which are commercially available and very inexpensive), the simple detection of glycoproteins on blots can be expanded to gain information about the sugar structure of the analysed glycoproteins. An additional technique, that can be

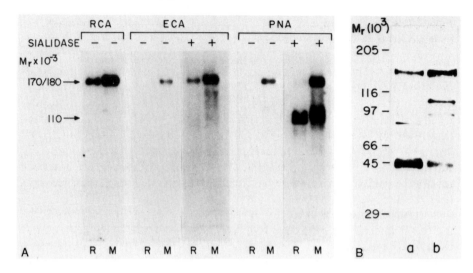

Figure 3. Analysis of glycoproteins by lectin overlays. *Panel A*. Plasma membrane proteins (50 µg) from rat (R) or mouse (M) thymocytes were separated by SDS-PAGE (7.5% polyacrylamide slab gel), blotted onto NC filters, and probed with ^{125}I-labelled lectins, RCA, ECA, and PNA. Some of the blots were *in situ* treated with sialidase (as indicated). The blots were exposed to X-ray films using intensifying screens. Observe the difference in recognition of glycoproteins by these three galactose-specific lectins; in addition, see the detection of new bands after the *in situ* treatment with sialidase. *Panel B*. Proteins (20 µg) from total cell homogenate (a) and plasma membrane fraction (b) of human polymorphonuclear leukocytes were electrophoresed (7.5% polyacrylamide slab gel), blotted onto NC filters and overalyed with Con A, and later with HRP. The HRP–Con A complex on the blot was developed with DAB. (Courtesy of Morella Rodriguez-Ortega.)

used in combination with lectin overlays, is the *in situ* modification of the sugar moieties by glycosylases. In other words, the blot is enzymatically treated to remove the most external sugar moieties, exposing new sugar residues that can now be recognized by lectins which otherwise will not bind to that particular glycoprotein. The most common *in situ* modifications of glycoproteins on blots is the treatment with sialidase (22, 23).

Sialic acid is a common terminal sugar of glycoproteins (especially those located on the cell surface). The presence of sialic acid can be recognized by lectins such as *Limulus polyphemus* agglutinin (LPA) and wheat germ agglutinin (WGA). The latter also interacts with GlcNAc residues of glycoproteins. Using WGA overlays of blots, either treated or untreated with sialidase, the presence of sialic acid (loss of WGA binding after sialidase treatment) versus terminal GlcNAc groups (WGA binding must be resistent to the enzymatic treatment) on glycoproteins becomes apparent. In addition, treatment with sialidase may reveal other glycoproteins with subterminal galactose residues which were masked by the presence of sialic acid (see

Figure 3a). The question arises: why treat the blots with sialidase if intact cells or glycoproteins in solution can also be treated with sialidase? The answer is very simple: modification of the sugar moieties of glycoproteins affects their electrophoretic mobility making it difficult to relate a glycoprotein to its modified product. To make that argument even stronger, the modified glycoprotein does not always migrate faster (with lower apparent molecular weight) than the native glycoprotein. For example, a mouse and human thymocyte surface glycoprotein with an apparent molecular weight of 110 kd migrates with an apparent molecular weight of 135 kd when treated with sialidase before electrophoresis (22, 23). The same observation has been reported for glycophorin, the major surface component of human red cells (24).

A very clever approach for the detection of lectin after the overlay is the use of a glyco-enzyme. This technique is similar to the sandwich methodology used for the immunoblots. The blot is first incubated with the native lectin (unmodified lectin), the excess of lectin is washed off, and the blot is further incubated with glyco-enzyme which can be natural such as HRP for the detection of concanavalin A agglutinin (Con A) as described by Hawkes (25) see *Protocol 5B* and *Figure 3b*. Neoglycoprotein enzymes (proteins that have been chemically modified by addition of a sugar moiety) can also be used, for example galatosyl alkaline phosphatase for the detection of RCA, ECA, or PNA. An alternative to this idea is to use a radiolabelled (iodinated) glycoprotein for the detection of the lectin bound to the immobilized glycoprotein on the blot. For example, ^{125}I-labelled fetuin can be used for the detection of sialic acid binding lectins such as WGA, LPA. Also ^{125}I-labelled asialofetuin has been used for the detection of RCA, ECA, and PNA.

Protocol 5. Lectin overlays

Two protocols are provided, modifications may be required to adjust them to particular cases. One protocol uses iodinated lectins (see *Protocol 4*). This protocol has been successfully tested with a great number of lectins. The second protocol uses HRP for the detection of Con A. In spite of several reports using enzyme-conjugated lectin probes, such conjugates have been found to display more non-specific binding than iodinated lectins.

A. *Lectin overlay protocol A*

This protocol is applicable to all lectins (23).

1. Quench blots with 1% haemoglobin (except when HRP is used to detect the signal), 2% PVP (especially good for WGA), or 2% BSA (except for overlays with PNA), all of them made in PBS. Perform

---

Protocol 5. *Continued*

    quenching at room temperature, with continuous agitation, for a minimum of 1 h (overnight works well).

2. Change the quenching buffer for fresh quenching buffer containing the appropriate lectin (for ^{125}I-labelled lectins, use $(0.5–2.0) \times 10^6$ c.p.m./ml). Incubate for 2 h at 25 °C (room temperature).

3. Discard the buffer containing the lectin (do not try to save this solution, it never works well a second time). Wash the blots with 0.1% Tween-20 in PBS for 3 h with changes every 30 min. Dry the blots and expose to X-ray films for 3–24 h.

B. *Lectin overlay protocol B*

This protocol is for the use of Con A and horseradish peroxidase (HRP) as detection system (26).

1. Quench blot with 2% (w/v) PVP–PBS for a minimum of 1 h.

2. Add Con A (50 μg/ml) in 2% PVP quenching buffer, incubate for 1 h at room temperature.

3. Remove Con A solution and rinse blots three times (5 min each) with PBS.

4. Add HRP (50 μg/ml) in PVP quenching buffer, incubate for 1 h at room temperature.

5. Wash blot with 0.1% (v/v) Tween-20–PBS for 1 h with changes of wash solution every 15 min.

6. Activity of HRP (bound to Con A) is assayed as described in Appendix 2. If molecular weight markers are included, ovalbumin (apparent molecular weight 45 kd) will give a positive signal, that is a very good positive control, the other molecular weight markers can act as negative controls. Alternatively ^{125}I-labelled glycoproteins can substitute for HRP.

5.1 Controls for lectin overlays

The only valid control for the lectin overlay is the co-incubation of the blot with the lectin and the corresponding sugar inhibitor. Monosaccharides and disaccharides are readily available and can be included in the incubation mixture. It is recommended to use a high concentration (up to 0.2 M which is the limit of solubility for most of them). The reason for employing such a large concentration of hapten monosaccharide sugars is that the affinity of the lectins for oligosaccharide is considerable greater than for monosaccharides (21). Because glycoproteins contain complex sugar chains, the lectin will bind more strongly to those residues than to the monosaccharides in solution. A list of the sugar hapten to be used with the most common lectins in blot overlays is provided in *Table 2*.

5.2 Sialidase treatment of blots

After quenching and before lectin overlay, incubate the blot with sialidase (0.005 U/ml) for 3 hours at 37 °C in the presence of 3% BSA–PBS. After rinsing the filters three times with PBS, proceed with *Protocol 5*.

6. Other protein blot applications

Protein blotting has been successfully used in the analysis of other interactions such as binding of viruses to their cell receptors (27), analysis of receptors by ligand and antagonist (28), interaction of cells with substrates (29), interaction of DNA with proteins (30, 31), purification of antibodies (32), and immunization of animals with proteins immobilized on the NC filter (33–35).

7. Concluding remarks

Today it is not necessary to convince people of the importance and utility of protein blotting as an auxiliary technique. In addition, protein blotting has induced a great deal of enthusiasm in many investigators who are still looking for new applications of the technology, improving the existing protocols, and even enriching the laboratory jargon. If you have not been blotting yet, what are you waiting for? Stand up and join the party!

Acknowledgements

I thank Morella Rodriguez-Ortega for sharing with me her protocols and extensive experience in protein blotting; Steve Beck for his assistance in standardizing the protocols described here, and for preparing *Figure 2*; Jonathan Gershoni for the enlightening discussions about the principles and applications of protein blotting; and Kasper Wang, Mark Clemens, Francehuli Dager, Jean-Michel Lebleautte, Elizabeth Miescher-Clemens, and Angel Hernandez for their constructive criticism. This work has been supported by the Robert Garrett Research Fund.

Appendix 1. Solutions

1. Gershoni's blotting buffer: 15.6 mM Tris/120 mM glycine, pH 8.3. This solution is prepared by combining 7.56 g of Tris-Base and 36 g of glycine in 4 litres of water (adjustment of pH should not be necessary). Make it the day before use and store at 4 °C (4).

2. Tris–NaCl stock solution: 20 × Tris–HCl buffer. For 2 litres of solution, dissolve 48.4 g of Tris-Base and 362 g of NaCl, add 59.3 ml of 6 N HCl.

3. Quenching buffer: 3% (w/v) BSA (Fraction V, Sigma #A–7906) dissolved in 10 mM Tris–HCl pH 7.4, 155 mM NaCl 0.02% NaN_3. To make 400 ml solution, add 20 ml 20 × Tris–HCl, NaCl stock solution, 380 ml of distilled water, 0.8 ml of 2% NaN_3 solution, and onto the surface of the liquid add 12 g of BSA. Leave the BSA to dissolve in solution without stirring. Store at 4 °C.

4. Probing buffer: 3% (w/v) BSA in 10 mM Tris–HCl pH 7.4, 155 mM NaCl, 0.3% (v/v) Tween-20 0.02% NaN_3. For 400 ml solution combine 20 ml 20 × Tris, NaCl stock solution, 12 ml 10% (v/v) Tween-20, 0.8 ml of 2% (w/v) NaN_3, 368 ml of distilled water, and add 12 g of BSA on top of the liquids as described for quenching buffer. Store at 4 °C.

5. Wash I: 10 mM Tris–HCl pH 7.4, 155 mM NaCl, 0.3% (v/v) Tween-20, 0.05% NP-40, 0.02% NaN_3. Mix 50 ml 20 × Tris, NaCl stock solution, 30 ml 10% (v/v) Tween-20, 5 ml of 10% (v/v) of NP-40, 2 ml of 2% (w/v) NaN_3, complete to 1 litre with distilled water. Store at room temperature.

6. Wash II: 10 mm Tris–HCl pH 7.4, 155 mM NaCl, 0.3% (v/v) Tween-20, 0.02% NaN_3. Mix 50 ml 20 × Tris, NaCl stock solution, 30 ml 10% (v/v) Tween-20, 2 ml of 2% (w/v) NaN_3, complete to litre with distilled water. Store at room temperature.

7. Wash III: 10 mM Tris–HCl pH 7.4, 155 mM NaCl, 10 mM EDTA, 0.3% (v/v) Tween-20, 0.05% NP-40, 0.02% NaN_3. Add 50 ml 20 × Tris, NaCl stock solution, 40 ml of 250 mM EDTA, 30 ml 10% (v/v) Tween-20, 5 ml of 10% (v/v) of NP-40, 2 ml of 2% (w/v) NaN_3, complete to 1 litre with distilled water. Store at room temperature.

8. Wash IV: 10 mM Tris–HCl pH 7.4, 155 mM NaCl, 0.02% NaN_3. Combine 50 ml 20 × Tris, NaCl stock solution, 2 ml of 2% (w/v) NaN_3, complete to 1 litre with distilled water. Store at room temperature.

Appendix 2. Solutions for developing enzymatic activities

1. HRP

Dissolve 30 mg of 3,3'-diaminobenzidine (DAB) (Sigma #D8001) in 100 ml of 50 mM Tris–HCl pH 7.4, add 70 μl of 30% H_2O_2. The solution of DAB should be prepared just before use. DAB is very toxic so be careful when weighing the powder. Also DAB is difficult to dissolve—vortexing or sonication helps. Before adding the solution to the blot, spin down (5 min, approximately 3000 r.p.m.) to remove any remaining solid. A brown band on the probed blot should be observed.

2. Alkaline phosphatase/naphthol/Fast Red
Dissolve 5 mg of naphthol AS–Mx phosphoric acid (Sigma #N4875) in 250 μl of 100% dimethylformamide. Dissolve 15 mg of Fast Red Tr salt (Sigma #F2768) in 50 ml of 100 mM Tris–HCl pH 8.4. Combine both solutions. A red or pink bank on the blot should be observed.

3. Bromochloroindolyl phosphate/nitro blue tetrazolium*
Dissolve 0.5 g of nitro blue tetrazolium (NBT) (Sigma #N6876) in 10 ml of 70% (v/v) dimethylformamide. In a separated tube dissolve 0.5 g of bromochloroindolyl phosphate disodium salt (BCIP) (Sigma #B6149) in 10 ml of 100% dimethylformamide. To 10 ml of alkaline phosphatase buffer (100 mM Tris pH 9.5, 100 mM NaCl 5 mM $MgCl_2$), add 66 μl of NPT solution, mix well and add 33 μl of BCIP solution, mix well. Incubate at room temperature. Stock solutions are good for one year, developing solution should be used within 1 h of being made. The appearance of a purple band on the blot is expected.

* Harlow, E. and Lane, D. (1988). *Antibodies. A Laboratory Manual*, (Cold Spring Harbor Laboratory).

References

1. Gershoni, J. M. (1988). *Meth. Biochem. Anal.*, **33**, 1–58.
2. Towbin, H., Staehelin, T., and Gordon, J. (1979). *Proc. Natl. Acad. Sci., USA*, **76**, 4350–44.
3. Bers, G. and Garfin, D. (1985). *BioTechniques*, **3**, 276–88.
4. Gershoni, J. M. and Palade, G. E. (1982). *Anal. Biochem.*, **124**, 396–405.
5. Gershoni, J. M., Davis, F. E., and Palade, G. E. (1985). *Anal. Biochem.*, **144**, 32–40.
6. Muilerman, H. G., Ter Hart, H. g. J., and Van Dijk, W. (1982). *Anal. Biochem.*, **120**, 46–51.
7. Aebersold, R. H., Leavitt, J., Saavedra, R. A., and Hood, L. E. (1987). *Proc. Natl. Acad. Sci. USA*, **84**, 6970–4.
8. Rohrinnger, R. and Holden, D. W. (1985). *Anal. Biochem.*, **144**, 118–27.
9. Burnette, W. N. (1981). *Anal. Biochem.*, **112**, 195–203.
10. Hancock, K. and Tsang, V. (1983). *Anal. Biochem.*, **133**, 157–162.
11. Johnson, D. A., Gautsch, J. W., Sportsman, J. R., and Elder, J. H. (1984). *Gene Anal. Tech.*, **1**, 3–8.
12. Bartles, J. R. and Hubbard, A. L. (1984). *Anal. Biochem.*, **140**, 284–92.
13. Batteiger, B., Newhall, W. J. and Jones, R. B. (1982). *J. Immunol. Methods*, **55**, 297–307.
14. Hunter, W. M. and Greenwood, I. C. (1962). *Nature*, **194**, 495–6.

15. Fraker, P. J. and Speck, J. C. (1978). *Biochem. Biophys. Res. Commun.*, **80**, 849–57.
16. Marchalonis, J. L., Cone, R. E. and Santer, V. (1971). *Biochem. J.*, **124**, 921–7.
17. Bolton, A. and Hunter, W. (1972). *Biochem. J.*, **133**, 529–39.
18. Eckhardt, A. E., Hayes, C. E., and Goldstein, I. J. (1976). *Anal. Biochem.*, **73**, 192–7.
19. Wilcheck, M., Spiegel, S., and Spiegel, Y. (1980). *Biochem. Biophys. Res. Commun.*, **92**, 1215–22.
20. Sandhu, G. S., Eckloff, B. W., and Kline, B. C., (1991). *BioTechniques*, **11**, 14–16.
21. Lis, H. and Sharon, N., (1986). *Ann. Rev. Biochem.*, **55**, 35–67.
22. De Maio, A., Lis, H., Gershoni, J. M., and Sharon, N. (1986). *FEBS Lett.*, **194**, 28–32.
23. De Maio, A., Lis, H., Gershoni, J. M., and Sharon, N. (1986). *Cell. Immunol.*, **99**, 345–353.
24. Gahmberg, C. G. and Andersson, L. C. (1982). *Eur. J. Biochem.*, **122**, 581–6.
25. Hawkes, R. (1982). *Anal. Biochem.*, **123**, 143–6.
26. Rodriguez-Ortega, M., Ofek, I., and Sharon, N. (1987). *Inf. Immunol.*, **55**, 968–73.
27. Gershoni, J. M., Lapidot, N., Zakai, N., and Loyter, A. (1986). *Biochim. Biophys. Acta.*, **856**, 19–26.
28. Gershoni, J. M., Hawrot, E., and Lentz, T. L. (1983). *Proc. Natl. Acad. Sci., USA*, **80**, 4973–77.
29. Hayman, E. G., Engvall, E., A'Hearn, E., Barnes, D., Pierschbacher, M., and Ruoslahti, E. (1982). *J. Cell. Biol.*, **95**, 20–3.
30. Bowen, B., Steinberg, J., Laemmli, U. K., and Weintraub, H. (1980). *Nucleic Acids Res.*, **8**, 1–20.
31. Aubertin, A. M., Tongre, L., Lopez, C., Obert, G., and Kirn, A. (1983). *Anal. Biochem.*, **131**, 127–34.
32. Olmsted, J. B. (1981). *J. Biol. Chem.*, **256**, 11955–7.
33. Anderson, P. J. (1985). *Anal. Biochem.*, **148**, 105–10.
34. Knudsen, K. A. (1985). *Anal. Biochem.*, **147**, 285–8.
35. Parekh, B. S., Mehta, H. B., West, M. D., and Montelaro, R. C. (1985). *Anal. Biochem.*, **148**, 87–92.

4

Protein blotting using polyvinylidene fluoride membranes

MICHAEL A. MANSFIELD

1. Introduction

Transfer of proteins from a polyacrylamide gel to a microporous membrane preserves the resolution of the electrophoretic transfer and permits further analysis using a broad array of techniques. Polyvinylidene fluoride (PVDF) was described as a protein blotting substrate in 1986 (1) and was found to be compatible with protocols defined for blotting to nitrocellulose (2). PVDF is a Teflon-type polymer composed of the basic repeating unit shown below

$$\overset{\delta+ \qquad \delta-}{(-CH_2-CF_2-)_n}$$

Proteins interact with the polymer non-covalently through dipolar and hydrophobic interactions. PVDF is chemically compatible with the aqueous buffer systems used in electroblotting and immunodetection. Since PVDF is resistant to most organic solvents, however, it can withstand harsh chemical conditions in which nitrocellulose membranes dissolve or decompose. For this reason, the methods available for protein analysis on PVDF membranes are much more extensive (*Table 1*; see (3) for review).

2. Membrane selection

2.1 Available membranes

There are currently numerous PVDF membranes available (*Table 2*). Most of these membranes comprise pure PVDF. Although the distribution of polymer lengths can vary in these membranes, the chemical nature of the protein/polymer interaction is the same. Differences in performance of pure PVDF membranes are due to differences in membrane structure (see Section 2.2.1). There are two PVDF membranes containing additional components. Westran consists of PVDF cast on a polyester web. The web does not interfere with electroblotting or alter the characteristics of the PVDF. Immobilon-CD is

Table 1. Post-transfer protein characterization techniques on PVDF membranes

Technique	References[a]
Protein staining	1, 4, 5–9
Glycoprotein analysis	6, 10–12
Lipopolysaccharide analysis	13
Phosphoprotein analysis	14–16
Receptor/ligand analysis	
DNA binding proteins	17–19
Growth factor receptors	20
Lectin binding proteins	11, 12
Ca^{2+} binding proteins	6, 21
Antibody production	22
Cell blotting	23
Immunodetection	
Colorimetric	1, 6, 14, 24–26
Radioactive	6, 15
Chemiluminescence	27, 28
Protein expression in bacteria	29
Reprobing	30
N-terminal sequencing	31–33
C-terminal sequencing	34
Peptide mapping	7, 15, 35–37
Amino acid analysis	33, 37–39
Phosphoamino acid analysis	16, 40, 41

[a] These references are representative of each technique.

Table 2. PVDF membranes for protein blotting

Membrane	Supplier
Low internal surface area[a]	
Hydrophobic PVDF	Gelman BioSciences
Immobilon™-P	Millipore Corporation
PolyScreen™	Du Pont NEN
PVDF Membrane	Pierce Chemical Co.
PVDF-Plus	Micron Separations, Inc.
Westran™	Schleicher & Schuell
High internal surface area[b]	
BIOTRANS™ PVDF	ICN Biomedicals, Inc.
FluoroTrans™	Pall BioSupport Corp.
Immobilon-P^{SQ}	Millipore Corporation
ProBlott™	Applied Biosystems
Trans-Blot^R PVDF	Bio-Rad Laboratories
Cationically modified PVDF	
Immobilon-CD	Millipore Corporation

[a] Low internal surface area membranes have about 400 cm^2 of internal surface area per cm^2 of frontal surface area and a BSA binding capacity of about 130 $\mu g/cm^2$.

[b] High internal surface area membranes have greater than 2000 cm^2 of internal surface area per cm^2 of frontal surface area and a BSA binding capacity of about 400 $\mu g/cm^2$.

unique among the PVDF blotting membranes in that the polymer surface is chemically modified to have a cationic charge. Although hydrophobic and dipolar interactions with the PVDF may contribute to protein binding, the primary binding interaction is ionic. Consequently, blots on Immobilon-CD have to be processed differently from other PVDF membranes (see Section 5).

2.2 Choosing a membrane

Optimal performance in blotting applications is dependent upon several factors. First, conditions must be chosen that maximize elution of proteins from the gel. Second, the membrane should be able to bind every protein molecule that elutes. Third, all of the protein bound to the membrane should be accessible for further analysis. Finally, the proteins should remain bound throughout analysis. Or in certain cases, such as peptide mapping, it should be possible to elute all bound molecules. While elution from the gel is dependent upon the solubility of each protein, optimal binding and retention, detection sensitivity, and elution from the membrane are dependent, in large part, on the membrane. For this reason, it is important to have a basic understanding of membrane structure and the implications of structure for performance.

2.2.1 Membrane structure and protein binding capacity

i. Pore size

Although pore size is commonly used to characterize membrane structure, this property actually describes the smallest diameter particle that is retained by the membrane when used as a filter. Proteins in solution, however, are not physically trapped on membranes. In fact, proteins greater than 1000 kd can diffuse through a membrane with a pore size of only 0.025 μm (42). Thus, pore size is only marginally useful in predicting performance. Of greater importance is the ability of the protein molecule to form a non-covalent interaction with the polymer surface.

ii. Internal surface area

A more useful parameter for predicting performance is the amount of internal polymer surface area that a protein can interact with when passing through the membrane. Relative internal surface areas can be measured by nitrogen adsorption (43). Based on this technique, PVDF membranes can be classified into two groups (*Table 2*): low internal suface area with about 400 cm^2 internal surface area/cm^2 frontal surface area and high internal surface area with greater than 2000 cm^2 internal surface area/cm^2 frontal surface area. Higher internal surface area correlates with increased protein binding capacity (see Section 2.2.1.*iii*). On Immobilon-CD, the most important factor determining binding capacity is the amount of cationic charge on the polymer surface, not the amount of internal surface area by itself.

iii. Binding capacity

Protein binding capacity is often used to predict membrane performance. Typically, the binding assay involves incubation of a membrane sample in a buffered saline solution containing the test protein (44). When binding reaches saturation, the membrane is washed and the amount of bound protein is measured. Membranes with high internal surface area bind substantially more protein than membranes with low internal surface area, 400 µg BSA/cm^2 as opposed to 130 µg BSA/cm^2. Although membranes with high internal surface area have fivefold greater internal surface area, the increase in BSA binding capacity is only threefold. It is likely that a large portion of the surface area available for nitrogen binding is sterically unavailable to large protein molecules.

In electroblotting, limitations in gel capacity prevent the amount of protein transferred from reaching the theoretical capacity of even the low internal surface area membranes. For instance, when loaded into a 5 mm wide well on an 8 × 10 cm, 10–20% polyacrylamide gel, 2.5 µg of BSA will resolve into a band occupying about 10 mm^2 of gel surface area. The corresponding area of a low internal surface area membrane theoretically binds about 13 µg. Yet, passage of protein through the membrane often occurs. It is important to recognize that electroblotting introduces factors that limit full utilization of the membrane's binding capacity. The chemical environment may contain methanol and SDS; the protein may be partially or fully denatured; and the electrical field will provide a force to drive the protein molecule through the membrane. In standard transfer systems, low internal surface area membranes will permit passage of most proteins with the degree of passage generally increasing as protein mass decreases. Protein retention during electroblotting can be improved by carefully modifying buffer conditions and field strength (see Section 3.5). High internal surface area membranes, in contrast, bind virtually all proteins greater than 15 kd and exhibit more efficient binding of proteins less than 15 kd (31).

2.2.2 Performance demands

With the exception of Immobilon-CD, the membranes listed in *Table 2* can be used interchangeably in different applications, albeit with varying degrees of efficiency. Obviously, any membrane should bind all of the protein transferred from the gel. If electroblotting conditions are modified to maximize protein binding, then the analytical method becomes the critical determining factor. In immunoblotting and receptor-ligand analyses, the following criteria are important for maximum sensitivity of detection:

● ease of blocking

- retention of target protein on the membrane during all incubation steps
- accessibility of antibodies to epitopes (ligands to receptors)

Low internal surface area membranes usually function better in immuno-detection. They are comparatively easy to block, and antibodies are better able to penetrate the more open pore structure. Subtle differences in the molecular structure of the polymer surface may be reflected in variable sensitivity, especially considering the diversity of blocking agents, detergents, and buffers used. In assays where maximum sensitivity is essential, testing of several membranes is advisable. Variable sensitivity can also arise from lot-to-lot variations that are not apparent from visual inspection of the membranes. Although high internal surface area membranes can be used in immunodetection, they are more difficult to block effectively; and the less open pore structure often limits antibody accessibility. In spite of their higher protein binding capacity, they usually exhibit only equivalent or reduced sensitivity.

In contrast to immunodetection, blocking is not required for amino acid sequencing, amino acid analysis, and peptide mapping. Protein accessibility is also not normally an issue because the reagents used in these procedures are not subject to the steric hindrance encountered by antibodies. Instead, the following criteria are important for optimal performance:

- retention of protein (amino acid sequencing only)
- lack of contaminants on membrane
- quantitative recovery of reaction products

High internal surface area membranes and Immobilon-CD generally meet these criteria in amino acid sequencing and amino acid analysis, although a blank sample of each lot of membrane should be tested for the release of contaminants that appear as spurious peaks on HPLC traces. Greater internal surface area increases the potential for contaminants. PVDF membranes may also exhibit low yields of certain amino acids (32, 33). Low yields of individual amino acids have not been observed on Immobilon-CD (45). If Westran is to be used in these applications, it should be tested for chemical compatibility as the polyester web may behave differently from the PVDF.

PVDF membranes are compatible with both enzymatic and chemical proteolysis (3). Unfortunately, high internal surface area membranes do not function well in peptide mapping because, in many cases, peptides are not released from the membranes surface. Peptide mapping is more effective on low internal surface area membranes, but hydrophobic peptides may be selectively retained (7). Immobilon-CD largely overcomes this problem. Because the binding mechanism is primarily ionic, peptide recovery is very efficient (7). HPLC traces of the recovered peptides appear nearly identical to traces from peptide digests generated in solution.

3. Blotting procedures

3.1 Handling membranes

Although PVDF membranes are flexible and comparatively resilient, damage to the microporous structure can reduce membrane performance. Also, the membranes bind protein indiscriminately. To minimize artefacts and prevent contamination, the following precautions should be followed:

(a) Do not remove the membrane from the protective interleaves until it is ready to be wet in alcohol (see Section 3.2).

(b) Wear powder-free gloves at all times.

(c) Cut the membrane with clean scissors, a clean razor blade, or a clean paper cutter.

(d) To label a blot, use a dull No. 2 pencil to write along the edge in an area where protein will not be transferred. Sharp pencils can tear the membrane, and ink can introduce unwanted contaminants. Note that writing on a membrane crushes the microporous structure.

(e) Handle the membrane at the edges with flat-tipped forceps (e.g. Millipore XX62 000 06). Alternatively, hold the membrane lightly at the corners with gloved hands. This is often preferable when aligning the membrane on a transfer stack.

(f) Prepare all solutions using high-quality reagents and deionized water (18.2 MΩ cm resistivity).

3.2 Membrane preparation

For electrical current and protein to pass through the membrane, air contained within the microporous structure must be replaced with buffer. The major difference between the preparation of PVDF and nitrocellulose membranes is the requirement for immersion of PVDF membranes in methanol before being placed in aqueous buffers (1) (*Protocol 1*). PVDF and nitrocellulose are both naturally hydrophobic. While nitrocellulose membranes can be manufactured with a surfactant such as glycerol or Triton X-100 to overcome the hydrophobicity, the manufacture of PVDF membranes does not allow for the inclusion of surfactants. Nevertheless, when laid on top of a concentrated alcohol solution (90–100% methanol, ethanol, or isopropanol), PVDF membranes wet out almost instantaneously. Complete wetting is evidenced by the membrane changing from opaque to semitransparent. The alcohol is then exchanged with water, and the water is exchanged with buffer. Immobilon-CD is an exception. The cationic derivatization process makes the membrane hydrophilic (7). Thus, it can be wet in either alcohol or water.

Protocol 1. Preparation of PVDF membranes for protein blotting

1. Cut a piece of membrane to the same dimensions as the gel.
2. Place the membrane in 100% methanol[a] for 15 sec.[b]
3. Place the membrane in deionized water (18.2 MΩ cm resistivity) for 5 min.
4. Place the membrane in the appropriate transfer buffer for at least 5 min.

---

[a] Ethanol or isopropanol may be substituted for methanol.
[b] This step may be omitted with Immobilon-CD.

3.3 Tank transfer

In tank systems, the transfer stack is immersed in a buffer reservoir and subjected to a uniform electrical field perpendicular to the plane of the gel (2). PVDF membranes are compatible with many commonly used transfer buffers (2, 3, 7, 31, 46), but the choice of buffer is often determined by the charge of the protein or by limitations of the post-blotting detection method. For immunodetection methods, transfer in Tris/glycine buffers (1, 2, 46) is standard (*Protocol 2A*), although any buffer that preserves antigenicity should be suitable (3). For N-terminal sequencing and amino acid analysis, the glycine contained in these buffers is a major interfering factor. To avoid this problem, proteins can be transferred in 10 mM Caps buffer (32) (*Protocol 28*, step **1**). Peptide mapping requires elution of the protein or peptides from the membrane. Although elution efficiency is protein and eluant-specific (3), the transfer buffer should be maintained below 20 °C to lessen the probability of strong protein/polymer interactions (47). In applications where protein is transferred from a non-denaturing gel, the transfer buffer should lack methanol and be of a composition that maintains protein conformation (1, 3, 48). When transferring from polyacrylamide isoelectric focusing (IEF) gels, brief equilibration in 0.2% SDS (*Protocol 2B*, step **2**) serves to enhance protein mobility (49). SDS is not required for transfer from agarose IEF gels (*Protocol 2B*, step **3**) (25).

Protocol 2. Tank blotting of proteins to PVDF membranes

- transfer buffer
- polyacrylamide gel containing resolved proteins
- container large enough to accommodate gel

Protocol 2. *Continued*

- two pieces of Whatman™ 3MM chromatography paper or equivalent, cut to the same dimensions as the gel
- PVDF membrane equilibrated in transfer buffer (see *Protocol 1*)
- tank transfer apparatus with gel holder and foam sponges (e.g. Scotch-Brite™ pads)
- power supply

A. *Transfer in Tris/glycine buffer*

1. Prepare sufficient Tris/glycine buffer (25 mM Tris, 192 mM glycine, 10% methanol[a]) to fill the transfer tank (refer to the instruction manual for your device), equilibrate the gel and membrane, and wet the Whatman 3MM paper. If bubble formation is a problem, degas the buffer for 5 min.

2. Remove the gel from its glass cassette, and trim away the stacking gel, if present. Stacking gels of low acrylamide concentration adhere to membranes and cannot be easily removed.

3. Equilibrate the gel in Tris/glycine buffer for 15 min. A 10 × 10 cm gel requires about 100 ml of buffer, a 20 × 20 cm gel requires about 200 ml.

4. Assemble the transfer stack.

   (a) Open the gel holder.

   (b) Place a foam sponge on the gel holder.

   (c) Immerse one piece of Whatman 3MM paper in fresh Tris/glycine buffer, and place it on top of the foam sponge.

   (d) Centre the equilibrated PVDF membrane on top of the Whatman 3MM paper. Using a test tube, gently roll out any trapped air bubbles.[b]

   (e) Place the equilibrated gel on top of the PVDF membrane. Roll out any trapped air bubbles.

   (f) Immerse the second piece of Whatman 3MM paper in fresh Tris/glycine buffer, and place it on top of the gel. Roll out any trapped air bubbles.

   (g) Place the second foam sponge on top of the transfer stack.

5. Close the gel holder and place it in the transfer tank.

6. Fill the tank with the required amount of Tris/glycine buffer.

7. Plug the leads into the power supply so that the gel is oriented toward the cathode (−) and the membrane is oriented toward the anode (+).

8. Adjust the voltage allowing 10 V/cm interelectrode distance.[c,d]

9. Transfer the proteins for 2 h.[d]

10. Remove the gel holder from the tank, and disassemble the transfer stack.

11. Place the PVDF membrane on a piece of clean Whatman 3MM paper to dry (see Section 3.6).[e]

B. *Alternative transfer systems*

1. *Caps buffer*. Follow *Protocol 2A* using 10 mM Caps, pH 11, 10% v/v methanol instead of Tris/glycine buffer.

2. *Transfer from polyacrylamide IEF gels*. Follow *Protocol 2A* changing step **3** as follows. Incubate the gel in 0.2% SDS for 15–20 sec, and then place it on top of the membrane.

3. *Transfer from agarose IEF gels*. Follow *Protocol 2A* using 20 mM Tris, 192 mM glycine, pH 8.3, 20% methanol, for the transfer buffer.

4. *Acid transfer of basic proteins*. Follow *Protocol 2A* using 0.7% v/v acetic acid, 10% v/v methanol for the transfer buffer. Assemble the transfer stack with the gel oriented toward the anode (+) and the membrane toward the cathode (−).

---

[a] Methanol concentrations from 0% to 20% can be used. Lower concentrations improve the solubility of high molecular weight proteins. Higher concentrations will promote partitioning of low molecular weight proteins on the membrane.

[b] Bubbles in the transfer stack block current flow and interfere with protein transfer to the membrane. If located between the gel and membrane, they completely block transfer.

[c] If excessive heat is generated during the transfer, the buffer should be prechilled. The unit should be cooled according to the manufacturer's instructions or, alternatively, placed in a cold room during transfer. If the protein is to be eluted from the membrane, the temperature should never exceed 20 °C.

[d] See Section 3.5 for optimization of voltage and transfer time.

[e] The gel should be stained for residual protein.

In the unique case of transfer from acid-urea gels, protein solubility will be dependent on maintaining an acidic pH (1, 50). The proteins have a net positive charge and will move toward the cathode. Thus, the membrane must be placed on the cathode side of the gel (*Protocol 2B*, step **4**).

3.4 Semi-dry transfer

PVDF membranes are compatible with semi-dry transfer systems (See Chapter 5). The three-buffer system described here (*Protocol 3*) was formulated by Kyhse-Andersen (51) to produce optimal transfer under isotachophoretic conditions. PVDF membranes perform well in this system, but conditions that generate too much heat can cause scorching of the membrane and gel. Also, because the field strength of semi-dry systems is stronger than in tank systems, transfer can be completed more rapidly.

Protocol 3. Semi-dry blotting of proteins to PVDF membranes[a]

- anode buffer I (0.3 M Tris, pH 10.4, 10% v/v methanol)[b]
- anode buffer II (25 mM Tris, pH 10.4, 10% v/v methanol)
- cathode buffer (25 mM Tris, 40 mM ε-aminohexanoic acid, pH 9.4, 10% v/v methanol)[c]
- polyacrylamide gel containing resolved proteins
- container large enough to accommodate gel
- six pieces of Whatman 3MM paper chromatography paper or equivalent, cut to the same dimensions as the gel
- PVDF membrane equilibrated in anode buffer II (see *Protocol 1*)
- semi-dry transfer apparatus (e.g. MilliBlot Graphite Electroblotter)
- power supply

A. *Transfer of one SDS gel*

1. Remove the gel from its glass cassette, and trim away the stacking gel. Stacking gels of low acrylamide concentration adhere to membranes and cannot be easily removed.
2. Equilibrate the gel in cathode buffer for 15 min. A 10 × 10 cm gel requires about 100 ml of buffer; a 20 × 20 cm gel requires about 200 ml.
3. Assemble the transfer stack.
   (a) Wet two pieces of Whatman 3MM paper in anode buffer I, and place them on the anode plate. Using a test tube, gently roll out any trapped air bubbles.
   (b) Wet one piece of Whatman 3MM paper in anode buffer II, and place it on top of the stack. Roll out any trapped air bubbles.
   (c) Centre the equilibrated PVDF membrane on top of the Whatman 3MM stack.[d]
   (d) Centre the gel on top of the PVDF membrane. Roll out any trapped air bubbles.[e]
   (e) Wet three pieces of Whatman 3MM paper in cathode buffer, and place them on top of the gel. Roll out any trapped air bubbles.

4. Place the cover on top of the unit.

5. Plug the leads into the power supply so that the cathode (−) is attached to the lid and the anode (+) is attached to the base.

6. Adjust the power supply to a current density of 1.5 mA/cm^2 of frontal membrane surface area.[f]

7. Transfer the proteins for 45 min.[f]

8. Turn off the power supply, unplug the leads, and open the unit.

9. Remove the top layers of Whatman 3MM paper and the gel.

10. Transfer the PVDF membrane to a fresh piece of Whatman 3MM paper to dry (see Section 3.6).[g]

B. *Transfer of multiple SDS gels*

1. Complete *Protocol 3A* up to step **3**(d).

2. Place one sheet of Whatman 3MM paper soaked in cathode buffer on top of the stack. Roll out any trapped air bubbles.

3. Place a piece of dialysis membrane (Spectrum Medical Industries #132677), cut to the same dimension as the gel and soaked in deionized water, on top of the transfer stack. The molecular weight cut-off of the dialysis membrane should be lower than the molecular weight of the proteins being transferred.

4. Place on top of the dialysis membrane, in the following order, one sheet of Whatman 3MM paper soaked in anode buffer II, a sheet of membrane equilibrated in anode buffer II, the equilibrated gel, one sheet of Whatman 3MM paper soaked in cathode buffer. Roll out any trapped air bubbles.

5. Repeat steps **B.3** and **B.4** for as many gels as your device can accommodate.

6. Place three sheets of Whatman 3MM paper soaked in cathode buffer on top of the stack. Roll out any trapped air bubbles.

7. Continue with step **4** of *Protocol 3A*.

C. *Transfer from agarose IEF gels*

1. Follow *Protocol 3A* using 20 mM Tris, 192 mM glycine, pH 8.3, 20% methanol, in place of the three buffer system.

2. Transfer the proteins for 1 h at a current density of 2.5 mA/cm^2.

D. *Transfer from polyacrylamide IEF gels*

1. Follow *Protocol 3A* omitting step **2**. Instead, soak the gel in 0.2% SDS for 15–20 sec, and place it on top of the membrane.

Protocol 3. *Continued*

2. Transfer the gel for 10–60 min at 0.8 mA/cm^2.

[a] This protocol is specific for the MilliBlot Graphite Electroblotter and similar devices with graphite plates. For devices with electrodes composed of other materials, consult the instruction manual for recommended buffers and transfer stack assembly.
[b] Methanol concentrations from 0% to 20% can be used. Lower concentrations improve the solubility of high molecular weight proteins. Higher concentrations will promote partitioning of low molecular weight proteins on the membrane.
[c] 40 mM glycine may be substituted for 40 mM ε-aminohexanoic acid. Adjust the pH to 9.4 with dilute NaOH.
[d] If the anode plate is porous, there may be a tendency for liquid to be drawn from the Whatman 3MM stack into the surface of the plate. This will make it difficult to position the PVDF membrane without introducing a large number of small air bubbles that are very difficult to roll out. To overcome this problem, the PVDF membrane should have a thin layer of buffer across its surface.
[e] To capture any proteins that migrate toward the cathode, a piece of PVDF membrane equilibrated in cathode buffer can be placed on top of the gel.
[f] See Section 3.5 for optimization of current density and transfer time.
[g] The gel should be stained for residual protein.

Single buffer systems can be used in semi-dry transfer (1, 33, 52), but the transfer efficiencies may be greatly reduced (*Table 3*). For example, when 25 pmol of BSA was transferred in 25 mM Tris, 192 mM glycine, over 69% of the protein remained in the gel regardless of methanol concentration. Using the three buffer system, less than 5% of the BSA was retained in the gel using buffer containing 0% and 10% methanol; and less than 10% was retained in buffer containing 20% methanol.

Table 3. Distribution of BSA after semi-dry transfer in different buffer systems[a]

Position	Three buffer system Methanol concentration			25 mM Tris, 192 mM glycine Methanol concentration		
	0%	10%	20%	0%	10%	20%
Gel	4.0[b]	4.2	9.2	70.8	69.0	74.7
Primary	78.8	84.4	74.2	25.0	30.0	24.6
Secondary	17.2	11.4	16.6	4.2	1.0	0.7

[a] 25 pmoles of BSA, trace-labelled with ^{125}I-BSA, was resolved by SDS-PAGE on a 10% to 20% polyacrylamide gel. Protein was transferred to Immobilon-P and Immobilon-P^{SQ} as primary and secondary membranes, respectively, for 1 h at 1.5 mA/cm^2 on a MilliBlot^{TM} Graphite Electroblotter. The gel and membranes were stained, and the BSA bands in each position were quantified by gamma-counting.
[b] Values are the mean of three determinations and represent the per cent of the total BSA recovered in each position.

3.5 Optimizing transfer

Since high surface area membranes effectively bind all transferred protein, optimal transfer is dependent upon maximizing protein elution from the gel. This can be affected by several factors. First, if the pH of the transfer buffer matches the isoelectric point of the protein, the protein will have no charge and will not migrate in the electrical field. The pH should be adjusted to greater than the isoelectric point to give the protein a net negative charge. Second, if methanol reduces protein solubility, the concentration should be reduced to less than 10% v/v. This problem is more significant for larger proteins. For tank transfer, reducing the methanol concentration may necessitate extending the gel equilibration period. Changes in gel size due to water absorption during transfer will reduce resolution on the membrane. Another method to improve solubility is to include up to 0.05% w/v SDS in the transfer buffer(s) (53).

Occasionally, protein bands will be smeared on high internal surface area membranes even when identical transfer conditions give well resolved bands on low internal surface area membranes. This artifact is a result of the smaller pore structure of these membranes. When proteins are transferred rapidly, there may be localized build-up of protein at the membrane surface. If the protein concentration becomes too high, the protein forms a gel that prevents migration of individual molecules into the pore structure. This phenomenon, well known from filtration applications, is called concentration polarization (54). When the gel and membrane are separated at the end of transfer, protein that has not penetrated the membrane will smear across the surface. This problem can be corrected by reducing the strength of the electrical field or the amount of protein resolved on the gel.

Efficient transfer to low internal surface area membranes depends on both gel elution efficiency and binding efficiency. Frequently, however, the above suggestions for enhancing elution often reduce binding efficiency. SDS is a major problem in this regard, especially for low molecular weight proteins (33). Unless SDS is necessary for protein solubility, it should be omitted from the transfer buffer and removed from the gel by equilibration in transfer buffer for at least 15 min. Residual SDS in the gel will cause a high degree of protein passage through the membrane. If the equilibration time is extended for too long, however, small proteins (less than 20 kd) may be lost from the gel. Binding of small proteins can be enhanced by using a methanol concentration of 20% (3, 33). For N-terminal sequencing, binding can be further enhanced by coating the membrane with polybrene prior to transfer (33), although this may cause large background peaks in the first few sequencing cycles (31). Another effective method for enhancing binding is to reduce the strength of the electrical field (33, 53). Binding efficiency is related in part to the residence time of the protein molecule in the membrane. Reducing the electrical field strength reduces the rate of migration, thereby increasing the residence time and the probability of interaction with the polymer. For tank transfer of a broad spectrum of proteins (14 to 400 kd), Otter *et al.* (53) recommended including 0.01% SDS and 20% methanol in the transfer buffer. The first hour of transfer is at low current density to enhance binding of low molecular weight proteins. Transfer for the next 16–20 h is at high current density to promote elution of high molecular weight proteins. A similar strategy should be effective in semi-dry transfer, although the time-frames will be shorter.

3.6 Post-transfer manipulations

When transfer is completed, the gel should always be stained for residual protein. Retention of protein throughout the gel indicates low transfer efficiency. Retention of an individual protein indicates low solubility of that protein. Patchy transfer of an individual protein may be caused by air bubbles in the transfer stack or by hydrophobic spots on the membrane.

In most instances, the membrane should be dried after blotting. Although the membrane can be processed immediately for most staining and immuno-detection protocols (1, 3), drying forces unbound protein molecules within the pore structure and molecules with limited membrane contact to bind more tightly to the polymer surface. Additionally, after drying, transfer quality can be assessed by transillumination (8) (see Section 4.1). Before incubation in blocking buffer, the membrane should be wet in 100% methanol and equilibrated in water (see *Protocol 1*). Membranes that are blocked immediately after blotting and then dried will not require wetting in methanol; the protein coating makes the membrane surface hydrophilic (3). If analysis of the bound protein requires the native conformation or enzyme activity, the membrane should not be allowed to dry out since subsequent wetting in methanol will denature the protein. Thus, immediate processing of the membrane is preferable.

4. Protein visualization

4.1 Transillumination

Transillumination is a simple and completely reversible visualization tech-nique (*Protocol 4*) (8). When the blot is placed in 20% methanol, areas of the membrane without protein will not wet, while areas containing protein will. The protein bands become transparent against an opaque background, and the image can be photographed for a permanent record of the transfer pattern. On low internal surface area membranes, the sensitivity of detection is close to that of Coomassie Blue. On high internal surface area membranes, sensitivity is lower because most of the protein will be localized on the side that was in contact with the gel. Since the side oriented away from the gel contains little protein, it fails to wet out and remains opaque, thereby reducing the amount of transmitted light.

Protocol 4. Transillumination of proteins on PVDF membranes[a]

- 20% v/v methanol
- blotted PVDF membrane
- light box

Method

1. Immerse the blotted PVDF membrane in 20% v/v methanol for 5 min.

2. Place the membrane on the light box.

3. To aid in visualizing the bands, mask the unused surface of the light box. The bands will appear transparent or semitransparent against an opaque background. Band or spot positions can be marked by piercing the blot with a needle. The blot may be photographed while immersed in 20% methanol.

4. When finished, place the membrane on a piece of Whatman 3MM paper to dry; or wet the membrane completely in 100% methanol (see *Protocol 1*) for further analysis.

[a] This procedure does not work on Immobilon-CD.

This technique is useful for several reasons. First, for immunodetection, the overall quality of transfer can be determined before expending costly immunoreagents. Second, unlike standard staining techniques, reversibility is not dependent upon extensive washing of the membrane in solutions that may also wash off protein. Third, in applications like N-terminal sequencing where protein modification must be kept minimal, the comparatively mild incubation in 20% methanol is unlikely to induce covalent alterations.

4.2 Coomassie Brilliant Blue

Staining with Coomassie Brilliant Blue is compatible with N-terminal sequencing and amino acid analysis (32, 39). The original protocol for staining PVDF membranes with Coomassie Blue specified incubation in the stain solution for 10–15 min (1). In practice, a 1 min incubation gives comparable sensitivity and simultaneously reduces the background (*Protocol 5*) (33). Background staining on high internal surface area membranes; and subsequent incubation in 90% methanol, 5% acetic acid, will be necessary to remove as much stain as possible. These conditions permit staining of most proteins but may lead to loss of small proteins (less than 5 kd) and peptides from the membrane. To enhance their retention, a milder staining technique was devised (*Protocol 6*) (9). If necessary, the stain can be completely removed from the protein but not without the loss of protein from the membrane (26).

Protocol 5. Protein staining with Coomassie Blue

- stain solution (0.1% w/v Coomassie Brilliant Blue R, 50% v/v methanol, 7.5% v/v acetic acid[a])
- destain solution A (50% v/v methanol, 7.5% v/v acetic acid[a])
- destain solution B (90% v/v methanol, 5% v/v acetic acid[a])
- staining tray

Method

1. Place the blot in the staining tray. Add stain solution and agitate for 1 min.[b]
2. Pour off the stain and quickly rinse the tray with deionized water.
3. Add destain solution A and agitate for 2–5 min.
4. (*Optional*) To fully destain the background, place the blot in destain solution B and agitate for 2–5 min.
5. Place the membrane on Whatman 3MM paper to dry.

   [a] For analysis requiring protein elution, eliminating the acetic acid may improve recovery (3).
   [b] If the membrane fails to wet in the stain solution, the methanol concentration may be lower than 50% due to evaporation of the methanol or dilution in the case of reused solutions. The stain should be freshly made, or the membrane should first be wet in 100% methanol.

Protocol 6. Peptide staining with Coomassie Blue

- stain solution (0.01%–0.02% w/v Coomassie Brilliant Blue R, 40% v/v methanol, 5% v/v acetic acid
- destain solution (40% v/v methanol, 5% v/v acetic acid)
- staining tray

Method

1. Place the blot in the staining tray. Add stain solution and agitate for 20–30 sec.

2. Pour off the stain and quickly rinse the membrane with deionized water.

3. (*Optional*) Add destain solution and agitate for 1 min.

4. Place the membrane on Whatman 3MM paper to dry.

4.3 Other stains

There is a wide array of other stains that are compatible with PVDF membranes including Ponceau S (1), amido black (1), copper phthalocyanine tetrasulphonic acid (CPTS) (4), India ink (1), and colloidal gold (1, 55). Ponceau S and CPTS are reversible (1, 4). Reports comparing the sensitivities of these stains on membranes are numerous (1, 4, 5). While the comparative performance of the stains is generally valid, absolute detection limits should be interpreted with these cautionary notes in mind. First, most of the data have been generated on samples where protein was directly applied to the membrane, not blotted from a gel. Second, it is assumed that there is no loss of protein from the membrane during staining and destaining. Third, where protein was transferred from a gel, it was assumed that all of the protein transferred from the gel and was retained by the membrane. Finally, different proteins exhibit different affinities for the same stain.

5. Special considerations for using cationically derivatized PVDF

While Immobilon-CD performs comparably with other PVDF membranes in standard transfer systems, the cationic charge introduces certain limitations. First, the membrane theoretically will not work for transfer of basic proteins in acetic acid (1, 50). The proteins will lack a negative charge and should be unable to bind to the membrane because of charge repulsion. Second, although the membrane is hydrophilic when removed from the box, it will become hydrophobic after transferring proteins from gels containing SDS. Experimental evidence suggests that anionic sulphate groups of the SDS interact with the membrane leaving the dodecyl chains exposed to make the surface hydrophobic (P. Barry, personal communication). If the membrane is allowed to dry after blotting, the hydrophobicity can be overcome by wetting in 100% methanol. Drying will also make elution of proteins and peptides more difficult. Third, Immobilon-CD is not generally recommended for immunoblotting or receptor-ligand analyses because of difficulty in blocking.

The stains discussed above do not work well on Immobilon-CD because they bind non-specifically to cationic charges on the membrane surface. Immobilon-CD Stain (Millipore ICDMQS060) is a negative stain formulated specifically for use on Immobilon-CD. This stain interacts only with the membrane, and the proteins appear as white bands or spots against a purple background (56) (*Protocol 7*). The sensitivity is comparable with Coomassie Brilliant Blue, and the stain is compatible with N-terminal sequencing and peptide mapping (55). Because the stain interacts with the membrane, the probability of protein modification is reduced. This stain is also compatible with other PVDF membranes.

Protocol 7. Staining with Immobilon-CD Stain

- stain solution A, enough to cover blot (stock diluted 1:12.5 with deionized water)
- developer solution B, enough to cover blot (stock diluted 1:12.5 with deionized water)
- water bath at 50 °C
- Immobilon-CD blot
- tray large enough to accommodate blot

Method

1. Heat the stain solution to 50 °C.
2. When transfer is completed, rinse the blot in deionized water and decant.[a]
3. Immerse the blot in stain solution A and agitate for 2–5 min at room temperature.
4. Pour off the stain and add developer solution B. Agitate the blot until the desired contrast is reached. Do not exceed 5 min.[b]
5. Rinse the blot in deionized water.
6. If proteins will be analysed by peptide mapping, seal the blot in a plastic bag with 1 to 2 ml of deionized water and store at −20 °C. For N-terminal sequencing, the blot can be air dried.[c]

[a] If the Immobilon-CD blot dries out, it must be wet in methanol and equilibrated in deionized water (see *Protocol 1*) prior to immersion in stain solution. The same is true for other PVDF membranes.
[b] On high internal surface area membranes, colour development is very rapid and should be monitored closely.
[c] For N-terminal sequencing, trim all extraneous membrane from the band or spot. To remove residual stain that might contribute to background in HPLC, rinse the membrane in 0.1% v/v cyclohexylamine in acetone before insertion in the sequencer cartridge.

References

1. Pluskal, M. G., Przekop, M. B., Kavonian, M. R., Vecoli, C., and Hicks, D. A. (1986). *BioTechniques*, **4**, 272.
2. Towbin, H., Staehelin, T., and Gordon, J. (1979). *Proc. Natl. Acad. Sci., USA*, **76**, 4350.
3. LeGendre, N. (1990). *BioTechniques*, **9**, 788.
4. Bickar, D. and Reid, P. D. (1992). *Anal. Biochem.*, **203**, 109.
5. Christiansen, J. and Houen, G. (1992). *Electrophoresis*, **13**, 179.
6. Gultekin, H. and Heermann, K. H. (1988). *Anal. Biochem.*, **172**, 320.
7. Patterson, S. D., Hess, D., Yungwirth, T., and Aebersold, R. (1992). *Anal. Biochem.*, **202**, 193.
8. Reig, J. A. and Klein, D. C. (1988). *Appl. Theoret. Electrophoresis*, **1**, 59.
9. Shultz, J. (1992). *Promega Notes*, No. 36. Promega Corp., Madison, WI.
10. Doerner, K. C. and White, B. A. (1990). *Anal. Biochem.*, **187**, 147.
11. Key, B. and Akeson, R. A. (1990). *J. Cell. Biol.*, **110**, 1729.
12. Wohlfart, P., Muller, H., and Cook, N. J. (1989). *J. Biol. Chem.*, **264**, 20934.
13. Stein, M. A., McAllister, S. A., Johnston, K. H., and Diedrich, D. L. (1990). *Anal. Biochem.*, **188**, 285.
14. Cowles, E. A., Agrwal, N., Anderson, R. L., and Wang, J. L. (1990). *J. Biol. Chem.*, **265**, 17706.
15. Hoeck, W. and Groner, B. (1990). *J. Biol. Chem.*, **265**, 5403.
16. Kamps, M. P. and Sefton, B. M. (1989). *Anal. Biochem.*, **176**, 22.
17. Grasser, K. D., Maier, U.-G., Haass, M. M., and Feix, G. (1990). *J. Biol. Chem.*, **265**, 4185.
18. Harrison, M. J., Lawton, M. A., Lamb, C. J., and Dixon, R. A. (1991). *Proc. Natl. Acad. Sci., USA.*, **88**, 2515.
19. Masumoto, H., Masukata, H., Muro, Y., Nozaki, N., and Okazaki, T. (1989). *J. Cell Biol.*, **109**, 1963.
20. Burrus, L. W. and Olwin, B. B. (1989). *J. Biol. Chem.*, **264**, 18647.
21. Le Maire, M., Lund, S., Viel, A., Champeil, P., and Moller, J. V. (1990). *J. Biol. Chem.*, **265**, 1111.
22. Dinjens, W. N. M., Van der Linden, E., Signet, C. M., Wijnen, J. T., Khan, P. M., Kate, J. T., and Bosman, F. T. (1990). *J. Immunol. Methods*, **126**, 175.
23. Metzelaar, M. J., Wijngaard, P. L. J., Peters, P. J., Sixma, J. J., Nieuwenhuis, H. K., and Clevers, H. C. (1991). *J. Biol. Chem.*, **266**, 3239.
24. Domingo, A. and Marco, R. (1989). *Anal. Biochem.*, **182**, 176.
25. Ogata, M., Suzuki, K., and Satoh, Y. (1989). *Electrophoresis*, **10**, 194.
26. Pryor, J. L., Xu, W., and Hamilton, D. W. (1992). *Anal. Biochem.*, **202**, 100.
27. Bronstein, I., Voyta, J. C., Murphy, O. J., Bresnick, L., and Kricka, L. J. (1992). *BioTechniques*, **12**, 748.
28. Sandhu, G. S., Eckloff, B. W., and Kline, B. C. (1991). *BioTechniques*, **11**, 14.
29. Skerra, A., Dreher, M. L., and Winter, G. (1991). *Anal. Biochem.*, **196**, 151.
30. Silverman, G. J. (1987). *Publication #RP241*, Millipore Corporation.
31. Baker, C. S., Dunn, M. J., and Yacoub, M. H. (1991). *Electrophoresis*, **12**, 342.
32. Matsudaira, P. (1987). *J. Biol. Chem.*, **262**, 10035.

33. Ploug, M., Jensen, A. L., and Barkholt, V. (1988). *Anal. Biochem.*, **181**, 33.
34. Zvaritch, E., James, P., Vorherr, T., Falchetto, R., Modyanov, N., and Carafoli, E. (1990). *Biochemistry*, **29**, 8070.
35. Iwamatsu, A. (1992). *Electrophoresis*, **13**, 142.
36. Crimmins, D. L., McCourt, D. W., Thoma, R. S., Scott, M. G., Macke, K., and Schwartz, B. D. (1990). *Anal. Biochem.*, **187**, 27.
37. Yuen, S. W., Chui, A. H., Wilson, K. H., and Yuan, P. M. (1989). *Bio-Techniques*, **7**, 74.
38. Nakazawa, M. and Manabe, K. (1992). *Anal. Biochem.*, **206**, 105.
39. Tous, G. I., Fausnaugh, J. L., Akinyosoye, O., Lackland, H., Winter-Cash, P., Vitorica, F. J., and Stein, S. (1989). *Anal. Biochem.*, **179**, 50.
40. Hildebrandt, E. and Fried, V. A. (1989). *Anal. Biochem.*, **177**, 407.
41. Murthy, L. R. and Iqbal, K. (1991). *Anal. Biochem.*, **193**, 299.
42. Gorisch, H. (1988). *Anal. Biochem.*, **173**, 393.
43. Gregg, S. J. and Sing, K. S. W. (1983). *Adsorption surface area and porosity*, 2nd edn., Academic, New York.
44. Pitt, A. (1987). *J. Parenteral Sci. Technol.* **41**, 110.
45. Denslow, N., Parten, B., Tran, N., Barry, P., and Pluskal, M. (1992). *9th Int. Conf. on Methods in Protein Sequence Analysis*, Abstract PI-45, p. 28, MPSA, Otsu, Japan.
46. Burnette, W. N. (1982). *Anal. Biochem.*, **112**, 195.
47. Szewczyk, B. and Summers, D. F. (1988). *Anal. Biochem.*, **168**, 48.
48. Wang, F. and Pan, Y. C. E. (1991). *Anal. Biochem.*, **198**, 285.
49. Knierem, M., Buchholz, J., and Pflug, W. (1988). *Anal. Biochem.*, **172**, 139.
50. Walsh, M. J., McDougall, J., and Wittman-Liebold, B. (1988). *Biochemistry*, **27**, 6867.
51. Kyhse-Andersen, J. (1984). *J. Biochem. Biophys. Methods*, **10**, 203.
52. Fausset, P. R., and Lu, S. H. (1991). *Electrophoresis*, **12**, 22.
53. Otter, T., King, S. M., and Witman, G. B. (1987). *Anal. Biochem.*, **162**, 370.
54. Brock, T. D. (1983). *Membrane filtration: a user's guide and reference manual*, p. 286. Science Tech, Inc., Madison, WI.
55. Moeremans, M., Daneels, G., and De Mey, J. (1985). *Anal. Biochem.*, **145**, 315.
56. Lopez, M. F., Barry, P., and Sawlivich, W. (1992). *Annual meeting of the Electrophoresis Society*, Abstract 604, Electrophoresis Society.

5

Protein blotting using semi-dry electrophoretic transfer equipment

GUNILLA JACOBSON

1. Introduction

Electrophoretic transfer of proteins from polyacrylamide gels to an immobilizing matrix is a widely used technique (1). When a protein is bound to a membrane it is more accessible to specific detection methods than in the gel and the separated bands are not broadened by diffusion. The technique has found wide application in detection, identification, and characterization of proteins and protein–protein interactions (2, 3). These applications are given in the remaining chapters of this text.

In semi-dry electrophoretic transfer a stack of wetted filter papers surrounding the gel and the blotting membrane is used as a buffer reservoir, instead of a tank as in conventional electrophoretic transfer (4, 5). The electrodes consist of conductive plates of at least the same size as the gel, which give an homogeneous electric field. The main advantages with semi-dry transfer are the ease of handling, the short time required for the transfer, and the low buffer consumption. Another important feature is that different buffers can be used at the anodic and the cathodic sides to improve the transfer. The short electrode distance gives a high voltage gradient despite low power. Thus the transfer requires a short time and cooling is normally not required since heat production is negligible.

This chapter describes the instruments and accessories required for semi-dry electrophoretic transfer. Procedures for performing the transfer are recommended and mechanisms of the transfer process are discussed. Finally, a trouble-shooting section is included, listing possible problems and remedies.

2. Composition of a transfer sandwich

The composition of a transfer sandwich consisting of the filter papers containing buffer, the blotting membrane, the gel and the electrode plates is shown in *Figure 1*. Transfer can be made simultaneously from several gels by stacking transfer sandwiches on top of each other separated by a dialysis membrane, which prevents cross contamination.

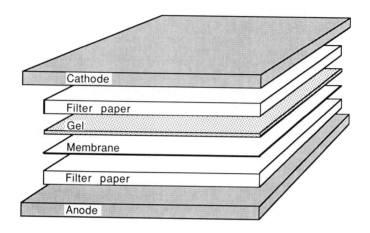

Figure 1. Composition of a transfer sandwich with electrode plates at the top and bottom. The electrophoresis gel is placed in contact with an immobilizing membrane and the transfer buffer is contained in filter papers on both sides.

3. Equipment

3.1 Instruments used for semi-dry electrophoretic transfer

3.1.1 Blotting apparatus

There are a large number of blotting units on the market. These consist mainly of two electrode plates, which may be made of graphite, stainless steel, or a conducting polymer. The electrode plates can either be connected to an existing horizontal electrophoresis instrument such as NovaBlot™—Multiphor® II (*Figure 2*) or PhastTransfer™—PhastSystem™ (both from Pharmacia Biotech) or built as a separate apparatus (Millipore, Sartorius). Some instruments are equipped with cooling either by water, a heat sink, or Peltier element. The electrode plates maintain good electrical contact between the gel, the membrane, and the filter papers, either by the weight of the lid, by applying an external weight, or by a locking mechanism. The plates are available in different sizes, the most common dimension being about 20 × 20 cm. Transfer can be performed from several gels at a time,

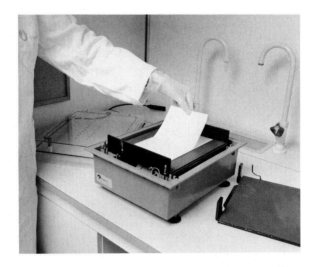

Figure 2. Apparatus for semi-dry electrophoretic transfer. The model shown is NovaBlot electrophoretic transfer unit connected to Multiphor II electrophoresis unit (Pharmacia Biotech). The transfer unit consists of two graphite plate electrodes with the dimensions 21 × 26 cm, which are positioned in the base unit of Multiphor and are covered by the safety lid during the run. The positioning of an immobilizing membrane on top of the anodic filter paper stack is shown.

either beside each other if the electrodes are large enough, or by placing several transfer units on top of each other.

3.1.2 Power supply
Because of the short electrode distance the voltage required seldom exceeds 100 V and is more often 10–20 V. On the other hand, because of the large cross-sectional area, the current passing through the transfer sandwich is fairly high, in the range 0.1–1 A depending on the gel size and the current density used.

3.1.3 Gel backing remover
If the gels are cast on a non-conductive plastic backing, they have to be removed from the backing prior to the electrophoretic transfer. This can easily be accomplished with the help of a gel backing remover (*Figure 3*), consisting of a mounting block, on which the gel is held in position by a clamp, and a cutting wire of thin stainless steel. The wire is pulled between the gel and the backing, thus separating the gel from its backing.

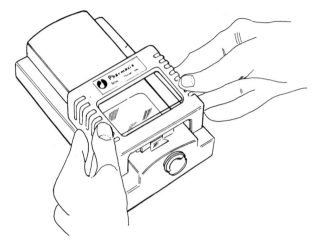

Figure 3. Gel backing remover for PhastGel media. The gel backing remover is a part of PhastTransfer semi-dry transfer kit, together with a semi-dry transfer electrode cassette for connection to PhastSystem (Pharmacia Biotech). The gel is attached to the bottom unit and the top unit holds the thin wire which separates the gel from the backing. A gel backing remover for large electrophoresis gels is also available from the same supplier.

3.2 Blotting membranes

A variety of immobilizing matrices have been used for electrophoretic transfer and are available from several suppliers (see details in Chapters 2 and 3). Nitrocellulose membranes are versatile and easy to use and are therefore the most widely used. The binding of proteins to nitrocellulose is probably due mainly to hydrophobic interaction but the mechanism is not fully understood (3). For electrophoretic transfer of small proteins, membranes with 0.1 or 0.2 μm pore size should be chosen (6, 7). If membranes stick to low-concentration gels after transfer then it may be more convenient to use membranes of 0.45 μm pore size. A drawback with these membranes is, however, that they are very brittle when dry.

Polyvinyldifluoride (PVDF, for example Immobilon™ from Millipore) has good mechanical strength and a protein binding capacity similar to that of nitrocellulose. Details of these membranes are given in Chapters 2 and 3. PVDF immobilizes proteins by hydrophobic interaction. In brief PVDF membranes are also compatible with gas-phase sequencers for subsequent determination of amino acid sequences. Many general protein stains are compatible with nitrocellulose and PVDF membranes.

Positively charged nylon membranes (for example ZetaBind™ from CUNO) are mechanically strong and have a high binding capacity. A disadvantage is their high non-specific binding which results in a high background after immunodetection. Most general protein stains are anionic

56

dyes and cannot be used with nylon membranes since they bind to these membranes.

3.3 Filter papers

Fine-quality filter paper, e.g. Whatman No. 1, should be used. The number of filter papers in a stack depends on the thickness of the papers; for Whatman No. 1 three sheets on each side could be used as a guideline. The number of filter papers does not seem to be critical (8). Most commercial instruments include filter papers as accessories and the recommended number of filter papers is also given. The filter papers should be cut to the size of the gel.

3.4 Buffer

3.4.1 Choice of buffer system

Usually the standard blotting buffers work satisfactorily for semi-dry electrophoretic transfer. For optimal transfer of a certain protein the conditions may, however, have to be modified. Many comparisons have been made between different buffers, but only moderate differences in their performance have been reported (8–10). On the other hand, addition of methanol and sodium dodecyl sulphate (SDS) to the buffers greatly influences the transfer result (see Section 3.4.2). Tris–glycine is the most commonly used buffer system for transfer. This buffer has been used in different concentrations and at different pH values, e.g. 25 mM Tris, 192 mM glycine, pH 8.3, which is the same as in the first published paper on electrophoretic transfer in a tank (1). A discontinuous buffer system with different anodic and cathodic buffer ions (4) is also widely used. The composition and preparation of these buffers are given in *Table 1*. Borate buffer (for example 50 mM borate, pH 9.0) has also been used (11, 12). Transfer from gels containing urea, and native gels in an acidic environment, can be performed in 0.7% acetic acid (13).

3.4.2 Modifications of the buffer systems

i. Methanol
Addition of 20% methanol to the transfer buffer increases the binding of protein to nitrocellulose and PVDF membranes, especially that of low molecular weight proteins (6, 9, 14). Methanol is not required for transfer to charged nylon membranes. Methanol facilitates the dissociation of SDS–protein complexes and increases the hydrophobic interaction between protein and membrane (3). On the other hand, for high molecular weight proteins, methanol can decrease the elution efficiency by denaturing the proteins or retarding the elution from the gel. In contrast to low molecular weight proteins, high molecular weight proteins do not require methanol for adequate binding to the membrane. As a

---

Table 1. Buffer systems for semi-dry electrophoretic transfer from SDS, native and IEF gels

Tris-glycine buffer

Anode and cathode buffer (pH 8.3)	25 mM Tris	3.0 g
	192 mM glycine	14.4 g
	20% methanol[a]	200 ml
	distilled water to	1 litre

Discontinuous buffer system

Anode buffer 1 (pH 10.4)	0.3 M Tris	36.3 g
(next to the anode)	20% methanol[a]	200 ml
	distilled water to	1 litre
Anode buffer 2 (pH 10.4)	25 mM Tris	3.0 g
(next to the gel)	20% methanol[a]	200 ml
	distilled water to	1 litre
Cathode buffer (pH 9.4)	25 mM Tris	3.0 g
	40 mM 6-amino-n-hexanoic acid	5.2 g
	20% methanol[a]	200 ml
	distilled water to	1 litre

[a] Methanol is not required when transferring to positively charged nylon membranes or from agarose gels; see also Section 3.4.2.

---

compromise between methanol and no methanol a concentration of 10% has been used (15). Methanol also prevents the gel from swelling during transfer (1), which can otherwise lead to loss of band sharpness.

ii. Sodium dodecyl sulphate (SDS)

As for methanol, the addition of SDS to the transfer buffer has both positive and negative aspects (5, 15). While addition of methanol to the transfer buffer increases the binding to the membrane but decreases the mobility of the proteins, SDS works the other way around by increasing the mobility and decreasing the binding.

SDS gives the proteins a higher mobility due to the higher charge. This means that the proteins migrate more quickly from the gel. Especially after isoelectric focusing, when the proteins have no net charge, an addition of SDS to the transfer buffer gives a charge to the proteins which thus migrate more easily. SDS, however, decreases the binding of the protein to both nitrocellulose and PVDF membranes. Thus if too much SDS remains bound to the protein, the protein migrates quickly from the gel but does not bind sufficiently to the membrane. If the SDS is stripped from the protein too quickly, the protein loses much of its electrophoretic mobility. The recommended concentrations of SDS vary between 0.01% for transfer from IEF gels, to 0.038% for transfer from SDS gels (8) and up to 0.1% SDS when SDS is used in the cathode buffer only (5).

In addition to using discontinuous buffer systems (as described in *Table 1*), the use of different anode and cathode buffers can be advantageous when utilizing the positive and overcoming the negative effects of methanol and SDS. The addition of SDS (for example 0.1%) to the cathode buffer gives the advantage of increased protein mobility while the addition of methanol in the anode buffer facilitates the dissociation of protein–SDS complexes, thus increasing the binding to the membrane (5).

iii. Ionic strength

An increased ionic strength results in increased binding of protein to nitrocellulose, but the transfer requires a longer time (9, 11). By diluting the buffer the transfer can be performed at higher voltage, and this in a shorter time, without excessive heat production.

4. Preparation of the transfer sandwich

Always wear gloves when handling gels and blotting membranes for personal safety and to prevent artifacts.

4.1 Removing the gel from the backing

If the gel is cast on a non-conductive backing, which is often the case in horizontal electrophoresis, it has to be removed from the backing before transfer. Fasten the gel on the mounting block of the gel backing remover. Place the cutting wire on the gel surface and carefully let it cut through the gel. When a gel consists of both stacking gel and separation gel, it is suitable to insert the wire between these two zones and only process the separation gel. Pull the wire slowly and steadily to separate the gel from the backing.

A small film of gel can remain on the backing after cutting. This usually constitutes only a few per cent of the total gel volume. As proteins almost invariably migrate near the surface layer of a gel during horizontal electrophoresis, the amount of protein left in residual traces of gel adhering to the backing is quite insignificant. Gels with a low polyacrylamide concentration, for example IEF gels, can be stabilized by applying the wetted blotting membrane on top of the gel prior to cutting.

4.2 Equilibration of the gel with transfer buffer

Generally equilibration is not necessary and may lead to loss of protein from the gel (9, 11), especially from horizontal gels where the proteins migrate mainly in the surface layer.

There are, however, some cases where an equilibration may be suitable:

(a) Equilibration of IEF gels in SDS-containing buffer, for example in 0.2% SDS for 10–20 sec (16), makes the proteins more mobile.

(b) IEF gels are more easily removed from the blotting membrane after the transfer if they are equilibrated in transfer buffer for a few minutes before the transfer.

(c) Excess SDS, which otherwise might prevent the binding of the protein to the membrane, can be washed away during an equilibration in transfer buffer for 15–30 min (15).

(d) Equilibration in transfer buffer for 5–20 min can be done to avoid swelling of the gels during transfer, since swelling leads to loss of band sharpness. This can also be avoided by including methanol in the transfer buffer.

When different buffers are used for the anodic and the cathodic side, the gel should be soaked in cathode buffer and the blotting membrane in anode buffer.

4.3 Assembling and dismantling the transfer sandwich

Rinse the graphite electrodes with distilled water before transfer to saturate them with liquid and remove excess water with an absorbent paper. Cut the membrane and filter papers to the size of the gel. If the filter papers are much larger than the gel, much of the available current passes beside the gel through the filter papers with lower transfer efficiency as a result. Wet the membrane and filter papers in transfer buffer by slow immersion to avoid trapping air bubbles. To avoid confusion over the orientation of the membrane relative to the gel, mark the membranes by writing on the wet membrane with a pencil or cut a mark at one of the edges either before or after the transfer.

For assembly of the different parts of the transfer sandwich see *Protocol 1*. This protocol assumes that the bottom electrode is the anode and that the proteins are negatively charged, which is generally the case in alkaline buffer systems.

Protocol 1. Assembly of the transfer sandwich

1. Place one set of wetted filter papers on the anode plate. Put one edge of the filter paper in contact with the electrode and slowly lower it onto the plate to avoid trapping air bubbles. Any air bubbles can be removed by gently squeezing or by rolling a glass rod over the paper stack. If a discontinuous buffer system with two anode buffers is used, then place the next set of anodic filter papers on top of the first.

---

2. Apply the wetted blotting membrane on top of the filter papers using the same technique as above (see also *Figure 2*).

3. Slowly lower the gel onto the membrane. If air bubbles become trapped, wet the surface of the gel with a few drops of transfer buffer, and gently squeeze out the bubbles.

4. Place a second pile of wetted filter papers on top of the gel.

5. If more than one gel—of the same type—is to be transferred simultaneously, rinse a dialysis membrane in water and place it on top of the filter papers. Then continue to assemble another transfer sandwich. Alternatively, the second sandwich can be placed beside the first on the electrode plate.

6. When all transfer sandwiches have been assembled place the wetted cathode on top and perform the transfer.

It is very important that the gel is not dislodged from its membrane after they have first come into contact. This may result in blurred or double protein bands since protein is rapidly transferred to the membrane by diffusion.

When very thin gels are being used it is convenient to first place the membrane on the gel, while the gel is still in the electrophoresis chamber or on the gel backing remover. Then carefully lift the gel and its membrane and place them with the membrane downwards on the filter papers.

It is sometimes valuable to have an immobilizing membrane on each side of the gel. This has often given very elucidating results, for example when performing the transfer at a pH where both positively and negatively charged proteins appear and move in opposite directions during the transfer.

After transfer, carefully disassemble the transfer sandwich and remove the membrane(s). Do not use any sharp instruments to remove the transfer sandwich, as this may damage the electrode plates. Mark the orientation of the membrane now if that wasn't done before the transfer. If the gel sticks to the membrane soak in buffer and carefully remove the gel.

5. Running conditions

5.1 Time and current

Semi-dry electrophoretic transfer is often performed at a current density of about 1 mA/cm^2, e.g. 100 mA for a 10 cm × 10 cm gel at this current density. Higher currents can be used; up to 5 mA/cm^2 has been recommended but this may require cooling. In this case the transfer takes a correspondingly shorter time. With higher current it has been observed that the recovery of low molecular weight proteins deteriorates (6, 11). One reason for this can be that the proteins move so fast that the time accessible for the binding reaction becomes too short.

The time required for the transfer varies with the properties of the proteins, especially their molecular weight, and with the thickness and the type of gel. A typical transfer time for a 1–1.5 mm SDS gel with 10–15% polyacrylamide is 1 h (4). Transfer from less concentrated polyacrylamide gels, such as IEF gels, and transfer from native polyacrylamide gels or agarose gels, can be completed in 30 min. A more extensive description of how different proteins move during different periods of the transfer is presented in Section 7.

In semi-dry electrophoretic transfer the experiments are often performed at a constant current, instead of at constant voltage. The current setting for a specified cross-sectional area can be kept constant irrespective of the number of filter papers in a stack or the number of transfer sandwiches used, provided they are stacked on top of each other. It is much more difficult to control the change of voltage to get the same transfer results in those cases, since the voltage depends on the distance and resistance between the electrodes.

5.2 Cooling

Semi-dry electrophoretic transfer is performed at room temperature. The temperature increase at a current setting of 1 mA/cm^2 is insignificant. At a current of about 2.5 mA/cm^2, however, a temperature increase to 40 °C inside the transfer sandwich has been observed after transfer for one hour (8). Using even higher currents such as 5 mA/cm^2, or transferring heat-labile proteins, is not recommended unless cooling is available.

6. Post-transfer treatment of the membrane

6.1 General protein staining

General protein staining of nitrocellulose and PVDF membranes can be performed using, for example, India ink (17, 18; see also Chapters 2, 3, 8–17) or colloidal gold (for example AuroDye® from Janssen). PVDF membranes for amino acid sequencing are usually stained with Coomassie Brilliant Blue (10). Staining of positively charged nylon membranes is not possible with these methods as the dyes bind to the membrane. Instead charged nylon membranes can be stained with Ferridye® (Janssen), which also works for nitrocellulose and PVDF membranes. In *Protocol 2* a silver staining technique (19), possessing many advantages over other general stains, is given. This method requires only 15 minutes and offers sensitivity comparable to colloidal gold. Contrary to the staining methods mentioned above, no pre-treatment with alkali or detergent-containing buffers to increase sensitivity and reduce the background is required.

Protocol 2. Silver staining of nitrocellulose and PVDF membranes

1. Prepare the staining solution: 0.5 ml 40% (w/v) Na_3-citrate, 0.4 ml 20% (w/v) $FeSO_4 \cdot 7H_2O$ (freshly prepared), and 9 ml distilled water. Under vigorous stirring, add 0.1 ml 20% (w/v) $AgNO_3$. This solution will be greenish brown.

2. Wash the membrane in distilled water for 2–5 min.

3. Stain the membrane in the staining solution for 5–10 min under gentle agitation.

4. Wash the membranes in distilled water for a few seconds.

If too much silver nitrate is used, a black precipitate forms in the solution which leads to weak or no staining. This can usually be prevented either by decreasing the amount of silver nitrate or by checking the iron sulphate solution which must be prepared fresh on the day it is used. A poorly stained membrane can be restained with fresh staining solution.

The above membrane silver-staining method has been successfully used for the detection of peptides. Due to their small size peptides are difficult to fix and are easily washed out during staining of the gel. As an alternative the peptides can first be transferred, either by semi-dry electrophoretic transfer or by diffusion transfer to an immobilizing membrane, and then stained. The time required for transfer and staining of the membrane will be about the same as the time required for direct staining of the gel.

6.2 Specific protein staining

Specific interactions such as antigen–antibody, receptor–ligand, glyco-protein–lectin, protein–ligand, and protein–DNA allow specific detection and identification of proteins. For details on the use of these techniques see Chapters 9–17 in this book and review articles on protein blotting (for example 2, 3).

6.3 Plastic embedding of nitrocellulose membranes

Embedding of blotting membranes in a polymer between plastic sheets offers great advantages. Provided that the refractive index of the polymer equals that of the membrane, the membrane will be transparent and the stained pattern will be open to evaluation by transmission methods. In *Protocol 3* a method is described where the refractive index of the polymer is the same as for nitrocellulose membranes. (Consequently this method cannot be used for other membranes.) The transparencies have good mechanical stability and may be handled and stored like dry electrophoresis gel on backing.

Most general detection methods (AuroDye, FerriDye, India ink, Amido Black, Fast Green, Coomassie Brilliant Blue) are compatible with this plastic embedding technique. Specific detection methods which are compatible with plastic embedding are AuroProbe™ BL (Janssen) and alkaline phosphatase-based methods (using BCIP and NBT as substrate). Some other specific detection methods are not compatible, i.e. the bands fade or disappear after embedding.

Protocol 3. Plastic embedding of nitrocellulose membranes

1. Prepare the monomer solution by dissolving 0.5 g benzoin methyl ether (Aldrich, art. no B870–3) in 25 ml TMPTMA (2-ethyl-2-(hydroxy-methyl)-1,3-propanediol trimethacrylate, Merck, art. no. 808187). Complete dissolution may require several hours. Store the solution at room temperature protected from light. For longer storage keep the solution at 4–8 °C. Avoid skin contact with the solution; TMPTMA is an irritant.

2. Dry the nitrocellulose membrane completely.

3. Cut two sheets of plastic, about twice as large as the membrane. A suitable plastic is PVC film supplied as write-on film for overhead transparencies.

4. For a 10 × 10 cm membrane, pour about 2 ml of monomer solution onto one of the plastic sheet halves. Spread the solution so that it covers an area equal to the membrane.

5. Put one edge of the membrane in contact with the solution and lower the membrane slowly onto the monomer solution. Allow the solution to soak through the membrane.

6. Apply a few droplets of monomer solution onto the membrane and cover it with the second plastic sheet.

7. Use a rubber roller to gently squeeze out all air bubbles between the membrane and the plastic sheets.

8. Irradiate each side of this sandwich for 10–15 sec using a fluorescent tube for sun tanning (for example the mini-solarium BaByliss® Active Sun type 787) or the MacroVue transilluminator (Pharmacia Biotech) or for 3 min using a long-wave UV light source (Osram UltraVitalux, Philips HPA/HPR or PolyScience UV lamp).

9. Cut the polymerized sandwich to size.

---

7. Transfer recovery

When designing and evaluating an electrophoretic transfer, it is valuable to consider the total process as consisting of three steps, where each step is of importance for the result. The first step is the migration of the proteins out of the gel. The second is the binding to the immobilizing membrane. Finally, in the third stage the proteins might eventually be lost from the membrane. Factors which favour one step may be less favourable for another. Such factors are the presence of methanol or SDS in the transfer buffer, length of transfer time, and molecular weight and other properties of the transferred proteins. Another factor which influences the rate of transfer is the concentration of the gel, since the elution time increases with increasing gel concentration.

Investigations with radioactive proteins have shown that there is never one moment during the transfer when all protein is eluted from the gel and at the same time still bound to the membrane (see *Figure 4*) (9). Especially if the binding to the membrane is poor, many of the proteins are easily lost from the membrane before the gel is completely emptied. This desorption reaction is always taking place, often, however, at a low rate. The conclusion is that an empty gel is no guarantee that the transfer is quantitative. Instead, the highest recovery in the membrane is obtained at different time intervals for different proteins. All this indicates that quantitative transfer procedures cannot be generalized. However, to obtain an optimal method for a reliable quantification of a specific protein or group of proteins is still quite possible. In reality, the point of time in the process where the maximum amount of bound protein is achieved must be regarded and accepted as optimal, whether or not protein is still found in the gel or in the filter papers.

It is often suggested that a second membrane can catch the molecules desorbed from the first. Actually a very small amount of the lost material binds to the second membrane (9), as shown in *Figure 4*. The desorption reactions are solid-phase reactions and have the same rate on both membranes irrespective of protein concentration. The rate of transport into the second membrane thus more or less equals the desorption rate on this membrane. As a consequence material is accumulated in the filter paper stack instead. On the other hand an overflow of material from the first membrane due to low capacity may of course be bound to a second membrane.

Low molecular weight proteins are more easily eluted from the gel, but generally they are also more easily lost from the membrane. On the other hand, high molecular weight proteins require longer times to elute from the gel but will remain attached to the membrane. So to achieve a high transfer efficiency, it is necessary to improve the yield of transfer from the gel to the membrane for high molecular weight proteins and to improve the retention of the proteins on the membrane for low molecular weight proteins.

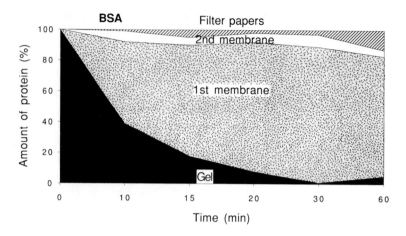

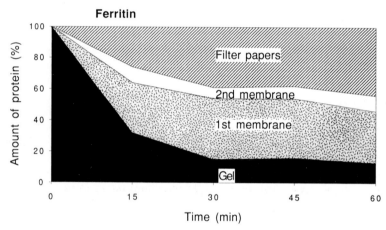

Figure 4. Semi-dry electrophoretic transfer of ^{125}I-labelled bovine serum albumin and ferritin to nitrocellulose membranes after SDS electrophoresis. Gel: PhastGel 10–15 (polyacrylamide gradient gel 10–15%, thickness 0.45 μm). Transfer buffer: 25 mM Tris, 192 mM glycine, pH 8.3, 20% methanol. The percentage of material present in the gel, the first and second membranes, and the filter papers is shown at different transfer times. (From (9) with permission.)

Ways to improve the elution of high molecular weight proteins include:

- increasing the transfer time
- omitting methanol from the transfer buffer
- the inclusion of SDS in the transfer buffer
- increasing the current

Ways to improve the binding of low molecular weight proteins include:

- decreasing the transfer time
- the inclusion of methanol in the transfer buffer
- omitting SDS from the transfer buffer
- increasing ionic strength of the transfer buffer
- decreasing the current

Unfortunately, optimizing the conditions for elution of high molecular weight proteins out of the gel will result in a poorer binding of low molecular weight protein to the membrane and vice versa: optimizing binding of low molecular weight protein to the membrane decreases the elution of high molecular weight proteins. The actual application will decide the choice of conditions.

8. Trouble-shooting

In this section common problems and pitfalls are listed, followed by suggested remedies.

8.1 Gel residues on the backing film

If there is only a thin layer of gel left on the backing, after using the gel backing remover, the protein losses will be insignificant, especially since proteins almost invariably migrate near the gel surface in horizontal electrophoresis. Gels of low polyacrylamide concentration, for example IEF gels and stacking zones, can be more difficult to remove from the backing.

(a) Stabilize the gel before by applying the wetted blotting membrane on top of the gel prior to cutting.

(b) Do not remove the low concentration gel in the stacking zone if no proteins of interest are expected there. Start cutting off the gel at the boundary between stacking gel and separation gel.

(c) Pull the wire on the gel backing remover steadily and do not interrupt the pulling.

8.2 Heating and/or voltage increase during transfer

This can be caused either by poor contact or by using transfer conditions which are too harsh.

(a) Take care when assembling the transfer sandwich that no air is entrapped.

(b) Ensure that the transfer sandwich is in good contact with the electrodes; use a weight if there are contact problems.

(c) Take care that the filter papers are sufficiently wetted with buffer.

(d) Electrodes made of conductive polymers have a limited life span and may need to be replaced.

(e) Decrease the current/voltage and/or use cooling.

(f) Decrease the ionic strength of the buffer.

8.3 Difficulties in separating the blotting membrane from the gel

Gels of low concentration, for example IEF gels and agarose gels, have a more sticky surface and can get stuck to the blotting membrane.

(a) Soak the membrane and gel in buffer after the transfer.

(b) Use blotting membranes with larger pore size such as 0.45 μm.

(c) Apply a low-binding membrane such as cellulose acetate between the gel and the immobilizing membrane.

8.4 No proteins are detected on the blotting membrane

(a) The wrong current polarity was used during the transfer.

(b) The membrane was placed on the wrong side of the gel. With alkaline buffer systems, transfer is normally in the direction of the anode (+) and the membrane should be placed on the anodic side of the gel. For acidic buffers transfer is in the direction of the cathode (−) and the membrane should be placed on the cathodic side of the gel. If there is a risk that proteins might migrate in both directions, use a membrane on both sides of the gel.

8.5 Disturbed pattern on the blotting membrane

8.5.1 Spots or areas without bands

Poor contact during transfer can lead to insufficient transfer from parts of the gel.

(a) Take care when assembling the transfer sandwich that no air is entrapped.

(b) Take care that the filter papers and membrane(s) are sufficiently wetted with buffer.

(c) Rinse graphite electrodes with water prior to assembling the transfer sandwich.

8.5.2 Diffuse bands

Diffuse bands can be caused by the gel swelling during transfer or by diffusion of proteins in the gel before transfer. Diffusion is fast especially for IEF gels.

(a) Minimize the time for assembly of the transfer sandwich.
(b) Do not equilibrate the gel before transfer or reduce equilibration time to avoid diffusion.
(c) Use methanol in the transfer buffer to avoid swelling.
(d) Equilibrate the gel before transfer to avoid swelling.

8.5.3 Additional band pattern
(a) Do not move the membrane once it has been placed on the gel surface. The proteins present on the surface of the gel diffuse immediately to the membrane as soon as contact is made.
(b) Use dialysis membranes between the transfer sandwiches when transferring from more than one gel at a time to avoid cross contamination.

8.6 Low recovery on the blotting membrane

When the recovery on the blotting membrane is too low, the proteins are either still in the gel or have migrated through the membrane and out into the filter paper stack. Staining of the gel shows if much material is still in the gel. To determine if the proteins are in the filter papers is not that straightforward. One way is to use radioactively labelled proteins.

8.6.1 Protein still in the gel
When insufficient amounts of protein have migrated out of the gel:

(a) Use a longer transfer time.
(b) Add SDS to the transfer buffer, or to the cathode buffer only, to increase the mobility of the proteins.
(c) Equilibrate IEF gels in SDS–buffer to increase the mobility of the proteins.
(d) Do not use methanol in the transfer buffer, especially not in the cathode buffer, or reduce the methanol content.
(e) If possible, use a lower gel concentration for the separation.
(f) Do not apply several transfer sandwiches on top of each other since the recovery has been shown to be lower from the gel closest to the cathode (8).
(g) Do not use filter papers larger than the gel, to prevent a large amount of the current from passing beside the gel.

8.6.2 Protein has been lost from the blotting membrane
When protein has migrated through the blotting membrane on to the filter paper stack:

(a) Use a shorter transfer time.

(b) Do not use SDS in the transfer buffer, especially not in the anode buffer.

(c) Use methanol in the transfer buffer, or in the anode buffer only.

(d) Decrease the current density.

(e) Do not equilibrate the gel before transfer or reduce equilibration time.

(f) Use a membrane with higher binding capacity.

Acknowledgements

I am grateful to Dr Per Kårsnäs for many valuable discussions, to Dr Nigel Tooke for critical reading and to Pharmacia Biotech for supporting the work.

References

1. Towbin, H., Staehelin, T., and Gordon, J. (1979). *Proc. Natl. Acad. Sci., USA*, **76**, 4350–4.
2. Towbin, H. and Gordon, J. (1984). *J. Immunol. Methods*, **72**, 313–40.
3. Beisiegel, U. (1986). *Electrophoresis*, **7**, 1–18.
4. Kyhse-Andersen, J. (1984). *J. Biochem. Biophys. Methods*, **10**, 203–9.
5. Svoboda, N., Meuris, S., Robyn, C., and Christophe, J. (1985). *Anal. Biochem.*, **151**, 16–23.
6. Lin, W. and Kasamatsu, H. (1983). *Anal. Biochem.*, **128**, 302–11.
7. Tovey, E. R. and Baldo, B. A. (1987). *Electrophoresis*, **8**, 384–7.
8. Bjerrum, O. J. and Schafer-Nielsen, C. (1986). In *Electrophoresis '86*, (ed. M. J. Dunn), pp. 315–27. VCH, Weinheim.
9. Jacobson, G. and Kårsnäs, P. (1990). *Electrophoresis*, **11**, 46–52.
10. Lissilour, S. and Godinot, C. (1990). *BioTechniques*, **9**, 397–401.
11. Jungblut, P., Eckerskorn, C., Lottspeich, F., and Klose, J. (1990). *Electrophoresis*, **11**, 581–8.
12. Menke-Möllers, I., Kurth, J., and Oette, K. (1992). *Electrophoresis*, **13**, 244–51.
13. Ricard-Blum, S., Hartmann, D. J., and Ville, G. (1990). *J. Chrom.*, **530**, 432–7.
14. Gershoni, J. M. and Palade, G. E. (1982). *Anal. Biochem.*, **124**, 396–405.
15. Mozdzanowski, J., Hembach, P., and Speicher, D. W. (1992). *Electrophoresis*, **13**, 59–64.
16. Knierim, M., Buchholz, J., and Pflug, W. (1988). *Anal. Biochem.*, **172**, 139–44.
17. Hancock, K. and Tsang, V. C. W. (1983). *Anal. Biochem.*, **133**, 157–62.
18. Sutherland, M. W. and Skerritt, J. H. (1986). *Electrophoresis*, **7**, 401–6.
19. Kovarik, A., Hlubinova, K., Vrebenska, A., and Prachar, J. (1987). *Folia Biol. (Praha)*, **33**, 253–7.

Principles and Methods for Preparing Samples for Protein Transfer

6

Transfer and blocking conditions in immunoblotting

A. VAN DAM

1. Introduction

Every scientist who performs immunoblotting techniques wishes to resolve proteins as distinguishable bands or spots at the site where specific antigen–antibody reactions occur. Additionally, no background staining should be obtained on other parts of the blot. Owing to a number of problems, distinct immunoblot patterns are not always obtained, and sometimes it is even difficult to distinguish specific staining from background reactions. These problems are, in the first place, related to the fact that the interaction between the blotting matrix and blotted antigens is not covalent, so that proteins can be lost from the matrix. Secondly, the antibody can often only react with the antigen if it is not denatured too much. Transfer and blocking conditions have great influences on the binding pattern of antigens and on their reactivity with antibodies. Finally, some problems are associated with the quality of the reagents (for example, conjugates) used in the technique.

The most common causes for low specific antigen–antibody interactions are that:

(a) The amount of antigen on the SDS gel is too low.

(b) The amount of specific antibody is too low.

(c) The antigen is denatured by SDS-PAGE procedures.

(d) There is inadequate transfer of the antigen from gel to blotting matrix.

(e) There is a loss of antigen from the blotting matrix during incubation with antibodies.

2. Effects of antigen and antibody concentration on immunoblotting

Successful results in immunoblotting depend on the amount of both antigen and antibody which have been used during the procedure. If other reaction conditions are optimal, protein bands which cannot be seen by silver staining of an SDS gel, can be detected by immunoblotting and amounts as low as 10 ng protein can be readily detected. Since approximatley 40 μl of a sample can be applied on a slot of an SDS gel, the antigen concentration of the sample must be at least 10 ng/40 μl, corresponding to 250 ng/ml. If antigen concentrations are below that limit, concentration procedures are likely to be necessary. Alternatively, specific substrates can be chosen, by which the detection limit of antigens can become as low as 0.1 ng (1) (to be described later).

The minimal antibody concentration is dependent on affinity of the antibody. Using purified, high-affinity monoclonal antibodies, 150 μg/ml IgG antibody was sufficient to detect antigens (2). This corresponds roughly to a 1/500 or 1/1000 dilution of a culture supernatant from a typical antibody-producing hybridoma cell line.

One of the major causes of an inadequate antigen–antibody reaction is denaturation of the antigen in SDS-PAGE. Boiling of samples in SDS leads to denaturation of antigens. During subsequent electrotransfer, blocking, and incubation, some renaturation of antigen occurs. It should be realized that proteins on immunoblots are not completely linearized and that a reaction of a protein with an antibody on an immunoblot does not prove that this antibody recognizes a linear epitope on the protein (3). Nonetheless, some antibodies which react well in other techniques such as ELISA (enzyme-linked immunosorbent assay) or immunoprecipitation do not react on immunoblots.

Transfer and blocking conditions influence the results of immunoblotting to a large extent. These will be discussed extensively in later sections.

High backgrounds have also a number of causes. Some of these are:

(a) inadequate blocking of empty binding sites on the blotting matrix

(b) crossreactivity of the antibodies used in the detection of the antigens

Many blocking agents have been advocated to diminish aspecific binding of antibodies to the blotting matrix. As will be discussed in more detail, most of them have the disadvantage that their application also leads to loss of antigens from the blotting matrix.

Whereas some crossreactions of antibodies are caused by the existence of similar epitopes on different antigens, aspecific banding patterns in immuno-blotting can be a consequence of the existence of broadly crossreactive antibodies by low avidity in an antibody preparation. The use of such antibody preparations should be avoided.

3. Experimental design to detect the antigen or antibodies

When the immunoblotting technique is used, the goal of the experiment is usually either to identify an antibody which reacts with a defined antigen or to recognize an antigen in a preparation by showing its reactivity with an antibody with known specificity. Although, in both cases, specificity and sensitivity should be optimized, the way to achieve this may depend on the aim of the study. If the technique is used as a tool to detect specific antibodies in polyclonal sera, background reactions caused by binding of non-specific IgG often play a major role. In this case, protocols should be directed at lowering these background reactions, especially if immunoblotting is aimed at the detection of antibodies in sera from patients when it is important to ensure the specificity of the reaction. In contrast, if one possesses a highly specific monoclonal antibody, and if studies are focused on antigen detection, protocols aimed at a high sensitivity can be used, since background reactions will be a minor problem.

4. How to determine protein loss and protein renaturation

4.1 Protein staining

A simple way to obtain an idea of transfer efficiency from SDS gel to blot is to cut a small part from the gel, to stain this part before transfer, and to stain the blotted gel after transfer. Coomassie Brilliant Blue staining gives an idea of transfer efficiency. The gel should be stained for 30 min with 0.25% (w/v) Coomassie Brilliant Blue in 50% methanol/10% acetic acid and destained in 7.5% methanol/5% acetic acid for 24 h. A comparison of the intensity of bands shows whether transfer of proteins has been virtually complete, or whether a large amount of protein has remained in the gel.

The nitrocellulose sheet can also be stained. A brief staining of small part of the sheet with Amido Black (0.5% in 50% methanol/5% acetic acid) followed by destaining with 50% methanol/5% acetic acid shows where proteins are located on the nitrocellulose sheet and gives an impression of the amount of transferred protein. The part of the sheet which has been stained with Amido Black cannot be used for antigen detection with antibodies. An alternative protein stain which can be used on nitrocellulose sheets is Ponceau S (Sigma, St Louis, MO, USA). Ponceau S should be used in a 0.5% (w/v) solution in 3% (w/v) trichloroacetic acid. The nitrocellulose sheet is stained for 30 sec and briefly destained (10–30 sec) with PBS, until protein bands on the nitrocellulose sheet can be distinguished. Although this staining procedure is somewhat less sensitive in comparison with Amido Black staining, it has the advantage that prolonged destaining of the nitrocellulose sheet in PBS leads to complete disappearance of the staining (see additional staining methods in Chapters 3 and 4). Once it is established that adequate transfer of protein has been achieved, proteins on the sheet can be detected with antibodies.

4.2 Radiolabelled proteins

Proteins which have been provided with a radioactive label have been of much use in the characterization of the efficiency of electrophoretic transfer as well as the quantitation of protein loss from blotting matrices in the presence of detergents and other agents. For this purpose, either radio-labelled purified proteins or a radiolabelled protein extract can be used. A description of techniques for the radiolabelling of proteins is beyond the scope of this chapter and the reader is referred to other texts (4). Radiolabelled proteins can be separated by SDS-PAGE, and both the amount of radioactivity transferred to the blotting matrix and the remaining radioactivity on the gel can be counted. After transfer, the blotting matrix can be incubated with different blocking and incubation buffers and loss of radioactivity into the buffer can be determined. To detect loss of antigen from immunoblotting membranes, radiolabelled protein can also directly be spotted onto the membrane, which can subsequently be incubated with the buffers. This type of study has been performed extensively, either to detect the efficiency of transfer from gel to blot, or to detect protein loss from blots. The results, as well as recommendations ensuing from the reports, will be discussed in the following sections. However, these studies have the important drawback that they do not take renaturation of protein into account. Therefore, it is of limited use to determine with a high accuracy protein loss from the blotting matrix during incubation with blocking and incubation buffers, since immunological recognition may increase at the same time, resulting in a net signal increase.

4.3 Protein renaturation

Buffers used for protein transfer, saturation of the blotting matrix, and incubation with antibodies have great effects on the final result of an immunoblot. These effects are not only due to influences on aspecific antibody binding or to antigen loss into the buffer. Buffers, and especially detergents used in those buffers, also have an important effect on the conformation of the nitrocellulose-bound antigen. Whereas proteins are denatured during SDS-PAGE, partial renaturation can take place during subsequent incubations.

The importance of protein renaturation in immunoblotting is highly dependent on the antigen–antibody interaction which is to be studied. If the antibody recognizes a linear epitope on the antigen, it will recognize the antigen both in the native and in the denatured conformation. If polyclonal or monoclonal antibodies originating from immunized animals are used, the reactivity of the antiserum with native and denatured antigen will depend on the conformation of the antigen which was used for immunization. Anti-bodies obtained from animals immunized with denatured antigen will also react predominantly with denatured antigen, whereas antibodies from animals that were immunized with native antigen will mainly recognize native antigen. Also, sera from patients will usually recognize native antigens. In the latter situations, antigen renaturation is highly important.

It is not possible to quantitate the extent of antigen renaturation. However, an idea of the combined result of electrotransfer of antigen, antigen loss from the blotting matrix, and antigen renaturation during saturation and incubation of the blot, can be obtained by titrating immune sera or monoclonal antibodies on an immunoblot. Since in immunoblotting it is the final amount of antibody which is of major importance, this is the best way to compare different transfer, saturation, and incubation conditions. If different conditions are compared, visual inspection is often sufficient to determine which condition is optimal for the studied antigen–antibody interaction. An example of such a protocol for human sera is given in *Protocol 1*.

4.4 Optimization of transfer conditions

The efficiency of electrotransfer of proteins depends on the size of the protein, the percentage acrylamide in the SDS gel, the electric current used for transfer, the transfer time, the blotting matrix and the pH of the buffer, and the presence of methanol of SDS in this buffer. (These factors are discussed in detail in Chapters 3 and 4 of this text and describe optimal transfer conditions relative to the type of blotting matrices used.)

4.5 Transfer efficiency

After separation of radiolabelled polypeptides on an SDS-PAGE gel containing 15% acrylamide, Lin and Kasamatsu (5) found, after 4 h transfer at 250 mA, a transfer efficiency of more than 80% of proteins with a molecular weight less than 70 kd, whereas 40% of a 92 kd protein was transferred. In contrast, after 13 h application of a current 70 mA, only proteins with a molecular weight of more than 30 kd were transferred at more than 70%, and only 9% of the 92 kd protein was transferred. Gershoni and Palade showed that high molecular weight proteins are better transferred from SDS gels containing lower concentrations of acrylamide (6).

The blotting matrix is of some importance, since not all blotting matrices retain all proteins (see Chapters 3, 4). Nitrocellulose with a pore size of 0.45 μm does not retain all proteins with a molecular weight of less than 20 kd, whereas nitrocellulose with a pore size of 0.2 μm binds such proteins better (5). Unfortunately, background levels increase on nitrocellulose with smaller pore sizes (7).

Originally, protein transfer from SDS gel to the blotting matrix was performed in a buffer containing 25 mM Tris–HCl, glycine 192 mM, pH 8.3, containing 20% methanol (8). A transfer buffer with a higher pH (NaHCO$_3$, 10 mM, Na$_2$CO$_3$ 3 mM, pH 9.0, also containing 20% methanol) has been advocated by Dunn (9). The pH of this transfer buffer is above the isoelectric point of most proteins, so most proteins have a negative charge in this buffer and will migrate, also independently of the presence of SDS, to the positive pool at which the nitrocellulose is situated. Both in the original publication (9) as well as in subsequent reports (10, 11), the use of this buffer has led to good results. Methanol is essential to improve binding of proteins to nitrocellulose. However, methanol leads also to fixation of proteins in the SDS gel, and concentrations higher than 20% should be avoided. Less fixation of proteins in the gel could also be responsible for the improvement seen after the use of higher currents (6, 9), up to 1 A, during the blotting procedure. If the proteins can be eluted out of the gel as quickly as possible, less protein can be fixated in the gel. Using high currents, transfer can be completed in 1 h. It is essential to use a blotting apparatus which can be cooled during the procedure; cooling only by performing the procedure in a room of 4 °C is insufficient. If nylon-based blotting matrices are used instead of nitrocellulose, methanol is not necessary to fix proteins and should be omitted from the transfer buffer (12).

4.6 Effects of SDS

The addition of 0.05% SDS to transfer buffers has been recommended (13). We found an increased transfer of proteins from gel to blot by adding 0.05% of SDS, but on nitrocellulose sheets, proteins were less well recognized by antibodies, probably because of denaturation (10, and unpublished work). Therefore, it is apparent that the addition of SDS to transfer buffers is dependent upon the nature of the proteins to be transferred. Moreover, we discard the transfer buffer after use, since used transfer buffer will be contaminated with SDS originating from gels.

4.7 Semi-dry blotting

A more recent development is the use of semi-dry blotting transfer systems which are described in detail in Chapter 5. By using these systems, the use of large amounts of transfer buffer is avoided. In addition, different buffers can be applied on the cathode and anode side of the gel. The addition of 0.1% SDS to the cathode buffer resulted in increased transfer of radioactive proteins from gel to blot (14); however, immunoreactivity of transferred proteins was not tested in this study. Serial packing of several gels and nitrocellulose sheets between both electrodes results also in increasing SDS concentrations towards the anode and leads, in our experience, to less reproducible results.

4.8 Renaturation

Another procedure to improve results in immunoblotting is to renature proteins in the SDS gel by putting the gel for 1 h in a buffer containing 20%

glycerol before electrotransfer of the proteins to the blotting matrix. Tris pH 7.4, 50 mM containing 20% glycerol gives good results (9–11), although 20% of the radioactive proteins can be lost in the renaturation buffer (10).

4.9 Drying of the blot

The efficiency of antigen binding improves greatly after air-drying of the blot, whereas, no reports have appeared commenting on loss of antigenicity of proteins because of this procedure. Therefore, it is recommended to air-dry the blot before continuing the procedure.

4.10 Glutaraldehyde fixation

Fixation of antigens by treatment of nitrocellulose sheets with 0.25% glutaraldehyde in PBS for 15 min at 4 °C after protein transfer has been reported to improve binding of monoclonal antibodies to the blot (15). Although we could not confirm these results with human sera, the procedure may be useful in specific cases.

4.11 Blotting matrices

Traditionally, proteins are transferred to nitrocellulose sheets in immuno-blotting (Chapter 3). A pore size of 0.45 μm is commonly used. As discussed in Section 3, nitrocellulose with a pore size of 0.2 μm can be considered with antigens with a molecular weight of less than 20 kd. Nitrocellulose is now available on a stronger support layer (BA-S 85, Schleicher and Schuell, Dassel, FRG), diminishing problems related to the fragility of this material. An alternative to nitrocellulose is Immobilon (Millipore, Bedford, USA) which is especially useful if the blotted protein has to be subjected to amino acid sequence analysis (see also Chapter 3). Nylon-based blotting matrices have been reported to bind a number of antigens more strongly than nitrocellulose (12), and some proteins such as haptoglobin and α-glyco-protein were found to bind to nylon, but not to nitrocellulose (16). A disadvantage of nylon-based matrices is the fact that after blotting, they have to be saturated overnight with 10% BSA at 47 °C in order to block aspecific binding.

4.12 Saturation and incubation conditions

To diminish non-specific binding of conjugate, as well as to renaturate the antigen, non-ionic detergents and blocking proteins can be used. In addition, incubation time and temperature influence the final result of blotting.

4.13 Detergents

The non-ionic detergents Tween-20, NP-40, and Triton X-100, have all been used in saturation and incubation buffers. All these detergents have one important drawback: they elute protein from blotting matrices. Protein elution from nitrocellulose has been extensively studied. Of the detergents, Tween-20 elutes the least amount of protein and is now regarded the best alternative. Up to a concentration of 0.01% Tween-20 proteins remained bound to nitrocellulose, but they were eluted by 0.05 or 0.1% Tween-20 (17). We found after transfer of radiolabelled proteins from SDS gels to 0.45 μm nitrocellulose sheets, that during subsequent incubation steps 30–50% of factor XII, the heavy chain and the light chain of IgG were still lost in PBS/ 0.1% Tween-20, compared with PBS only. The addition of Tween-20, however, leads also to recognition of bands which are not or are only barely recognized in the absence of detergent (10, 18, 19), probably by renaturing antigens. According to our experiences, the renaturing effects of Tween-20 will usually outweigh the disadvantages of antigen loss, at least if human sera are to be tested. Moreover, good results have been obtained by performing all saturation and incubation reactions in the presence of Tween-20 only, and omitting blocking proteins (20). It has been reported that the addition of 0.05% Tween-20 can lead to recognition of irrelevant antigens by monoclonal antibodies (21); however, the dilution of culture supernatant was 1:2.5, which results in a rather high antibody concentration. If higher antibody dilutions are used, these problems will probably be circumvented.

4.14 Blocking proteins

BSA (1%) is often used as a blocking agent. As a cheaper alternative, 5% low-fat dried milk has been advocated (22). They can be added to the saturation buffer as well as to the buffers in which primary and secondary antibody are diluted (see *Protocol 1*). However, low-fat dried milk also elutes proteins from nitrocellulose, resulting in a protein loss of 10% after 1 h, increasing to 25% after 24 hours (23).

If the amount of background is still too high, the addition of non-specific, non-conjugated immunoglobulin in the incubation with the second antibody can be helpful in diminishing aspecific binding. If a goat anti-mouse, a goat anti-rabbit, or a goat anti-human conjugate is used, one can add 5% normal goat serum to the incubation buffer in which this conjugate is diluted. If the conjugate is from rabbit origin, normal rabbit serum can be used. If a mouse monoclonal anti-Ig antibody is used as a conjugate, the addition of normal mouse serum to the buffer is expensive, and thus not practical.

4.15 Time and temperature

Since prolonged incubation of immunoblots in buffers containing detergents or low-fat dried milk leads to increasing loss of antigen from the membrane, saturation and incubation times should not be chosen to be longer than necessary. Saturation for 1 h, incubation of primary antibody for 1 or 2 h, and incubation of conjugate for 1 h, all at room temperature, are usually sufficient. Performing incubations at 37 °C does not have advantages over incubations at room temperature and can lead to higher backgrounds (24).

There are two alternatives to be considered:

(a) If the primary antibody is of high avidity, and if only a limited amount of this antibody area is available, prolonged incubations (for example, overnight) will lead to some increase of antibody binding.

(b) With low-avidity antibodies, prolonged incubations at room temperature are not useful due to rapid dissociation of the antigen–antibody binding. However, one can consider overnight incubation at 4 °C. This procedure has also reported to result in less background (25).

4.16 Choice of second antibody and substrate

After incubation with the primary antibody and washing, one can choose between a radioactive and an enzyme-conjugated second antibody. With a radioactive second antibody, one can vary the time of autoradiography, and sharp bands can be produced. Disadvantages of the radioactive second antibody are all drawbacks related to working with radioactivity. In addition, one has to wait until the next day before a result can be obtained, since autoradiography has to be performed at least overnight.

If an enzyme-labelled second antibody is chosen, one has the choice between a horseradish peroxidase (HRP) conjugated antibody and an alkaline-phosphatase (AP) conjugated antibody. All substrates used for visualization of bands are carcinogenic and should thus be used with care. Since enzyme activity is sometimes inhibited by the presence of detergents, a final wash of blots in PBS without detergent is recommended just before developing.

The use of AP in combination with the substrates nitro blue tetrazolium (NBT) and 4-bromo-3-chloro-indolyl phosphate (BCIP), can result in the sharpest bands if the specificity of the conjugate is optimal. With HRP, one can choose between several substrates: 4-chloro-1-naphthol (4C1N), diaminobenzidine (DAB) and tetramethylbenzidine (TMB). All can be obtained through Sigma (St Louis, MO, USA). 4C1N is dissolved in ethanol (10 mg/ml); 1 ml of this stock solution can further be diluted into 100 ml PBS, to which 40 µl H_2O_2 is added just before developing the blot. DAB is also best dissolved in ethanol or methanol (10 mg DAB in 5 ml, 10–15 min, stirring necessary). This is added to 45 ml PBS, to which 30 µl H_2O_2 is added as above. TMB must also be dissolved in ethanol; for the reaction DONS (dioctylsulphosuccinate, Sigma) is also necessary. Its use is described in *Protocol 2*. Of these substrates, TMB has the highest sensitivity and can be used if the primary antibody is highly specific for the antigen, as is often the case with monoclonal antibodies. DAB has an intermediate sensitivity and 4-chloro-1-naphthol has a rather low sensitivity. The use of this last substrate can be considered if one is studying human sera, which often give rise to high background reactions. A highly sensitive combined staining by 4C1N and DAB is recommended by Young (1). 10 mg DAB and 30 mg 4C1N are together dissolved in 5 ml methanol, which is subsequently added to 40 ml PBS. Just before developing, 30 µl H_2O_2 is added.

4.17 Binding of proteins on dot-blots

In dot-blotting, the antigens can be bound in any buffer to nitrocellulose. A comparison of different binding buffers has been made by Hoffman *et al.* (25). Radiolabelled antigens bound equally well in acidic, neutral, and basic buffers, as well as in 8 M urea or 6 M guanidine hydrochloride. During subsequent incubation with 1% low-fat dried milk, most antigen that was bound at neutral pH was lost most readily from the filters. However, if binding of radiolabelled antibody to the proteins was studied, the amount of bound antibody was highest if the antigen had been bound in acid buffers (0.1 M phosphate, pH 3) in 8 M urea (pH 7), or in neutral buffers. After correction for protein loss, most antibody was bound to antigens incubated with nitrocellulose at neutral pH. This study illustrates that efficient binding in denaturing buffers interferes with antigenic recognition; which effect predominates is not predictable and differs for each antigen–antibody interaction.

4.18 Quality control

It can be concluded that many variables determine the final result in immunoblotting. Incomplete transfer of antigens from gel to blot, variable antigen loss from the blotting matrix during subsequent incubations, and variable antigen renaturation in the presence of detergents can all lead to the day-to-day variations which are so familiar to users of this technique. With repeated testing of the same four reference sera for antibodies against HIV, false-positive reactions (2.0%) and false-negative reactions (1.7%) were obtained, thus illustrating incomplete reproducibility of the test (26).

Particularly if immunoblotting is used as a diagnostic tool for the presence of antibodies in human sera, one should include adequate control sera on each blot. These control sera should comprise at least one negative serum as positive sera for each of the bands which are to be scored. If the reaction of the positive control serum with the band is insufficient, all sera tested on that blot should be retested. In addition, it is useful to include other control sera at regular intervals; the person who does the interpretation of the blot should not be aware when such additional control sera are included. This procedure results in an important additional quality check of utmost importance in a technique in which so many variables play a role.

Protocol 1. How to determine optimal electrotransfer, saturation, and incubation conditions in immunoblotting

1. Separate the antigen by standard SDS-PAGE electrophoresis.

2. Take the gel out of the glass plates and perform electrotransfer onto a nitrocellulose sheet, pore size 0.45 μm. As a standard condition, overnight transfer in $NaHCO_3$, 10 mM, Na_2CO_3 3 mM, pH 9.0, also containing 20% methanol at 50 mA can be used.

3. Take the blot out of the blotting apparatus and let it dry on a tissue. The blot can be stored for a prolonged period, up to one month, at this stage.

4. Saturate the blot. Use as a standard condition an incubation with PBS, containing 0.1% Tween-20 and 1% BSA (PTB), at room temperature, for 1 h.

5. Put the blot in an incubation apparatus or cut it into strips (most easy when the blot is wet).

6. Perform incubation for 2 h with a positive and a negative control serum. Usually, the positive control serum should be tested at five fourfold dilutions, starting at a 1/50 dilution. For the negative control serum, a 1/50 and a 1/200 dilution are sufficient. Dilutions can be made in PTB. The incubation can be performed at room temperature.

7. Wash the strips three times, 5 min each, with PBS/0.1% Tween-20.

8. Incubate the strips for 1 h with the appropriate radiolabelled or enzyme-labelled conjugate at the dilution suggested by the manufacturer. Dilute the conjugate in PTB and perform the incubation at room temperature.

9. Wash the strips three times, 5 min each, in PBS/0.1% Tween-20 and rinse them once in PBS without Tween-20.

10. Perform the substrate reaction or autoradiography.

Alternative procedures which have been described as useful:

(a) Incubate the gel for 1 h in Tris, pH 7.4/50 mM containing 20% glycerol before electrotransfer for renaturation of proteins.

(b) Perform electrotransfer for 1 A for 1 h. Cooling apparatus for blotting buffer is essential!

(c) Use an alternative blotting matrix. Nitrocellulose with a pore size of 0.2 μm has been recommended for proteins of low molecular weight (less than 20 kDa). Immobilon (Millipore) can also be used, and some proteins bind better to nylon-based matrices.

Protocol 1. *Continued*

(d) Omit Tween-20 from the saturation, incubation, and washing buffers to diminish antigen elution from blots.

(e) Omit BSA from the saturation, incubation, and washing buffers.

(f) Replace BSA with 5% low-fat dried milk in the saturation, washing, and incubation buffers.

(g) Perform incubation with primary antibody at 4 °C or at room temperature or overnight.

Protocol 2. Developing of blots incubated with an HRP conjugate and the substrate tetramethylbenzidine (TMB)

1. Prepare stock Na citrate buffer: 0.0243 M citric acid, 0.0512 M Na_2HPO_4, pH 5.0.

2. Dissolve 48 mg TMB and 160 mg dioctylsulphosuccinate (DONS) in 20 ml ethanol at 60 °C.

3. Mix the ethanol, in which TMB and DONS have been dissolved, with 12 ml Na citrate buffer stock and 60 ml water.

4. Add 40 µl H_2O_2 immediately before developing.

5. Develop the blot for 2–10 mins. Stop developing by rinsing the blot with water.

6. Since the staining pattern fades away, good results which have to be stored should be photographed immediately.

References

1. Young, P. R. (1989). *J. Virol Methods*, **24**, 227–36.
2. Towbin, H. and Gordon, J. (1984). *J. Immunol. Methods*, **72**, 313–40.
3. Habets, W. J., Hoet, M. H., DeJong, B. A., Van der Kemp, A., and Van Venrooij, W. J. (1989). *J. Immunol.*, **143**, 2560–6.
4. Johnstone, A. and Thorpe, R. B. (1987). *Immunochemistry in practice*. Blackwell Scientific, Oxford.
5. Lin, W., and Kasamatsu, H. (1983). *Anal. Biochem.*, **128**, 302–311.
6. Gershoni, J. M. and Palade, G. E. (1983). *Anal. Biochem.*, **131**, 1–15.
7. Tovey, E. R., Ford, S. A., and Baldo, B. A. (1987). *J. Biochem. Biophys. Methods*, **14**, 1–17.

A. Van Dam

8. Towbin, H., Staehelin, T., and Gordon, J. (1979). *Proc. Natl. Acad. Sci., USA*, **76**, 4350–4.
9. Dunn, S. D. (1986). *Anal. Biochem.*, **157**, 144–53.
10. Van Dam, A. P., Van den Brink, H. G., and Smeenk, R. J. T. (1990). *J. Immunol. Methods*, **129**, 63–70.
11. Bastagno, M., Cerino, A., Riva, S., and Astaldi Ricotti, G. C. B. (1987). *Biochem. Biophys. Res. Commun.*, **146**, 1509–14.
12. Gershoni, J. M. and Palade, G. E. (1982). *Anal. Biochem.*, **124**, 396–405.
13. Monk, B. C. (1987). *J. Immunol. Methods*, **96**, 19–28.
14. Lissilour, S. and Godinot, C. (1990). *BioTechniques*, **9**, 397–401.
15. Ikegaki, N. and Kennett, R. H. (1989). *J. Immunol. Methods*, **124**, 205–10.
16. Miribel, L. and Arnaud, P. (1988). *J. Immunol. Methods*, **107**, 253–9.
17. Hoffman, W. L. and Jump, A. A. (1986). *J. Immunol. Methods*, **94**, 191–6.
18. Spinola, S. M. and Cannon, J. G. (1985). *J. Immunol. Methods*, **81**, 161–5.
19. Tovey, E. R., Ford, S. A., and Baldo, B. A. (1989). *Electrophoresis*, **10**, 243–9.
20. Mohammed, K. and Esen, A. (1989). *J. Immunol. Methods*, **117**, 141–5.
21. Bird, C. R., Gearing, A. J. H., and Thorpe, R. (1988). *J. Immunol. Methods*, **106**, 175–9.
22. Johnson, D. A., Gautsch, J. W., Sportsman, J. R., and Elder, J. H. (1984). *Gene Anal. Technol.*, **1**, 3–8.
23. Den Hollander, N. and Befus, D. (1989). *J. Immunol. Methods*, **122**, 129–35.
24. Thean, E. T. and Toh, B. H. (1989). *Anal. Biochem.*, **177**, 256–8.
25. Hoffman, W. L., Jump, A. A., Kelly, P. J., and Ruggles, A. O. (1991). *Anal. Biochem.*, **198**, 112–18.
26. Edwards, V. M., Mosley, J. W., and the Transfusion Safety Group (1989). *Am. J. Clin. Pathol.*, **91**, 75–8.

7

Sample preparation for protein electrophoresis and transfer

VAUGHAN H. LEE and BONNIE S. DUNBAR

1. Introduction

A critical yet often overlooked step in the process of analysing proteins by electrophoresis and transfer is the method used for solubilization. We have found for many protein samples that the method of sample preparation is the most important consideration for optimal results with protein blotting after one-dimensional or two-dimensional polyacrylamide gel electrophoresis (PAGE). The best method for solubilization of a protein sample is dependent on the type of protein sample and the physicochemical nature of the individual proteins to be analysed. There is no one method that will give optimal solubilization and/or resolution of all proteins. It is therefore necessary in the initial studies of a given protein to empirically determine the optimal procedure for protein sample solubilization. This chapter should be helpful in understanding the principles of protein solubilization that are critical for carrying out electrophoresis for most studies involving protein transfer.

2. General principles

Sample preparation of proteins typically involves some degree of denaturation of the protein. The molecular process of protein denaturation is the reversible or irreversible process in which the native conformation of a protein is changed without altering the primary structure (1, 2). In order to have a working understanding of this process it is necessary to be familiar with the basic terminology applied to the conformation of the native protein (1, 2):

(a) *Primary structure*: denotes the sequence of amino acid residues in the protein molecule.

(b) *Secondary structure*: signifies that hydrogen bonds are involved in a higher-order structure, such as α-helix formation.

(c) *Tertiary structure*: refers to the pattern of folding into a compact globular molecule.

(d) *Quaternary structure*: signifies the non-covalent asociation of two or more subordinate entities, subunits which may or may not be identical.

In the living organism proteins exist in their native state which is dependent upon the physiological conditions for the normal functions of each protein. It is therefore important to acknowledge that the physical and chemical properties of any protein or polypeptide removed from its biological environment for analysis *in vitro* may be quite different from its properties *in vivo*.

2.1 Denaturation by urea

Urea (H_2NCONH_2) has been, and still is, one of the most widely used denaturants. Extensive physicochemical studies have been carried out to analyse the extent of denaturation of a variety of different proteins (1). The extent of protein denaturation in urea has been shown to depend on temperature, pH, and ionic strength. Usually, its effectiveness is obtained only at relatively high concentrations (> 8 M) and still there remain many proteins which do not undergo complete denaturation (3). As with other denaturants to date, most physicochemical studies on the denaturation efficacy of urea have been carried out using highly purified, homogeneous proteins.

Urea is most commonly used to solubilize protein samples for isoelectric focusing. Urea works by disrupting hydrogen bonds, and has the advantage for some applications that it does not affect the intrinsic charge of proteins so that separation of constituent polypeptides will be on the basis of size and charge, in contrast to the use of sodium dodecyl sulphate (4). The major disadvantage is that urea must be present during electrophoresis to maintain the denatured state of the protein.

2.2 Denaturation by detergents

Ionic as well as non-ionic detergents have long been known to bring about various degrees of denaturation. In general, however, the ionic detergents are more active. In addition to bringing about denaturation, it has been demonstrated that, at low concentrations, they can protect proteins from heat coagulation or from denaturation by urea and guanidinium chloride (1, 3, 5, 6).

2.2.1 Non-ionic detergents

Non-ionic detergents are commonly used to solubilize proteins from membranes or to solubilize proteins in a manner which may not affect the biological activity of that protein. To date, the most commonly used non-ionic detergents include Triton X-100 (7, 8), Lubrol and Sarkosyl (9) and Nonidet P-40 (NP-40).

While the solubilization of complex proteins is not fully understood, some basic studies using purified proteins have been carried out to help determine the mechanisms by which these detergents interact with proteins. Triton X-100 (TX-100) has been concluded to interact predominantly by binding hydrophobically to certain proteins (10). In these studies, it was observed that some proteins, including horse myoglobin and human IgG, did not bind TX-100, while other proteins did bind (in decreasing order: human sera albumin, bovine serum albumin, and β-lactoglobulin).

2.2.2 Anionic detergents

In general, ionic detergents are more effective in solubilizing proteins than are non-ionic detergents. The most commonly used detergents are sodium dodecyl (lauryl) sulphate (NaDodSO$_4$; CH$_3$(CH$_2$)$_{10}$CH$_2$OSO$_3$Na; SDS) and sodium deoxycholate. Although sodium deoxycholate is an ionic detergent, it resembles non-ionic detergents in its low denaturing effects. Since in addition sodium deoxycholate does not bind to membrane proteins in significant quantities, it also causes fewer conformational changes than strongly ionic detergents such as SDS. SDS has been shown to dissociate larger proteins into subunits, unfolding the polypeptide chains to form rod-like complexes of proteins to which SDS molecules are bound, mainly by hydrophobic bonds (11, 12). To date, several detailed investigations have used the interaction between bovine serum albumin and anionic detergents as a model to understand the mechanism of denaturation (3, 13, 14).

More recently, detailed studies utilizing equilibrium dialysis have been carried out to elucidate the role of SDS binding to proteins with special reference to PAGE (15). In these studies, binding of detergent (in 50 mM sodium phosphate buffer at 25 °C, pH 7) was found to occur in two phases with an initial, gradual increase in binding (0.3–0.6 g/g protein) followed by a subsequent steep increase up to 1.2–1.5 g/g protein. The binding which varied from protein to protein was found to be complete at an SDS concentration below the critical micelle concentration.

2.3 Disulphide bond reducing agents

Many proteins contain disulphide bonds which maintain protein conformation by covalently crosslinking two different parts of the same polypeptide chain or two different chains. It is therefore necessary to reduce these disulphide bonds for effective resolution of proteins or protein subunits in SDS-PAGE. This is generally accomplished using such reagents as β-mercaptoethanol or dithiothreitol (DTT). We have described three solubilization solutions which contain β-mercaptoethanol as the reducing reagent (see *Protocols 1* and *2*). Although, the standard SDS-PAGE 'solubilization buffers' are at pH 6.8, this is below the optimal pH for most disulphide bond reducing agents. (Note: the theory for the low pH is that this is the same pH as the stacking gel. Because the anionic detergent, SDS, is used in these systems, however, this negates the need for the stacking gel used in non-denaturing electrophoresis.) The SDS solubilization solution described in *Protocol 2* therefore works best with most protein samples because of the higher pH (9.5).

3. General solubilization solutions for one- and two- dimensional PAGE

In general, it is apparent that the process of protein denaturation and solubilization is an extremely complex one and that no generalizations can be made which will be optimal for every protein sample, especially for complex protein mixtures. We have found, however, that most protein or peptide antigens can be resolved with the following procedures.

Protocol 1. Sample preparation for one-dimensional SDS-PAGE (16)

Reagents
- SDS (BioRad)
- Trizma base (Sigma)
- β-mercaptoethanol (BioRad)
- glycerol (Fisher)

Equipment and supplies
- 1–3 ml glass vials with screwtops
- 20 and 100 µl Hamilton syringes
- ultracentrifuge (for removing insoluble material and nucleic acids from samples)
- Beckman Ti-42.2 rotor (this rotor is convenient for small samples, but other angular rotors can also be used)
- Beckman airfuge (can be used for SDS solubilization but is not advised for urea solubilization, as heating samples can cause carbamylation of proteins)
- Amicon centrifugation concentrator tubes (Centricon 10, #4205) (optional but very useful for concentrating samples without increasing salt concentration)

- 0.2 μm syringe filters (Nalgene Labware 190–2020; Nalge Co., Sybron Corp.)
- microdialyser (Health Products)

A. *Preparation of solubilization buffer stock solution (pH 6.8)*
1. Take 2% SDS, 2 g and add 0.0625 M Trizma Base, 0.75 g.
2. Add 10% glycerol, 10 ml and fill to 100 ml.
3. Filter with 0.2 μm syringe filter.
4. Take 2–5% β-mercaptoethanol and add fresh to small aliquot.

B. *Procedure*
1. Add solubilization buffer to sample.
2. Heat at 95 °C in boiling water bath. (It may be adequate and sometimes advantageous to incubate sample for 2–3 h at 25 °C before boiling if proteases are not present in sample.)
3. Ultracentrifuge at 100 000–200 000 g for 1–2 h to remove nucleic acids or insoluble material if necessary.

Protocol 2. Sample preparation for isoelectric focusing in two-dimensional PAGE (2)

Reagents
- SDS (BioRad)
- cyclohexylaminoethane (CHES) (Calbiochem)
- Glycerol (Fisher)
- β-mercaptoethanol (BioRad)
- urea (Ultrapure) (BioRad)
- Nonidet P-40 (non-ionic detergent) (Accurate Chemical)
- Ampholytes (pH 3.5–10: BioRad, LKB, or Pharmacia; pH 2–11: Serva). This wide-range mixture is adequate for most routine samples. Other pH range or combinations of brands of ampholytes may be used in some instances (2).
- H_2O deionized with mixed bed resin (Continental Filter System) or deionized double-distilled H_2O

Equipment and supplies
As *Protocol 1*

Protocol 2. *Continued*

A. *Preparation of stock solutions*

   (a) SDS solubilization buffer for isoelectric focusing (IEF)
1. Take 0.05 M CHES, 100 mg, 2% SDS, 200 mg, and 10% glycerol, 1 ml.
2. Bring to 10 ml with H_2O and pH to 9.5. Add a very small amount of bromophenol blue.
3. Filter with 0.2 μm syringe filter and store at room temperature.
4. Add β-mercaptoethanol (2%) to small aliquot just prior to use.

   (b) Urea solubilization buffer for IEF (make fresh before use)
1. Take 9 M urea, 54 g, and (4%) Nonidet P-40, 4 ml.
2. Add water to a final volume of 100 ml and filter with a 0.2 μm filter.
3. Add 2% β-mercaptoethanol and 2% ampholytes to the small aliquot of solubilization buffer just prior to use. (Use either 3.5–10 LKB or 9–11 Serva ampholytes.)

B. *Procedure*
1. Prepare sample prior to solubilization. Most protein samples can be solubilized directly. If tissues are used, they may be homogenized in an ice bath but for better solubilization of tissues use tissues frozen in liquid nitrogen. These can be pulverized in liquid nitrogen. Solubilize the pulverized tissue directly or extract it with water and centrifuge to remove insoluble from water-soluble proteins.
2. Concentrate the sample. If necessary, concentrate the protein sample using Amicon microconcentrator tubes or lyophilize the sample directly or following dialysis against ammonium bicarbonate (pH 7.5) or H_2O to remove salts. Alternatively, use a two-times concentrated sample buffer so that the sample will not be diluted as much.
3. Solubilize the sample.
   (a) *Urea solubilization.* Suspend samples in the urea solubilization solution and incubate at room temperature for 2 h. *Do not heat,* or you will generate charge artifacts.
   (b) *SDS solubilization.* Suspend samples in SDS solution buffer, place in a tightly capped glass vial, and heat for 5–10 min in a boiling waterbath. (Thick plastic tubes such as microfuge tubes are insulated and interfere with heating.) It may be necessary to solubilize some samples at room temperature for 2–3 h with or without heating.
4. Centrifuge the sample. Following the incubation, samples are centrifuged to remove non-solubilized material and nucleic acids that

may interfere with focusing or cause 'streaking' in one- and two-dimensional PAGE (100 000–200 000 *g* for 2 h is suggested). We recommend using a Beckman Ti-42.2 rotor, which holds 72 tubes. A main advantage of this rotor is that small sample volumes (20–200 μl) can be prepared in these tubes (Beckman 342.303). A problem encountered occasionally is that some proteins of interest may be removed during centrifugation if they are not adequately solubilized. Centrifuge at 25 °C to prevent either urea or SDS from precipitating out of the solubilization buffer.

5. Load the sample. Following centrifugation, remove supernatants from the tube and apply them to IEF gels. While some samples can be frozen at −70 °C and run at a later date, best results are obtained if samples are run immediately after solubilization.

4. Sample preparation for different types of proteins

Initial factors to consider when choosing the best method of sample preparation are the general characteristics of the protein and the cellular localization of the protein in question. The cytosolic protein content of cells, whether they are prokaryotic or eukaryotic, is typically quite complex.

4.1 Subfractionation of samples for electrophoresis

It is critical that the investigator who is just initiating experiments be aware of the limitations of the analysis of total cellular or biological fluid samples which may contain thousands of proteins. Most of the abundant cellular proteins are 'housekeeping' proteins which are essential for the life of the cell. It is frequently not possible to observe discrete minor differences which might be brought about by experimental variables if total cellular protein is analysed. It is therefore usually necessary to carry out some form of protein subfractionation prior to protein analysis in order to analyse minor proteins in a sample.

4.1.1 Organelle fractionation using centrifugation and electrophoresis

Classical methods for subfractionating cellular components utilizing centrifugation have been described in detail previously (17, 18). While these methods have been invaluable in studies on the structure and function of specific organelles of cells, they are time-consuming and limited for several aspects of protein analysis:

(a) Only small numbers of samples can be easily processed.

(b) These methods take long periods of time, therefore, endogenous proteolysis can cause alterations in protein prior to electrophoretic analysis.

(c) Detailed analyses must be carried out to prove the quality of the preparation (for example, electron microscopy and enzyme identification).

4.1.2 Water-soluble fractionation

For the rapid fractionation of cells or tissue, it is possible to rapidly homogenize (before or after pulverization of tissue in liquid nitrogen) in distilled H_2O. The samples can then be centrifuged at 100 000–200 000 g for one hour and the water 'insoluble' as well as the water-soluble fractions can be analysed. Because this method is rapid and simple, it is usually the method of choice if tissue or cell samples are available only in limited amounts.

Alternative protein fractionation methods have been developed for protein analysis that rely on independent and more expedient chemical extractions (19). These methods have allowed the fractionation of cells into subcellular fractions corresponding to water-soluble, membrane, microfilament, intermediate filament, microtubule, polysomal, and nucleic protein fractions. Care must be taken throughout these procedures to insure that proteins are not proteolysed or chemically modified prior to protein analyses. More recently, new methods and equipment have been developed for the electrophoretic purification of cells and membranes (20–22). These new methods of free-flow electrophoresis should prove invaluable in future studies of cell isolation and fractionation.

4.1.3 Chemical extraction methods for protein analysis

A variety of methods are available for extracting proteins directly from cells or tissues for analysis by PAGE. Generally, these require multiple samples for different extraction procedures. One series of chemical extractions has been developed to analyze seven subcellular fractions corresponding to:

- water-soluble proteins
- membrane proteins
- microfilaments and other deoxycholate-soluble proteins
- intermediate filaments
- microtubules
- polysomes and
- nuclei (19)

It should be pointed out that while cell fractionation methods are important for analysis and comparison of complex protein samples, it is more difficult to definitively establish that a protein is a constituent of a particular cellular organelle. It will eventually be necessary to prove the cellular localization of a protein using such methods as immunocytochemical localization.

4.2 Solubilization of membrane proteins

The solubilization of membrane proteins for purification is accompanied by several methods. Some proteins are associated with the external or internal surface of the membrane while others are intercalated in the lipid bilayer. The strategy for isolating your protein of interest will depend on its interaction with the lipid bilayer of the cellular membranes. Since proteins may be associated with membranes in a variety of ways, it will be necessary to design your experiments to dissociate or solubilize your protein accordingly. A detailed list of membrane proteins and the methods for isolation has been described by Guidotti (23). A minor portion of membrane proteins are loosely bound to or associated with membranes. Some of these can be dissociated by changing the ionic strength or pH of the medium or by chelating the divalent cations which are involved in the binding of some proteins to the membrane (24). For example, basic proteins such as cytochrome C are positively charged at neutral pH and are therefore bound to membrane phospholipids by electrostatic bonds which can be disrupted by high salt concentrations. In general, we have found that either the urea solubilization or sodium dodecyl sulphate solubilization methods for iso-electric focusing or for SDS-PAGE are adequate for optimal resolution of most membrane proteins when one- or two-dimensional PAGE is used.

Although PAGE is commonly used to separate and identify soluble enzymes, membrane enzymes and other proteins are more difficult to identify, presumably due to their lipoprotein character. Because large lipoprotein molecules or aggregates are unlikely to enter even 5–10% acrylamide gels or fail to resolve adequately if they do, it is necessary to solubilize or disaggregate these prior to electrophoresis (25). Many solubilization methods used to extract proteins from the lipid portion of the membranes are frequently accompanied by irreversible inactivation of membrane enzymes or alteration in the physicochemical properties of the molecules to be analysed. Essentially, all methods using organic solvents for lipid extraction cause some degree of protein denaturation. Organic solvents (such as 2-chloroethanol or n-butanol) have been used to solubilize membranes because they have the capacity to separate membrane lipids from proteins (26). Acetic acid has also been used, since at low concentrations (10%) it has been reported to act as an acid by dissociating the loosely bound membrane proteins. At high concentrations ($> 50\%$), however, it acts mainly as an organic solvent and weakens the hydrophobic bonds within the protein subunits as well as between the protein and lipid molecules (24).

Generally, ionic detergents are more effective than non-ionic detergents in solubilizing membranes. However, if maintenance of enzymatic or biological activity is important, ionic detergents may be unacceptable. As with other protein samples, the degree of membrane solubilization depends on the detergent concentration. This optimal concentration has been shown to be dependent on the weight ratio of detergent to membrane protein rather than on the absolute detergent concentration (27, 28). As described above, membranes have also been solubilized with a combination of detergents (for example, deoxycholate and TX-100). A non-denaturing, zwitterionic detergent, CHAPS (3-(3-chloroamidopropyl)dimethylammonio)-1-propane sulphonate) has been reported to be effective at breaking protein–protein interactions (29). While this detergent may not be universally useful, it behaves as a zwitterion and possesses no net charge over a large pH range. It therefore does not interfere with ion exchange or isoelectric focusing methods to the extent that many other detergents do.

4.3 Concentration of proteins for gel electrophoresis from conditioned medium using diatomaceous earth

It is frequently advantageous to partially fractionate a concentrated protein before it is analysed by electrophoretic methods. Optimal methods for this involve procedures which are rapid and take a minimal amount of time to carry out so that large numbers of samples can be processed without proteolysis of proteins, etc. Affigel Blue (BioRad Chemical Co.) is frequently used to remove albumin from serum or plasma samples so that minor serum proteins can be more easily identified (30). We have found, however, that other proteins may also be removed by this or other charged bead matrices which are commonly used for protein fractionation.

A convenient, inexpensive method for rapidly concentrating proteins for analysis by electrophoresis using celite/diatomaceous earth has recently been developed (31). This method is useful because small amounts of protein may be absorbed and concentrated with minimal loss of protein and without the simultaneous concentration of salts which will interfere with isoelectric focusing. This method is outlined below (*Protocol 3*).

This procedure is used to concentrate medium conditioned by tissue-culture cells in order to study secretory proteins by two-dimensional PAGE. It is an excellent method with which to compare serum-free medium from cell cultures under various conditions (the ubiquitous serum proteins make it difficult to analyse differences in gel patterns). Large numbers of small-quantity media samples can be concentrated quickly and inexpensively for gel electrophoresis without the resultant artifacts generated by the high concentration of salts in samples concentrated by other methods. Initial studies should be done on a particular system to optimize the amount of diatomaceous earth needed, its length of incubation with the medium, and how much urea buffer will be used. The procedure described below (*Protocol 3*) has been optimized for our system and should be used as a guideline.

Protocol 3. Concentration of proteins for gel electrophoresis
from conditioned medium using diatomaceous
earth (31)

Reagents

• diatomaceous earth, 97.5% SiO_2 (Sigma, grade III #D-5384) (of the three
grades offered by Sigma grade III has been found to be most useful for
this method)

Equipment

• microcentrifuge (Beckman B microfuge, Fisher model 235B)

A. *Preparation of stock solutions*

(a) 10% diatomaceous earth

1. Take 1 g of diatomaceous earth.
2. Wash by adding at least 20 ml distilled water, shake, centrifuge the
diatomaceous earth into a pellet, and remove the water.
3. Repeat washing. Add 10 ml distilled water and use this as a 10%
solution.

(b) Urea gel electrophoresis solubilization buffer

1. Prepare as in *Protocol 2*.

B. *Procedure*

1. Remove cellular debris from medium conditioned by cells in culture by
centrifugation. Add the diatomaceous earth solution (making sure it is
well suspended) to the conditioned medium in a plastic tube to make a
final concentration of 2% diatomaceous earth solution (i.e. 200 µl 10%
diatomaceous earth added to 800 µl conditioned medium). Mix gently
and continuously by using a rocker platform or rotator for 2 h at room
temperature.
2. Pellet the diatomaceous earth by centrifugation. A quick way to do this
is to put the mixture into Eppendorf tubes and centrifuge. Remove the
supernatant. Add urea gel electrophoresis solubilization buffer to the
pellet; the amount will depend on how much protein was in the
medium and how much sample can be loaded onto the gels (we use
30–70 µl of urea buffer per original ml of serum-free medium). Stand at
room temperature for 2 h vortexing every 15 min. Pellet the
diatomaceous earth and load supernatant onto a gel.

5. General rules for choosing a solubilization method

There are no set rules to determine the best solubilization procedure other than empirically for your protein of specific interest. Knowledge of the physicochemical characteristics of the molecule will allow you to make an educated guess based on the solubilization mechanisms described above. We have found that the three solubilization methods as outlined in this chapter (16, 32) can be used for most protein samples (see *Protocols 1* and *2*). You may have to try each the first time to determine the method and concentrations to be used in order to optimize solubilization of some samples. Different solubilization methods may affect the apparent pI of some proteins. The solubilization solutions may be altered for detection of specific types of proteins. One example is the detection of DNA-binding proteins as described in Chapter 13. In this example the reducing agent is omitted, the SDS concentration is lowered to 0.5%, and the samples are not boiled.

It is critical that the ratio of solubilization buffer to sample be optimized. Although you will have to optimize the solubilization method for your specific samples, we have found the following ratios of protein to sample buffer adequate (*Table 1*).

Table 1. Suggested sample to solubilization buffer ratios for different sample types

Sample	Sample amount	Solubilization buffer (vol.)
Tissue homogenates	200–500 µg	2 ml
Cell pellets	20–50 µl	300 µl
Soluble proteins	10–200 µg	30–50 µl
Cell culture cellular proteins	1×10^6 cells[a]	500 µl
Cell culture media proteins	Proteins from 1 ml medium	30–70 µl

Note: 5–30 µl of each of the above samples should be adequate for identification of abundant proteins by Coomassie Blue or of minor proteins by silver stain for two-dimensional gel patterns.

6. Protein quantitation in solubilization samples

6.1 Modified Bradford protein assay for samples in urea solubilization buffer (33)

This is an excellent method for quickly determining the amount of protein in a sample that has been solubilized in urea gel electrophoresis solubilization buffer for isoelectric focusing. It is often the case that the amount of protein in a sample cannot be assayed before solubilization. For example, cells and sometimes tissues are put directly into solubilization buffer, or the buffer is required to obtain the sample from an inert support. The use of ovalbumin is the standard for this assay, but the investigator should select the standard protein that responds similarly to most of the proteins in the sample (i.e. BSA for serum proteins).

Protocol 4. Modified Bradford protein assay for samples in urea solubilization buffer

Reagents
- protein for standard (for example, BSA, ovalbumin)
- Coomassie Brilliant Blue G-250 dye reagent (BioRad, Pierce)

Stock solutions
- urea electrophoresis solubilization buffer (see *Protocol 2*)
- standard protein stock (BSA, ovalbumin, or protein standard of your choice)
- 0.1 N HCl in distilled H_2O
- Coomassie dye reagent: this can be made according to Bradford (34) or brought from Pierce (ready to use: 23200) or BioRad (concentrate that must be diluted and filtered before use: 500–0006).

1. Prepare protein standard samples in duplicate to contain 1–50 μg protein in 10 μl urea buffer.
2. Add 10 μl 0.1 N HCl to each tube and bring the volume up to 100 μl with 80 μl distilled water.
3. Prepare unknown samples similarly. For example, bring 5–7 μl of a protein sample solubilized in urea buffer up to 10 μl with more urea buffer, add 10 μl 0.1 N HCl and bring to 100 μl with 80 μl distilled water.
4. Add 3.5 ml Coomassie dye reagent to each tube, mix thoroughly.
5. After 5 min, read the absorbance at 595 nm with a spectrophotometer.
6. Use a blank containing all reagents except protein to set the zero.

6.2 Modified protein assay for samples in SDS solubilization buffer

SDS will interfere with the standard Lowry assay in concentrations above 12.5 mg/ml (35). However, if the amount of solubilization buffer in each assay sample is adjusted to an equivalent amount, a relative measure of the amount of sample solubilized in SDS can be obtained. This is important when attempting to load equal amounts of solubilized proteins.

Protocol 5. Modified Lowry protein assay

Reagents

- sodium carbonate ($Na_2CO_3 \cdot H_2O$) (Sigma)
- sodium hydroxide pellets (NaOH) (Sigma)
- copper sulphate ($CuSO_4 \cdot 5H_2O$) (Mallinckrodt)
- sodium potassium tartrate (NaK tartrate$\cdot 4H_2O$) (Sigma)
- bovine serum albumin (BSA) (Sigma)
- Folin-Ciocalteu's phenol reagent, 2.0 N (Sigma)

Equipment

- spectrophotometer (Milton Roy, Spectronic 1001 Plus)

A. *Preparation of stock solutions*

(a) Solution A

1. Take 2% Na_2CO_3, 2 g and 0.1 N NaOH, 0.4 g.

2. Bring to 100 ml in distilled H_2O and store in a dark bottle.

(b) Solution B_1

1. Take 1% $CuSO_4 \cdot 5H_2O$, 0.5 g.

2. Bring to 50 ml in distilled H_2O.

(c) Solution B_2

1. Take 2% NaK tartrate$\cdot 4H_2O$, 1 g.

2. Bring to 50 ml in distilled H_2O.

(d) Solution C

1. Take 100 part A, 1 part B_1, and 1 part B_2.

(e) BSA standard

1. Take BSA 100 mg.

2. Bring to 100 ml in distilled H_2O. Check the UV absorbance of the standard on a spectrophotometer at 280 nm. The absorbance of BSA at 1 mg/ml is 0.58. Freeze 1.0 ml aliquots for use.

B. *Procedure*

1. Prepare protein standards, each in duplicate or triplicate: pipette aliquots of BSA stock into 12 × 75 mm tubes (5–40 μl will give absorbance readings in the linear range of the assay). Add solubilization buffer (volume equal to that of unknown sample to be added) and distilled H_2O to bring volumes to 200 μl. A blank should be included with the solubilization buffer, distilled H_2O, and all other reagents except BSA.

2. Prepare protein samples, also in duplicate or triplicate: pipette an aliquot of sample containing approximately 5–30 μg of protein into tube and bring volume to 200 μl with distilled H_2O. Try 10, 50, or 100 μl aliquots if protein concentration is totally unknown.

3. Add 1.0 ml solution C to each tube, mix, and incubate 10 min at room temperature.

4. Add 50 μl Folin-Ciocalteu's reagent and vortex immediately.

5. Incubate for at least 30 min at room temperature.

6. Read absorbance at 660 or 750 nm with spectrophotometer (tungsten light setting). Blank against appropriate reagent blank. Plot amount of BSA in standards against the average absorbance for each, and use this standard curve to determine amount of protein in samples.

7. Artifacts of protein solubilization

7.1 Detergent concentration and interaction

The solubilization of proteins with detergents is a complex process. Inadequate levels of detergent may result in inadequate solubilization, so that proteins do not enter the polyacrylamide gel. If more than one detergent is used (for example anionic and non-ionic), they may also interact if used simultaneously and form aggregates that will interfere with proteins entering polyacrylamide gels or will cause streaking.

Boiling SDS samples in plastic tubes will frequently result in inadequate solubilization because the thick plastic wall of the tube will insulate the sample. It is important to heat samples in glass tubes for optimal sample solubilization. It is also critical *not* to store SDS-solubilization solutions in the freezer since this detergent will aggregate and optimal solubilization cannot be obtained even after heating the reagent again.

7.2 Chemical modification of proteins

Many side chains of amino acid residues of globular proteins easily react with a variety of specific chemical reagents. While these reactions can readily be used to detect and quantitate levels of proteins, they can also induce changes in protein that may alter charge or structure. These changes would therefore affect the mobilities of proteins in IEF or in SDS-PAGE. The most common modifications that can occur during protein sample preparation or solubilization are carbamylation and deamidation.

Carbamylation is the process of adding a carbamyl group (NH_2CO-) to an amino group. This can occur when protein samples are allowed to heat in the presence of urea. Under these conditions, the cyanate generated from urea will cause carbamylation of proteins, and may dramatically alter their charge properties. For these reasons, proteins should never be heated in the presence of urea prior to analysis by IEF unless you are processing proteins to make internal charge standards (2).

Deamidation is the removal of an amino group (NH_2) from an amino acid. Deamidation occurs when primary amino groups are converted into hydroxyl groups. This can occur if proteins are treated by acetic acid or nitric acid in dilute HCl (36).

7.3 Protein concentration

Common methods used for concentrating protein samples include lyophilization, centricon microconcentrators (e.g. Centricon microconcentrator, Amicon, Beverly, MA, USA), trichloroacetic acid (TCA) precipitation, and ammonium sulphate precipitation. Lyophilization of protein samples will also concentrate salts and other contaminants which can interfere with isoelectric focusing or cause 'streaking' of samples in one- or two-dimensional PAGE. If samples are lyophilized to dryness, proteins will often aggregate and become more difficult to denature. Likewise, TCA and ammonium acetate precipitation can alter protein migration patterns in gels. Centricon microconcentrators are used for small sample volumes but these membranes may bind some proteins lowering the recovery of sample after this procedure.

7.4 'Insoluble' proteins

Some proteins are difficult to solubilize or may interact with other proteins even in the presence of high concentrations of either detergents or denaturing reagents, or both. It is important that a systematic study be carried out utilizing different solubilization methods in conjunction with one- as well as two-dimensional PAGE to determine the best method with which to analyse your protein samples. In extreme cases, it may be necessary to carry out proteolysis of samples in order to at least evaluate the peptide composition of proteins that cannot be evaluated with conventional methods.

References

1. Lapanje, S. (1978). *Physiochemical aspects of protein denaturation*. Wiley, New York.

2. Dunbar, B. S. (1987). *Two-dimensional electrophoresis and immunological techniques*. Plenum, New York.
3. Tanford, C. (1968). *Adv. Protein Chem.*, **23**, 121.
4. Hames, B. D. (1981). In *Gel electrophoresis of proteins: a practical approach*, (ed. B. D. Hames and D. Rickwood), pp. 1–91. IRL Press, Oxford.
5. Tanford, C. (1970). *Adv. Protein Chem.*, **24**, 2.
6. Steinhart, J. and Reynolds, J. A. (1969). *Multiple equilibrium in proteins*. Academic, New York.
7. Makino, S., Reynolds, J. A., and Tanfor, C. (1973). *J. Biol. Chem.*, **239**, 3687.
8. Dewald, B., Dulaney, J. T., and Touster, O. (1974). *Methods Enzymol.*, **32**, 82.
9. Newby, A. C. and Chrambach, A. (1979). *Biochem. J.*, **177**, 623.
10. Green, F. A. (1971). *J. Colloid. Interface Sci.*, **35**, 481.
11. Reynolds, J. A. and Tanford, C. (1970). *Proc. Natl. Acad. Sci., USA*, **66**, 1002.
12. Reynolds, J. A. and Tanford, C. (1970). *J. Biol. Chem.*, **245**, 5161.
13. Decker, R. V. and Foster, J. F. (1966). *Biochemistry*, **5**, 1242.
14. Reynolds, J. A., Herbert, S., Polet, H., and Steinhart, J. (1967). *Biochemistry*, **6**, 930.
15. Takagi, T., Tsujii, K., and Sherahama, K. (1975). *J. Biochem. (Tokyo)*, **77**, 939.
16. Laemmli, U. K. (1970). *Nature*, **277**, 680.
17. Fleischer, S. and Kervina, M. (1974). *Methods Enzymol.*, **31**, 6.
18. Reid, E. and Williamson, R. (1974). *Methods Enzymol.*, **31**, 713.
19. Lenstra, J. A. and Bloemendal, H. (1983). *Eur. J. Biochem.*, **135**, 413.
20. Menashi, S. and Crawford, N. (1980). *Eur. J. Cell Biol.*, **22**, 598.
21. Menashi, S., Weintroub, H., and Crawford, N. (1981). *J. Biol. Chem.*, **256**, 4095.
22. Morre, D. J., Morre, D. M., and Heidrich, H. G. (1983). *Eur. J. Cell Biol.*, **31**, 263.
23. Guidotti, G. (1972). *Ann. Rev. Biochem.*, **41**, 731.
24. Razin, S. (1972). *Biochim. Biophys. Acta*, **265**, 241.
25. Dewald, B., Dulaney, J. T., and Touster, O. (1984). *Methods Enzymol.*, **32**, 82.
26. Zahler, P. and Weibel, E. R. (1970). *Biochem. Biophys. Acta*, **219**, 320.
27. Selinger, Z., Klein, M., and Amsterdam, A. (1969). *Biochem. Biophys. Acta*, **183**, 19.
28. Engelman, D. M., Terry, T. M., and Morowitz, H. J. (1967). *Biochem. Biophys. Acta*, **135**, 381.
29. Hjelmeland, L. M. (1980). *Proc. Natl. Acad. Sci., USA*, **77**, 6368.
30. Tracy, R. P. and Young, D. S. (1984). In *Two-dimensional gel electrophoresis of proteins: methods and applications*, (ed. J. E. Celis and R. Bravo), pp. 193–240. Academic, New York.
31. Maresh, G. and Dunbar, B. S. (1988). *Electrophoresis*, **9**, 54.
32. Tollaksen, S. L., Anderson, N. L., and Anderson, N. G. (1984). In *Operation of the ISO–DALT system*, 7th edn., p. 1, ANC–BIM–81–1.
33. Ramagli, L. S. and Rodriguez, L. V. (1985). *Electrophoresis*, **6**, 599.
34. Bradford, M. M. (1976). *Anal. Biochem.*, **72**, 248.
35. Peterson, G. L. (1983). *Methods Enzymol.*, **91**, 95.
36. Haurowitz, F. and Tunca, M. (1945). *Biochem. J.*, **39**, 443.

8

Strategy for purification of organelles from parasites: protein blotting as one of the initial steps

DAVID W. SAMMONS

1. Introduction

Purification of organelles is essential for studies of the cell biology of eukaryotic cells and their parasites, and is essential for the complete understanding of the host/parasite membrane organizational and spatial interrelationships. Organelle-specific antigens or structures can be manipulated to assist in the isolation and purification of organelles; however, it is sometimes technically difficult to achieve unless consideration is made of all separation alternatives. Available principles of separation are size, density, charge, immunoaffinity, paramagnetic, and combinations of these in the presence of various buffers and detergents.

Immunoblotting furnishes an ideal starting point for the molecular characterization of organelle-specific proteins; however, generation of antibodies to the organelle's protein must first be achieved. Purification of the organelle-specific protein to be utilized in generation of the antibody is greatly simplified if the intact organelle is purified from the other cellular components. While several purification approaches are possible, an individual strategy may have to be developed that fits the uniqueness of the organelle's properties and considers special problems that arise as a result of these properties. Detergent solubilization and subsequent centrifugation (size and density) have been the workhorses of organelle purification for decades; however, large quantities of organelles free from contaminants can seldom be achieved when only these two approaches are utilized. Free-flow electrophoresis (charge) has been very effective in some instances for the purification of mammalian organelles, and immunoaffinity methods have become increasingly popular as beads capable of being derivatized with specific antibodies have become available.

In my laboratory we are studying the molecular structure, biological organization, and biochemical function of the membranes of the *Plasmodia falciparium* food vacuole, a parasite organelle found in the trophozoite stage of infected erythrocytes. The food vacuole has gained a place of importance in research in the past few years since findings suggested that the mechanism of action of chloroquine resides with an enzyme in this organelle (1). The food vacuole contains proteases responsible for the degradation of haemoglobin (2–5), haem polymerase involved in the polymerization of haem (1), and several other uncharacterized proteins essential for the detoxification pathway. To facilitate studies of the food vacuole proteins and their interactive functions, it is necessary to have preparative amounts of pure food vacuole for biochemical analysis. This chapter offers several of the approaches that we are using for the isolation of the parasite and this essential organelle. Perhaps some of the purification strategies will be applicable to the isolation of other organelles in different biological systems

2. General strategy for the purification of parasite organelles

The isolation strategy for the *Plasmodia* food vacuole organelle illustrates a typical approach that one can take to purify any specialized parasite organelle. The strategy encompasses the following general steps:

(a) Collect parasite-infected host cells; culture *in vitro* if possible (*Figure 1*).

(b) Identify an organelle-specific subelement's unique feature and evaluate its potential use with one of the separation principles.

(c) Purify the organelle subelement and its associated proteins (*Figure 2*).

(d) Generate antibodies and characterize by immunoblot with the subelement proteins (*Figure 3*).

(e) Separate intact parasites from host cell membranes (*Figure 4*).

(f) Use organelle subelement unique features to purify intact organelles from parasite contaminants including other parasite stages that are devoid of the organelle subelement.

(g) Use the antibodies raised against the purified organelle subelement to characterize antigen distribution on organelle and membranes (*Figure 5*).

(h) Capture isolated organelles on antibody-derivatized acrylamide beads for the morphological and biochemical analysis of structure and function of intact organelles (*Figure 6*).

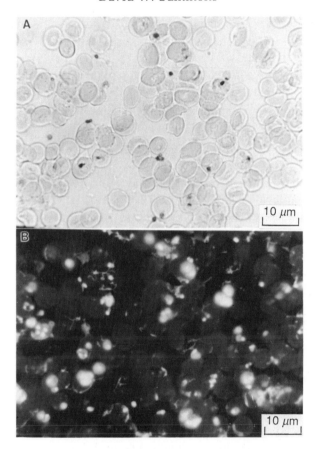

Figure 1. *In vitro* culture of *P. falciparum* in human erythrocytes. A, Infested erythrocytes; B, parasite infested erythrocytes detected by staining nucleic acids with acridine orange dye.

3. Isolation of *P. falciparum* food vacuoles

Protocol 1. In vitro culture of *P. falciparum* and collection of infected erythrocytes

1. Culture *P. falciparum* FCR3 TC strain (Gambia, Africa) in culture using the candle jar method of Tragger and Jensen (6).

2. Culture in 15 cm petri dishes at a haematocrit indicating approximately 2–4% human erythrocytes using culture medium of RPMI 1640 supplemented with 25 mM Hepes, 23 mM NaHC O$_3$ 1% Penicillin/streptomycin (v/v), and 5% human serum (v/v).

Protocol 2. Purification of organelle subelement and associated proteins

1. Culture 15 culture plates for isolation and electrophoretic characterization of associated protein. Note: Since haemozoin is abundantly expressed in the trophozoite stage of the intraerythrocytic cycle, this number of plates should be adequate.

2. Isolate haemozoin directly from malarial tissue using established methods (10).

   (a) Collect pellet of parasite-infested erythrocytes from culture by centrifugation at 650 × *g* for 10 min.

   (b) Lyse pellet by adding 10 × volume of distilled water.

   (c) Pellet haemozoin after centrifugation at 40 000 × *g* for 25 min at 25 °C.

   (d) Wash pellet successively with 0.2% SDS until supernatant absorbance (280 nm) has leveled off. Note: the free haemozoin has 'sticky' properties after removal of the SDS therefore replacement PBS buffer may result in aggregation.

Figure 2 illustrates a cluster of purified haemozoin as seen with scanning electron microscopy. There is a protein coat surrounding each haemozoin crystal that is not solubilized by 0.1% SDS but this can be removed with higher concentrations of anionic detergents.

Protocol 3. Preparation of haemozoin-associated protein from the purified haemozoin crystal

1. Dissolve crystal in 0.1 M NaOH.

2. Precipitate the released protein with the addition of 3% volume of HCL-acetone chilled at −70 °C.

3. Recover protein after storage of the mixture overnight at −20 °C and centrifuge at 12 500 g for 15 min at 4 °C.

4. Wash protein pellet twice with 0.5 ml of 0.1 M Tris–HCl buffer, pH 7.2 by centrifugating at 100 000 g for 30 min.

5. Proteins are generating using established protocols.

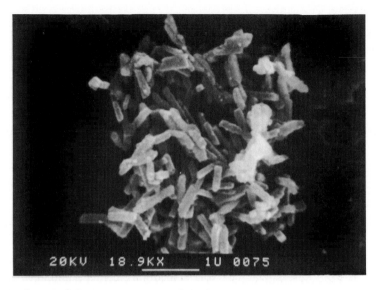

Figure 2. Scanning electron micrograph of purified haemozoin.

Protocol 4. Immunoblot analysis of antibodies against haemozoin proteins

1. Carry out SDS electrohphoresis using the procedure of Laemmli (19).

    (a) Use 12% or 15% mini slab acrylamide gels (1.0 mm thick, 5.5–6.0 cm long).

    (b) Solubilize haemozoin protein:

        • 2% SDS

        • 5% B-mercaptoethanol

        • 0.125 M Tris–HCl, pH 6.8

        • 10% glycerol

        • 0.1% bromophenol blue

        • heat at 100C for 5 min

    (c) Load gel and carry out electrophoresis at 100v for run through stacking gel and at 140 v for electrophoresis in separation gel.

2. Immunoblot of haemozoin protein following transfer protein to nitrocellulose filter.

    (a) Transfer buffer:

        • 2.9 g Tris

109

Protocol 4. *Continued*

- 14.5 g glycine
- 200 ml methanol in 100 ml water

(b) Transfer gel at 60 V in transfer buffer.

(c) Block nitrocellulose membrane with 5% milk for 30 min while shaking.

(d) Dilute primary antibody containing rabbit anti-haemozoin protein serum 1/100 in 5% milk.

(e) Incubate antibody with membrane for 45 min at 24 °C.

(f) Wash membrane four times for 5 min in PBS-Tween buffer (0.5% Tween).

(g) Incubate in secondary antibody (goat anti-rabbit IgG/HRP diluted 1/5000 in mile and incubate 45 min at 25 °C.

(h) Was as in (f) above.

(i) Incubate with substrate (1 hydroxyl-4 chloro-1 napthol).

Figure 3 illustrates as immunoblot using the rabbit antisera to haemozoin proteins. There are several immunodominant proteins with molecular weights in the range of 31–55 kd but none of the lower molecular weight proteins is detected. The identity of these proteins remains unknown at this time.

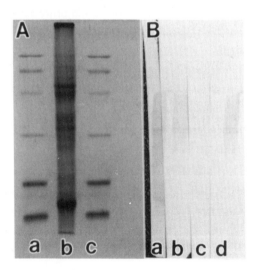

Figure 3. Immunoblot characterization of haemozoin associated protein. A, Sodium dodecyl sulfate electrophoretic analysis of the Acetone/HCl extracted haemozoin proteins. B, Western blot analysis of the rabbit anti-haemozoin proteins.

David W. Sammons

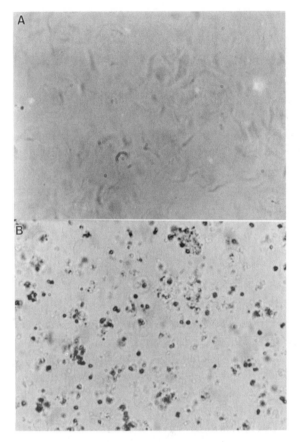

Figure 4. Separation of erythrocyte membranes from intact parasites. A, erythrocyte membranes after separation from the parasites and centrifugation at 1 000 000 × g. There are a few contaminate particles that stain with anti-haemozoin fluorescent antibodies. B, *P. falciparum* parasites after separation from the erythrocyte membranes after pelleting at 16 000 × g. Note the trophozoites represented by the circular structures surrounding the dark bodies (food vacuoles containing birefringent haemozoin) and the dark bodies not enclosed in the circular structure (parasitophorous vacuole membrane).

Protocol 5. Separation of parasites from erythrocyte membranes

1. Culture of trophozoite-stage infected erythrocytes.

   (a) Treat infected erythrocytes to a final concentration of 0.1% (w/v) saponin.

   (b) Separate by differential centrifugation as described previously (20).

Protocol 5. *Continued*

    (c) Released parasites can be identified by the presence of the parasitophorous vocuolar membrane surrounding many of the paracytes (See *Figure 4*).

2. Fractionation of erythrocyte membrane fractions.

    (a) Lyse cells as described in Section 3.2 above.

    (b) Collect erythrocyte membrane fractions from a 100 000 *g* spin and evaluate for the presence of parasites (*Figure 4*) show several fluorescent particles which can be identified when stained with the anti-haemozoin antibody although numbers are small in comparison to erythrocyte membrane quantity.

3. Release of food vacuoles from intact parasite.

    (a) Triturate parasite sample 20 times with 27 gauge needle as previously described (5, 21).

    (b) Food vacuoles can be observed as round and dense particles as seen in *Figure 4b*.

    (c) Intact trophozoite stage of the parasite are identified with the parasitophorous vacuole membrane surrounding its dark malaria pigment.

Protocol 6. Purification of intact organelles from contaminants using organelle subelement feature (paramagnetic property).

Note: Often organelles have unique features that can be utilized to assist in their purification, and polymerized haem of haemozoin is such an example. Its paramagnetic property is due to the electron valence state of the iron atom in the haemozoin. In a previous study, infected erythrocytes with parasites in the trophozoite stage were successfully separated from the non-haemozoin-bearing erythrocytes as a mixture of infected erythrocytes and uninfected erythrocytes were passed through a magnetic field (18) as outlined below.

1. Triturated parasites are suspended in 1 ml PBS buffer and loaded into a separation column with a 1 ml pipette with an open-bore orifice (to prevent shear).

2. Customized magnet prepared as a small 5 × 5 × 8.5 cm permanent, rare earth alloy (neodymium, cobalt, iron) with steel jacket.

3. Fit a plastic insert filled with 0.1 g randomly packed smooth steel

allow wire (No. 430, Molecular-Wire Corporation) into a 1 ml eppindorph centrifuge tube.

4. Place insert within centrifuge tube and cut bottom off with a razorblade.

5. Connect a 1 ml plastic tip designed for the eppindorph pipette to the bottom of the modified centrifuge tube to create a small exit orifice that is connected to a silicon tube threaded through a peristaltic pump (Model P-1, Pharmacia).

6. Fill entire separation assembly with PBS and place against the magnet.

7. Allow the force of the magnet to hold the assembly against the crevice of the magnet.

8. Suspend a 1 ml aliquot of triturated parasites to the steel wire and pump fluid at a rate of 0.5 ml/min until 3 ml of PBS has passed.

9. Remove wire and fluid from the magnetic field and to retain food vacuoles which can be recovered.

10. Use biofringent microscopy to determine purity of haemozoin-containing food vacuoles. (Because the food vacuoles may still have parasitophorous membranes from the trophoozoites, it is possible to use the birefringent property to evaluate and use in the purification strategy.)

11. Close scrutiny of these samples will show at least two sizes of birefringent food vacuoles. Centrifugation and elutriation methods (size and density) can be used to separate the two sizes of food vacuoles or they can be separated by free-flow electrophoresis (charge).

Protocol 7. Antibody binding to purified haemozoin food vacuoles

1. Identification of impure food vacuoles which have not been purified by percoll centrifugation as described by Goldberg *et al.* (5) can be visualized with polarized light at 1000 × magnification (see *Figure 5a*).

2. To identify the same sample for food vacuoles, stain sample with primary rabbit anti-haemozoin antibody followed by goad anti-rabbit IgG Biotin with streptavidin-PE.

3. Use fluorescence microscopy to observe each structure having the corresponding birefringent food vacuole (*Figure 5b*). Note: In some instances structures with faint fluorescence may not fluoresce. This

Protocol 7. *Continued*

suggests that proteins of the haemozoin are also present in other membranes of the parasite that are not part of the food vacuole. In this case further immunofluorescence with sub-fractionation of parasite samples will be needed to elucidate the exact correlation of the antigen location on other membranes of the parasite.

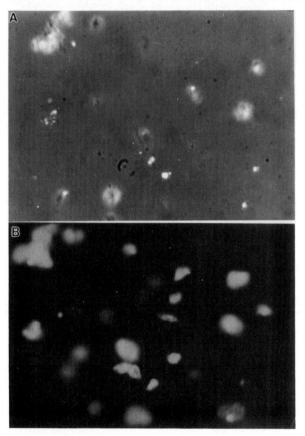

Figure 5. A, Capture of food vacuoles coated with rabbit anti-haemozoin protein antibodies by acrylamide beads coated with goat anti-rabbit IgG. B, Parasites stained with FITC labelled goat anti-rabbit antibody prior to addition of the 3M Emphaze biosupport beads.

These studies demonstrate that the haemozoin antigen are expressed on the surface of the food vacuoles. These methods also demonstrate that the usefulness of the antibodies in the purification strategy for isolating food vacuoles with immunoaffinity techniques may be compromised if the proteins are found on all parasite membranes. Because protocols outlined above demonstrate that food vacuoles expressing protein epitopes are recognized by the anti-haemozoin antibodies, it may be necessary to further purify these.

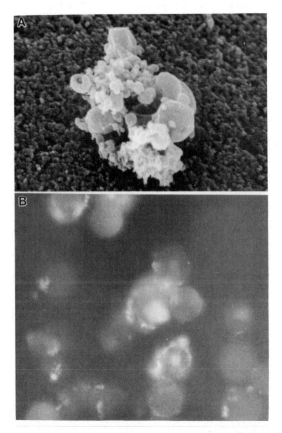

Figure 6. Scanning electron micrograph of a food vacuole attached to the 3M Emphaze Bead. The food vacuole is attached to the intracellular membranous structures, however the parasitophorous vacuole membrane is gone.

Protocol 8. Use of Immunoaffinity beads to purify food vacuole from parasite membranes and other structures

1. Bind rabbit anti-haemozoin antibody to 3M-EMPHAZE activated chromatography beads (3M Company) using procedures outlined by company instructions. (These beads are suitable since they are hydrophilic and highly crosslinked with copolymers of bis-acrylamide/azalactone.

2. Incubate beads food vacuoles and the with goat anti-rabbit IgG antibody.

Protocol 8. *Continued*

3. Use scanning electron microscopy to characterize food vacuoles (*Figure 6*). This step of purification illustrates the presence of fluorescent food vacuoles that are attached to the beads. At this level of magnification it is impossible to discern whether just food vacuoles and free haemozoin are binding to the surface of the bead. Scanning electron microscopic analysis demonstrates that membranous components are also attached to the beads. This observation is to be expected since findings shown above show that the haemozoin antigens are distributed on parasite membranes other than food vacuoles.

Protocol. 9. Magnetic purification of haemozoin-bearing food vacuoles

1. Take parasite fractions from the magnetic separation outlined in *Protocol 6*.

2. Separate parasite fractions from the magnetic separation and pellet.

3. Link fraction *s* to the 3M beads as described in **Protocol 8**.

4. Fix coated beads in 3% glutaraldehyde in cacodylate buffer.

5. Fix beads for 1 h and wash three times in PBS before post-fixing in 0.15 osmium tetroxide for 1 h.

6. Wash post-fixed sample three times in deionized water for 10 min before blocking in 3% uranyl acetate in water for 30 min.

7. Dehydrate in alcohol (30, 50, 70, 95%) at 5–10 minutes per alcohol concentration.

8. Incubate twice more in 100% alcohol for 5–10 min before placing dehydrated block in freon TF two times for 30 min.

9. Analyse spatial orientation of parasite food vacuole by scanning electron microscopy.

The scanning electron micrograph of *Figure 6b* shows the spatial organization of the parasite food vacuole in relation to the parasite's other membraneous structures. This structure is presumably the food vacuole, typically the largest birefringent object. It remains to be determined whether the smaller birefringent particles are indeed the mature coalesced food vacuoles as previously described (22) and whether they can be isolated without the associated membranes apparent in *Figure 6b*.

Finally, with a solid matrix such as an acrylamide bead it is possible to bind intact purified organelles via immunological linkages to antigens on the surface of the organelle. With this technology, it is possible to anchor intact and physiologically functional organelles with proper spatial orientation. These beads permit studies to characterize the structural and functional elements of the food vacuole. With intact food vacuoles, studies may be performed *in vitro* to elucidate the mechanism of drug resistance and for the development and testing of new drugs that can reverse chloroquine resistance that is currently a significant problem worldwide (23).

If needed, a final purification step can be done with an additional centrifugation step with a gradient that can separate the target organelle and the final contaminant. One can also use the magnetic properties of an organelle to separate the organelle from structures that are devoid of haemozoin. Preliminary results confirm that it is possible to separate different stages of malarial parasites with free-flow electrophoresis (24). These two separation methods utilize free solution and have several advantages of their own. Clearly, each method will have to be evaluated individually and at each step of the strategy to obtain the best final protocol for purifying the *P. falciparum* food vacuole.

References

1. Slater, A. F. and Cerami, A. (1992). *Nature*, **355**, 167–9.
2. Rudzinska, M. A., Trager, W., and Bray, R. S. (1965). *J. Protozool.*, **12**, 563–76.
3. Aikawa, M. (1971). *Exp. Parasitol.*, **30**, 284–320.
4. Sherman, I. W. (1979) *Microbiol. Rev.*, **43**, 453–95.
5. Goldberg, D. E., Slater, A. F., Cerami, A., and Henderson, G. B. (1990). *Proc. Natl. Acad. Sci., USA.*, **87**, 2931–5.
6. Trager, W. and Jensen, J. B. (1976). *Science*, **193**, 673–5.
7. Schaudinn, F. (1903). *Arbeiten Kaiserlichen Gesundheitsante*, **19**, 169–250.
8. Sherman, I. W., Ting, I. P., and Ruble, J. A. (1968). *J. Protozool.*, **15**, 158–64.
9. Homewood, C. A., Jewsbury, J. M., and Chance, M. L. (1972) *Comp. Biochem. Physiol.*, **43B**, 517–23.
10. Homewood, C. A., Moore, G. A., Warhurst, D. C., and Atkinson, E. M. (1975). *Ann. Trop. Med. Parasitol.*, **69**, 283–7.
11. Yamada, K. A. and Sherman, I. W. (1979). *Exp. Parasitol.*, **48**, 61–74.
12. Ginsberg, H., Rosenzweig, M., Willenz, A., Zangvill, M., and Bauminger, E. R. (1987). *Abstracts, 3rd International Conference on Malaria and Babesiosis, Annency*, p. 26.
13. Ashong, J. O., Blench, I. P., and Warhurst, D. C. (1989). *Trans. R. Soc. Trop. Med. Hyg.*, **83**, 167–72.
14. Goldie, P., jun., Roth, E. F., Oppenheim, J., Vanderberg, J. P. (1990). *Am. J. Trop. Med. Hyg.*, **43**, 584–96.
15. Lawrence, C. and Olson, J. A. (1986). *Am. J. Clin. Pathol.*, **86**, 360–3.
16. Heidelberger, M., Mayer, M. M., and Demarest, C. (1946). *J. Immunol.*, **52**, 325–33.

17. Paul, F., Melville, D., Roath, S., Warhurst, D. C., and Osisanya, J. O. S. (1981). *The Lancet*, **11**, 70–71.
18. Fairlamb, A. H., Paul, F., and Warhurst, D. C. (1984). *Mol. Biochem. Parasitol.*, **12**, 307–12.
19. Laemmli, U. K. (1970). *Nature*, **227**, 680–5.
20. Hsiao, L. L., Howard, R. J., Masamichi, A., and Taraschi, T. F. (1991). *Biochem. J.*, **274**, 121–32.
21. Cowman, A. F., Karcz, S., Galatis, D., and Culvenor, J. G. (1991). *J. Cell Biol.*, **113**, 1033–42.
22. Slomianny, C. (1990). *Blood Cells*, **16**, 369–78.
23. Peters, W. (1987). *Chemotherapy and drug resistance in malaria*. Academic, London.
24. Heidrich, H. G., Mrema, J. E. K., Jagt, D. L. V., Reyes, P., and Rieckmann, K. H. (1982). *J. Parasitol.*, **68**, 443–50.

Detection Methods and Uses in Immunoblotting

9

Radiometric methods for detection in blots

R. A. LASKEY

1. Introduction

Radioisotopes are used extensively to label probes for many blotting applications. This chapter considers the best methods for detecting them efficiently.

The most widely used methods involve autoradiographic detection on X-ray film. Autoradiographic methods can provide a good combination of sensitivity and resolution, and they do not require investment in expensive capital equipment. In spite of claims to the contrary, accurate quantitation can be achieved easily. For direct autoradiography without intensifying screens or scintillators, the response of the film is inherently linear until it reaches saturation (1, 2). When intensifying screens or fluorographic scintillators are used to increase sensitivity, the response of film to the light they produce is non-linear but it can easily be made linear by pre-exposing the film to a flash of light (1, 2).

Phosphorimagers offer a new alternative to film detection methods. Although they involve a high initial capital expense, they offer increased sensitivity for most of the radioisotopes commonly used in biological sciences, the exception being tritium (^{3}H). They also offer linearity over a wide dynamic range.

Within the range of autoradiographic methods available, there are differences in sensitivity and resolution. The greatest resolution is offered by direct autoradiography, in which a β-particle or γ-ray interacts directly with the silver halide crystals in the emulsion of a radiographic film. However, greater sensitivity can often be achieved by converting the emissions to blue or ultraviolet light, either by using an intensifying screen or by using an organic scintillator impregnated into the sample. These indirect methods superimpose a photographic image over the autoradiographic image, decreasing exposure time but also decreasing image resolution.

This chapter starts by considering the most appropriate method for detecting each of the commonly used radioisotopes bound to a blotted membrane and the sensitivities that the methods achieve. Section 3 describes specific protocols for radioisotope detection. Sections 4 and 5 attempt to clarify the confused question of quantitative accuracy of isotope detection methods and to summarize briefly their underlying theory. Further details of the underlying theory and detection methods for other types of sample are described elsewhere (3).

Since chemiluminescence and bioluminescence detection methods, which are described in Chapters 10 and 11, also function by detecting light on radiographic film, some comparisons of the methods are included here.

2. Choosing a detection method

2.1 When to use direct autoradiography

Nitrocellulose and other membranes used for protein blotting provide excellent sample geometry for radioisotope detection as there is relatively little absorption of the radioactive emissions by the sample. Therefore direct autoradiography on radiographic film is relatively efficient for isotopes such as ^{14}C, ^{35}S, or ^{33}P (*Table 1*) as the film absorbs most of the energy emitted towards it.

2.2 When to use fluorography

The very weak emissions from ^{3}H (*Table 1*) are mostly absorbed within the sample. Therefore for samples containing ^{3}H the membrane should be impregnated with an organic scintillator such as PPO (2,5-diphenyloxazole) to produce a fluorographic exposure (4).

Table 1. Characteristics of radioisotopes commonly used in biological sciences

Radioisotope	Half-life	Emissions (max) (MeV)
^{3}H	12.4 years	β 0.0186
^{14}C	5730 years	β 0.156
^{35}S	87.4 days	β 0.167
^{33}P	25.4 days	β 0.249
^{32}P	14.3 days	β 1.709
^{125}I	60 days	γ 0.035 (+ 0.027 MeV X-rays) (+ 0.030 MeV electrons)
^{131}I	8.0 days	γ 0.364 (+ 0.61 MeV β)

2.3 When to use an intensifying screen

Although direct autoradiography records emissions from ^{14}C, ^{35}S, or ^{33}P efficiently, it wastes much of the energy from more penetrative emissions

Table 2. Recommended film detection method for blotted membranes

Radioisotope	Procedure[a]	Description
^{3}H	Fluorography dip or spray	Protocol 2
^{14}C ^{35}S ^{33}P	Direct autoradiography (with possible slight increase in sensitivity by fluorography)	Protocol 1
^{32}P	Intensifying screen for optimum sensitivity	Protocol 3
^{125}I and all other γ-emitters	Direct autoradiography for optimum resolution	Protocol 1

[a] With the exception of ^{3}H the other radioisotopes listed are also suitable for detection by phosphorimager (Section 2).

such as ^{32}P or γ-emitting isotopes like ^{125}I or ^{131}I. These emissions pass through and beyond the film, which absorbs only a small fraction of their energy. This wastage is overcome by placing an intensifying screen, consisting of a high-density inorganic fluor beyond the film (2) (see *Table 2*). Emissions which pass beyond the film are absorbed by the screen, which fluoresces to emit blue or ultraviolet light. This passes back through the film superimposing a fluorographic image over the autoradiographic image.

Intensifying screens increase sensitivity for penetrative emissions. They have no effect on less energetic emissions such as ^{3}H, ^{14}C, or ^{35}S. Intensifying screens also decrease image resolution because they emit light from sites which may be more remote from the source of the radioactive emission.

The widespread practice of placing two screens inside a single cassette (5) causes a substantial further loss of resolution, although it does increase sensitivity further. Light from the screen next to the sample can still pass back through a translucent membrane or filter and add a lower-resolution image to the film. Therefore it is better to use only one screen in the cassette when reasonable resolution is required.

2.4 When to use a phosphorimager

When a phosphorimager is available, it can increase sensitivity and thus decrease exposure time significantly (6). Manufacturers claim that exposure times are typically reduced by about a factor of 10. Phosphorimagers are based on a similar principle to intensifying screens, namely fluorescent emission of light after absorbing the energy from radioactive emissions, but there is one crucial difference. The fluorescent emission is delayed so that energy is stored in the cassette rather than in a photographic film. This energy can be released instantaneously by scanning the cassette with laser light and the resulting fluorescence is imaged using photomultipliers. Electronic measurement of the fluorescence overcomes the inherently low quantum efficiency of photographic emulsions. It also overcomes the non-linear response of film to low intensities of light produced by intensifying screens or fluorography, though other ways of overcoming this problem are described in Sections 4 and 5.

Phosphorimagers are not suited to detection of tritium because the weak β-particles emitted by ^{3}H are internally absorbed within the sample. However, they are suitable for most of the other radioisotopes used frequently in biological sciences. This includes ^{35}S and ^{14}C in dried samples, even though film detection of these isotopes is not improved by intensifying screens. The reason for this paradox is the complete absorption of their β-particles by the film so that no energy reaches the intensifying screen beyond the film. However, in phosphorimaging there is no film between the sample and the fluorescent fluor so β-particles from ^{35}S and ^{14}C can still reach the fluor to record an image.

3. How to use the detection methods

This section describes the use of the various isotope detection methods (see *Table 3*). It focuses on film-based methods, because the detailed use of each model of phosphorimager is described in the manufacturers' manuals.

Table 3. Approximate sensitivities of detection methods

Radioisotope	Approximate d.p.m./cm² required for detectable film image in 24 h ($A = 0.02$)			d.p.m./cm² required for detectable image in 1 h
	Direct auto-radiography	Fluorography	Intensifying screen	Phosphorimager
^{3}H	$> 10^6$	8000	—	—
^{14}C	$\geqslant 400$	400	—	400
^{35}S	$\geqslant 400$	400	8	
^{32}P	525		50	50
^{125}I	1600		100	~ 50

Data for the newly introduced isotope ^{33}P were not available. Other data for film detection are from references (1–3) and Laskey and Mills unpublished observations, and for phosphorimager detection from reference (8).

3.1 General considerations for working with radiographic film

Safety requirements for working with radioisotopes lie outside the scope of this short chapter. They are described in detail elsewhere (7).

Perform all manipulations involving undeveloped film in a dark-room with low-intensity dark-red safelights suitable for medical radiography film. Store unused film at 4 °C well away from radioisotopes for optimal shelf-life. Record the orientation of the sample relative to the film by marking at least two corners of the sample either using ink mixed with small amounts of radioisotope or by writing in normal pen on commercially available luminous tape, such as Trackertape™ from Amersham. This leaves a negative image of the ink marks on the film.

For exposure, press the film tightly to the dry sample. This is most easily achieved using an X-ray cassette available from most radiographic film manufacturers. When the film is exposed at −70 °C (see Sections 3.3 and 3.4) the cassette should be allowed to warm to room temperature before developing.

Develop and fix exposed films according to the manufacturer's instructions. Automatic bench-top processors are available at relatively low cost.

3.2 Procedure for direct autoradiography

Direct autoradiography without screens or scintillators provides close to optimum sensitivity for film detection of ^{35}S, ^{14}C, and ^{33}P on membrane blots and optimum resolution for these and more energetic isotopes. It is extremely inefficient for ^{3}H. The images produced are linearly related to the amount of radioactivity up to the saturation limit of the film and are therefore suitable for quantitation.

Protocol 1. Procedure for direct autoradiography

1. Ensure that the membrane is dry.

2. When exposing ^{32}P the membrane may be covered by thin plastic film such as Saranwrap™, but this should not be used for direct autoradiography of weaker β-emitters such as ^{14}C, ^{35}S, or ^{33}P as their emissions are absorbed by it.

3. Select a radiographic film. Optimum sensitivity for direct auto-radiography is obtained from a 'direct' type of film such as Hyperfilm β-max from Amersham or Direct Exposure Film from Kodak. 'Direct'-type films have a high silver content and no anti-scratch plastic coating. Alternatively, 'screen-type' films such as Kodak XAR-5, Fuji RX, or Amersham Hyperfilm MP can be used for direct autoradio-graphy at slightly lower efficiency than their 'direct' alternatives.

4. Clamp the film and the sample together tightly in a film cassette.

5. Expose direct autoradiographs at ambient temperature. There is no gain in sensitivity by exposing at lower temperatures, nor is there any advantage in pre-exposing the film.

6. During exposure of ^{32}P or γ-emitting isotopes such as ^{125}I, avoid stacking cassettes together to prevent phantom images from adjacent

---

Protocol 1. *Continued*

samples. One way of overcoming this problem is to use intensifying screens as barriers, either between cassettes or inside cassettes. Provided exposure is at ambient temperature, the screen will not contribute to the film image and so it will not decrease the resolution.

7. After exposure remove and process the films in a dark-room following the manufacturer's instructions.

3.3 Procedure for fluorography of weak β-emitters

β-particles from ^{3}H are too weak to escape from the sample to reach the film. However, ^{3}H can be detected efficiently by converting its radiation to light and recording a fluorographic image on film instead of a radiographic image.

The more energetic β-particles from ^{35}S and ^{14}C can be detected efficiently on membrane blots by direct autoradiography. It is possible that there is slightly improved sensitivity for these isotopes by fluorography, but there is a shortage of clear evidence on this question. A similar doubt exists for the slightly more energetic ^{33}P, though as these emissions are stronger still, improvement by fluorography is even less likely. Detection of ^{32}P and γ-emitters such as ^{125}I is not improved significantly by fluorography. For these highly penetrative emissions use direct autoradiography (Section 3.2) for optimum resolution or intensifying screens (Section 3.4) for optimum sensitivity.

Blotted membranes are easily impregnated with fluorographic scintillators. *Protocol 2* describes Southern's procedure (4) for impregnation with PPO. For this procedure the membrane must be completely dry. Alternatively aqueous fluorographic reagents such as Amplify™ and Enlightening™ can be used, in which case step **3b** replaces step **3a** in *Protocol 2*.

It is important to ensure uniformity of impregnation or a patchy image will result. Uniform impregnation can be confirmed by viewing the membrane under ultraviolet illumination after impregnating and drying. The whole membrane should fluoresce at the same intensity. The commonest reason for patchy impregnation with the non-aqueous method in *Protocol 2* is residual water in the membrane.

Protocol 2. Procedure for fluorography of weak β-emitters

1. Ensure that the membrane is completely dry.

2. Work only in a ventilated fume hood.

3. (a) Soak the dried membrane in 20% w/v PPO (2,5-diphenyloxazole) in toluene or ether. This procedure involves toxic hazard and fire hazard *or* (b) Soak the membrane in Amplify™ or Enlightening™.

4. Air dry the membrane and check that impregnation is complete by uniform fluorescence under ultraviolet illumination. If fluorescence is patchy, re-dry the membrane thoroughly and repeat the impregnation procedure.

5. Expose the filter to pre-flashed 'screen-type' radiographic film at −70 °C.

Because the fluorographic scintillator divides the energy of an emitted β-particle into smaller quanta of light it is necessary to expose fluorographs at −70 °C. In addition a quantitative response of the film and maximum sensitivity for small amounts of radioactivity are only obtained when a reversible stage of image formation is by-passed by pre-exposing the film to an instantaneous flash of light (pre-flashing) (1). The reason for this requirement is briefly explained in Section 5.

The conversion of β-particles to light has additional consequences. First it becomes necessary to use a screen-type film such as Kodak XAR 5, Fuji RX, or Amersham Hyperfilm MP in order to achieve maximum sensitivity. Second, resolution is decreased because both the β-particles and the secondary light emissions disperse.

3.4 Use of intensifying screens to increase sensitivity for ^{32}P or γ-ray emitters

Intensifying screens increase the detection efficiency of ^{32}P or γ-emitters such as ^{125}I or ^{131}I, by trapping emissions which pass through and beyond the film and converting them to light which passes back through the film superimposing a photographic image over the autoradiographic image (2). The most widely used intensifying screens are composed of calcium tungstate. Although several other materials are available, these have been less suitable for isotope detection for a variety of reasons (2).

Although intensifying screens are used routinely in medical radiography, at least one additional step is required for the longer exposures used in radioisotope detection. This arises because the initial step of photographic image formation is reversible, as explained in Section 5. However, this problem can be partly overcome by exposing the film at −70 °C and completely overcome by combining low-temperature exposure with pre-exposure of the film to an instantaneous flash of light to by-pass the reversible stage of image formation (2). Pre-exposure is essential if image quantitation is required.

Although intensifying screens increase detection efficiency, they decrease resolution because both the radioactive emissions and the secondary light generated disperse. 'Screen-type' X-ray film such as Kodak XAR-5, Fuji RX, and Amersham Hyperfilm MP should be used with intensifying screens, as their spectral sensitivity is matched to each other.

A wide range of X-ray intensifying screens is available from manufacturers such as Du Pont, Fuji, Kodak, CAWO, or Amersham. In general screens made of calcium tungstate (for example Du Pont, Cronex Lightning Plus, Fuji Mach II, Amersham Hyperscreen, or CAWO) give the best combination of high resolution and low background for radioisotope detection. Screens containing either europium-activated barium fluorochloride or terbium-activated rare-earth oxysulphides (lanthanum, gadolinium, or yttrium) may offer greater sensitivity, but with decreased resolution and greatly increased background. Although these problems are not revealed during medical radiography, for which the screens are designed, they become acute in long exposures when the reversible stage of image formation is manipulated by exposing at −70 °C or by pre-exposure of the film (2).

Protocol 3. Procedure for use of intensifying screens to increase sensitivity for ^{32}P and γ-emitters (2)

1. Dry the membrane or cover with Saranwrap™.

2. Select only 'screen-type' radiographic film such as Kodak XAR-5, Amersham Hyperfilm-MP, Fuji RX, or Du Pont Cronex 4.

3. For quantitative accuracy or maximum sensitivity for small amounts of radioactivity, pre-expose the film to an instantaneous flash of light. (See Section 4 for pre-flashing procedure and Section 5 for an explanation of its effect.)

4. Mark two corners of the sample with different symbols using radioactive ink or luminous tape (see Section 3.1).

5. Place one sheet of X-ray film (pre-flashed if required) over the sample.

6. Select an X-ray intensifying screen according to the criteria described in Section 3.4. Clean and dry the screen if necessary.

7. Place the intensifying screen, face down, on top of the film so that the film is enclosed between the screen and the sample.

8. Clamp sample, film, and screen tightly together, ideally in a medical X-ray cassette.

9. Expose at −70 °C. If the film has been correctly pre-flashed exposure can also be performed at ambient room temperature, but at only 50% of the efficiency obtained at −70 °C. Without pre-flashing, exposure at −70 °C is essential to achieve any benefit from intensifying screens.

10. Sensitivity can be increased further by placing a second screen outside the sample so that the order is screen 1, gel, film, screen 2.

> Although this can increase sensitivity up to twofold, it substantially decreases resolution (5). This point should be remembered when using a cassette which already contains two screens for a high-resolution sample.
>
> 11. After exposure, develop the film according to the manufacturer's instructions.

4. Quantitation of film images, including chemiluminescent and bioluminescent images

Images obtained by direct autoradiography on direct or screen-type films in the absence of intensifying screens or organic scintillators are directly proportional to the distribution of radioactivity. The absorbance of the autoradiographic image increases linearly with increasing radioactivity until the film begins to saturate. Therefore images obtained by direct autoradiography can be quantitated accurately.

However, when the radioactive emissions are divided into many smaller quanta of light, by either fluorographic scintillators or intensifying screens, then the response of the film is non-linear. Small amounts of radioactivity are seriously under-represented. Because this problem is worst for small amounts of radioactivity in long exposures, it is easily underestimated.

The reason for the different responses of film to ionizing radiation or to the smaller quanta of light is explained briefly in Section 5, but the most important practical consequences are:

(a) Fluorographs and intensifying screens must be exposed at −70 °C to slow the back-reaction of the reversible first stage of image formation in the film (see Section 5).

(b) Quantitation of images from fluorography and intensifying screens is only meaningful when the reversible stage of image formation is by-passed by pre-exposing film to an instantaneous flash of light (1–3).

The theoretical basis of these two procedures is explained briefly in Section 5 and in more detail elsewhere (1, 3). In addition to allowing accurate quantitation, pre-exposure also increases detection efficiency for small amounts of radioactivity. It has only marginal effects on large amounts of radioactivity (see Section 5). Neither exposure at low temperature nor pre-exposure affects the efficiency or linearity of direct autoradiography (1, 2).

For pre-exposure to hypersensitize a film it is essential that the flash should be short, of the order of 1 msec. This can be achieved by attenuating the output from a photographic flash gun. Longer flashes only increase the background fog level of film without hypersensitizing it.

Provided that the flash is of the order of 1 msec, then the increase in background fog level can be used as a convenient index to monitor hypersensitivity. The background absorbance should be increased to between 0.15 and 0.2 (A_{540}) above the absorbance of untreated (but developed) film.

The intensity of the flash from a photographic flash gun can be attenuated by wavelength filtration. Thus orange filters (Wratten number 21 or 22) taped to the units decrease the output to approximately the correct level. Further adjustments can be made by adding neutral-density filters, by varying the aperture in an opaque mask, or by varying the distance of the flash unit from the film. A suitably attenuated unit is available from Amersham. Trial exposures can be made on a single film by changing the position on the film of a clear window in an opaque mask. The fog levels achieved can be measured using a densitometer or by placing pieces of the film in a spectrophotometer.

It is important to note that the film will only yield a linear response to the amount of radioactivity when the fog level has been raised between 0.1 and 0.2 (A_{540}) above that of untreated film. Whereas unflashed film under-represents small amounts of radioactivity, film which has been pre-flashed to densities of 0.2 over-represents small amounts of radioactivity (1).

Bioluminescent or chemiluminescent detection methods described in Chapter 5 also record photographic images on radiography film. Therefore they are subject to the same principles as detection by fluorography or intensifying screens. However, the intensity of light produced is much greater, requiring much shorter exposures, and therefore not requiring exposure at −70 °C. This is fortunate since the light-producing reactions would be inhibited and ineffective at such a low temperature.

Nevertheless, pre-exposure of the film is necessary for optimal sensitivity and essential for accurate quantitation (3). Although the greater intensity of light production by chemiluminescence and bioluminescence compared with radioactive sources improves linearity of the film response, the need to expose at ambient temperature completely off-sets this advantage. Therefore these processes are severely non-linear unless pre-flashed film is used. For the same reason very faint bands can be greatly enhanced by pre-exposing the film.

Quantitation of film images obtained on pre-flashed film can be achieved by scanning the film with one of the many commercially available densito-meters. Verification of the quantitative accuracy can be confirmed when necessary by slicing the membrane and counting pieces of membrane in a liquid scintillation counter.

5. The underlying principles of radioisotope detection by X-ray film

Photographic emulsions are composed of silver halide crystals (grains of the film), each of which behaves independently. To produce a developable image each silver halide crystal requires several photons of light (approximately five in average emulsions), each of which produces an atom of metallic silver. These then catalyse the reduction of the entire silver halide crystal by the developer.

A single hit by a β-particle or γ-ray can produce hundreds of silver atoms rendering the grain fully developable. Hence direct autoradiography is a linear 'single-hit' process in which all emissions are recorded equally until the film is saturated.

However, once the ionizing radiation is converted to multiple photons of light by an intensifying screen or fluorographic scintillant, the response of film is fundamentally different. Each photon produces only a single atom of silver. Although two or more silver atoms in a silver halide crystal are stable, a single silver atom is unstable and it reverts to a silver ion with a half-life of about 1 sec at room temperature. We have suggested previously that this is the reason why exposure at -70 °C is necessary for the low light intensities produced by fluorography and intensifying screens (1–3). Lowering the temperature slows the thermal reversion of the single silver atom, increasing the time available to capture a second photon and thus produce a stable pair of silver atoms.

The probability of a second photon being captured by a grain before the first silver atom has reverted is greater for large amounts of radioactivity, and hence higher photon flux, than for small amounts. Therefore small amounts of radioactivity are under-represented for both fluorography and intensifying screens, even when exposed at -70 °C. Pre-exposing film to an instantaneous flash of light overcomes this problem because it provides many of the grains of the film with a stable pair of silver atoms. Thereafter each photon which arrives has an equal chance of contributing to the growth of the latent image. Consequently, correctly pre-flashed film responds linearly to the amount of radioactivity from intensifying screens and fluorographs. For the same reason pre-exposure largely (but not completely) by-passes the need to expose at -70 °C.

There is confusion in the literature over the need to pre-flash in order to obtain maximum sensitivity from intensifying screens. This has arisen because the effect of pre-exposure is negligible when tested using large amounts of radioactivity in short exposures. Only *small* amounts of radioactivity are under-represented when radiation is converted to light and there is no effect for large amounts. The practical consequence of this confusion is that serious errors arise when faint bands are compared with dark bands in long exposures of 1 week or more using intensifying screens with untreated film. Under these conditions errors of eightfold have been observed, using ^{32}P and intensifying screens for peak comparisons on unflashed film. However, this problem does not occur for direct autoradiography and it is completely overcome for screens and fluorography by pre-flashing the film. Hence the purpose of this final section is to stress the importance of understanding the underlying principles to ensure success with the 'practical approach'.

References

1. Laskey, R. A. and Mills, A. D. (1975). *Eur. J. Biochem.*, **56**, 335.
2. Laskey, R. A. and Mills, A. D. (1977). *FEBS Lett.*, **82**, 314.
3. Laskey, R. A. (1993). *Efficient detection of biomolecules by autoradiography, fluorography or chemiluminescence*, Review 23. Amersham International, Amersham.
4. Southern, E. M. (1975). *J. Mol. Biol.*, **98**, 503.
5. Swanstrom, R. and Shank, P. R. (1978). *Anal. Biochem.*, **86**, 184.
6. Johnston, R. F., Pickett, S. C., and Barker, D. L. (1990). *Electrophoresis*, **11**, 355.
7. Slater, R. J. (ed.) (1990). *Radioisotopes in biology: a practical approach.* IRL, Oxford.
8. Molecular Dynamics (1990). *Molecular Dynamics 400 A phosphorimager specification.* Molecular Dynamics, Sunnyvale, California.

10

Bioluminescence-enhanced detection systems in protein blotting

REINHARD ERICH GEIGER

1. Introduction

Bioluminescence is a natural phenomenon found in many lower forms of life (1–3). Naturally occurring bioluminescent systems differ with regard to the structure and function of enzymes and cofactors as well as in the mechanism of the light-emitting reactions (4, 5). Because of its high sensitivity, firefly (*Photinus pyralis*) bioluminescence has been used for many years for the sensitive determination of ATP (6). More recently, further highly sensitive bioluminescent and chemiluminescent methods have become available for many different analytes (7–10). Recently, bioluminescent detection of nucleic acid hybridization and protein blotting have been reported (11, 12).

2. Principle and application

A new type of enzyme substrate based on luciferin derivatives, which are highly sensitive for the corresponding enzymes in the test detection systems, are described. These new substrates (13, 14) can be used for unmodified enzymes and for enzyme conjugates, applied in enzymatic activity test systems, in reporter gene tests (15), in enzyme immunoassays (16), in protein blot analysis (17, 18), and ion nucleic acid hybridization tests (12, 19).

The test principle of these new substrates is the release of D-luciferin from D-luciferin derivatives by the action of hydrolytic enzymes:

$$\text{D-luciferin-}\beta\text{-D-galactoside} \xrightarrow{\beta\text{-galactosidase}} \text{D-luciferin} + \beta\text{-D-galactose} \quad (1)$$

$$\text{D-luciferin} + O_2 + \text{ATP} \xrightarrow[\text{Mg}^{2+}]{\text{luciferase}} \text{Oxyluciferin} + h\nu + \text{AMP} + \text{PP}_i. \quad (2)$$

Reaction (1) is the release of luminometrically active D-luciferin from D-luciferin-*o*-*ß*-galactoside (20) by the action of *ß*-galactosidase and (2) is the production of light by the oxidation of D-luciferin by firefly (*Photinus pyralis*) luciferase. Released D-luciferin can be quantified by as luminometric detection system (see *Figure 1*). The high sensitivity of these bioluminogenic substrates is obtained on one hand by the amplification which occurs in the releasing step (for example one molecule of alkaline phosphatase can convert 1000 molecules of D-luciferin-*o*-phosphate to D-luciferin per second) and on the other hand by the very sensitive bioluminescence system (*Photinus pyralis*, concentrations of 5×10^{-13} mol/litre of D-luciferin can be detected (13).)

The bioluminescent detection system described can be applied in protein blotting experiments using all types of proteins and antigens. When using the bioluminescence system antibodies have to be labelled with enzymes.

Bioluminescence-enhanced detection systems require convenient and reliable light-measuring instruments. In the last few years established manufacturers of photometric microtitre plate readers have also introduced readers for chemiluminescent or bioluminescent measures. This equipment can now be used for measuring bioluminescence- or chemiluminescence-enhanced enzyme immunoassays in microtitre plates. If protein blotting experiments can be performed in microtitre plate wells (for example microtitre plate wells having nitrocellulose membranes at the bottom, and others) convenient and highly sensitive measuring equipment is available. For electronic measuring of emitted photons produced on nitrocellulose sheets it is recommended to use photon-counting camera systems (Hamamatsu Photonics Deutschland GmbH, D 82211 Herrsching or Astromed Ltd, Cambridge, UK). This innovative and precise measuring equipment can detect photons within a very short time and with an extremely high sensitivity (1 photon/qcm sec). Further, magnetic storage of pictures on diskettes for later data analysis is easily possible.

Detection of protein blotting can also be performed using photographic films for light detection. Photographic films have been used from Kodak AG and Polaroid GmbH (for example Tri X pan, 380 ASA, or polaroid films). The films should be developed according to the procedures given by the manufacturers.

3. Bioluminescence-enhanced detection: detection scheme

The standard scheme for biluminescence-enhanced detection is performed as follows (*Figure 1*):

(a) application of antigens to nitrocellulose

(b) binding of the labelled antibodies to the proteins

(c) incubation of the antigen/antibody-conjugate/complex with bioluminogenic substrate and simultaneous measuring of emitted light
Protocol 1 and *2* detail the standard procedure and *Figure 2* shows
detection of a protein blot using a photon-counting camera system.

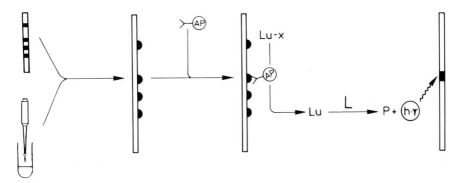

Figure 1. Scheme and principle of the bioluminescent detection system. AP, respective
enzymes used, for example alkaline phosphatase or β-galactosidase; Lu-x, = corresponding D-luciferin derivative; Lu, D-luciferin; L, luciferase; P, oxyluciferin; B, nitrocellulose
sheet with proteins; >—AP, antibody–enzyme conjugate; hγ, emitted light.

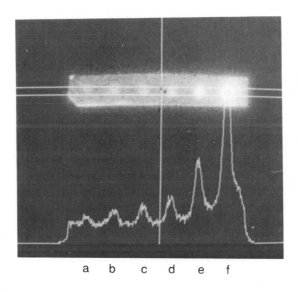

a   b   c   d   e   f

Figure 2. Detection of a protein blot by the use of a photon-counting camera system
(Argus-100): a, control, no IgG added; b, 5 fg; c, 50 fg; d, 500 fg; e. 5 pg; f, 50 pg of rabbit
IgG.

Protocol 1. Bioluminescence-enhanced detection using alkaline phosphatase as an enzymatic label

Standard reagents

- nitrocellulose or nylon filters
- ATP (disodium salt), $MgCl_2$, DTT (offered by known suppliers)
- *Photinus pyralis* luciferase, native or recombinant (offered by known suppliers)
- D-luciferin-*o*-phosphate (BioAss, D 86911 Diessen, Germany)

Standard solutions

- D-luciferin-*o*-phosphate solution: 2 mmol/litre D-luciferin-*o*-phosphate
- buffer solution: 41 mmol/litre Hepes, 2.6 mmol/litre ATP, 7.8 mmol/litre diethanolamine, 5 mmol/litre $MgCl_2$, 2.5 mmol/litre DTT, pH 8.0
- luciferase solution: 1 mg luciferase (*Photinus pyralis*)/ml, 0.5 mol/litre Tris/succinate buffer, pH 7.7, containing 3 mmol/litre DTT
- alkaline phosphatase label (antibody–alkaline phosphatase conjugate)
- light detection solution: 1 ml buffer solution, 0.01 ml luciferase solution and 0.01 ml D-luciferin-*o*-phosphate solution

Method

1. After antigens have been transferred and alkaline phosphatase label has been bound wash the filter (nitrocellulose or nylon) with phosphate-buttered saline and briefly dip into light detection solution (about 6 ml in a Petri dish).
2. Transfer filter to a transparent plastic basin.
3. Place basin (in the dark) in the light-tight chamber of a photon-counting camera.
4. Perform light detection using the photon-counting camera. Count and integrate photons for 5 sec, 5 min or 20 min depending on the photon counting camera system used. Blotted protein will be visualized as bright spots.
5. Semiquantity results using computer programs supplied with the photon-counting camera.

Protocol 2. Bioluminescence-enhanced detection using β-galactosidase as an enzymatic label

Standard reagents

- Nitrocellulose or nylon filters
- ATP (disodium salt), MgCl$_2$, DTT (offered by known suppliers)
- *Photinus pyralis* luciferase, native or recombinant (offered by known suppliers)
- D-luciferin-*o*-β-galactoside (BioAss, D 86911 Diessen, Germany)

Standards solutions

- D-luciferin-*o*-β-galactoside solution: 0.25 mmol/litre luciferin-*o*-β-galactoside
- Buffer solution: 41 mmol/litre Hepes, 5 mmol-litre MgCl$_2$, 2.6 mmol/litre ATP, pH 7.75; ATP is added shortly before use
- Luciferase solution: 1 mg luciferase (*Photinus pyralis*)/ml 0.5 mol/litre Tris/succinate buffer, pH 7.7, containing 3 mmol/litre DTT.
- Antibody-β-galactosidase conjugate
- Light detection solution: 1 ml buffer solution, 0.005 ml luciferase solution, and 0.05 ml D-luciferin-*o*-β-galactoside solution

Method

1. After transferring proteins and binding of β-galactosidase label wash the filter with phosphate-buffered saline and briefly dip into light detection solution (about 6 ml in a Petri dish).
2. Transfer filter to a transparent plastic basin.
3. Place basin (in the dark) in the light-tight chamber of a photon-counting camera.
4. Perform light detection using the photon counting camera. Count and integrate photons for 5 sec, 5 min or 20 min depending on the photon-counting camera system used. Blotted protein is visualized as bright spots.

4. Special hints for application and trouble-shooting

Many advantages in handling and sensitivity have been obtained using a photon-counting camera system instead of photographic films (12). The detection limits can be lowered by powers of 10 even at a shorter detection time (5 to 10 min). The method is relatively simple to perform, but one has to be careful when using nitrocellulose. It has been demonstrated that different types of nictrocellulose purchased from different distributors may contain substances which interfere with firefly luciferase (*Photinus pyralis*). A reducing effect of luciferase activity was obtained by adding buffer to the test system in which nitrocellulose was soaked or stored only for a short time. The luciferase may be inhibited or may be denatured by compounds existing in the nitrocellulose sheets. Furthermore, the use of high-quality water is recommended.

In earlier stages of synthesis of D-luciferin-*o*-phosphate very small amounts of free D-luciferin could be detected in the preparations using the highly sensitive bioluminescence reaction after purification of D-luciferin-*o*-phosphate. These traces of D-luciferin sometimes influenced the blank values. By improving the purification methods D-luciferin-*o*-phosphate is now available in a highly purified grade. After dissolving D-luciferin-*o*-phosphate in water or 0.05 mol/litre ammonium acetate, pH 6.5, aliquots should be taken and stored at −80 °C or −30 °C until use. For each experiment a fresh aliquot should be used. If users wish to purify their own D-luciferin-*o*-phosphate, purification methods using high-performance liquid chromatography are published in (13).

It is recommended that D-luciferin-*o*-β-galactoside be dissolved in highly pure water or in 0.05 mol/litre ammonium acetate, pH 6.8. Aliquots should be taken and stored at −80 °C or −30 °C until use. For each experiment a fresh aliquot should be used. D-luciferin-*o*-β-galactoside has a very low blank value.

References

1. Deluca, M. A. (1978). *Bioluminescence and Chemiluminescence*, Methods of Enzymology, Vol. 57. Academic, New York.
2. Deluca, M. and McElroy, W. D. (1986). *Bioluminescence and Chemiluminescence, Part B*, Methods of Enzymology, Vol. 133. Academic, New York.
3. Herring, P. J. (1987). *J. Biolumin. Chemilumin.*, **1**, 146–63.
4. Burr, G. J. (1985). *Chemi- and bioluminescence*. Marcel Dekker, New York.
5. Schölmerich, J., Andreesen, R., Kapp, A., Ernst, M., and Woods, W. G. (1987). *Bioluminescence and Chemiluminescence, New Perspectives*. John Wiley, Chichester.
6. Lundin, A., Richardsson, A., and Thorpe, A. (1976). *Anal. Biochem.*, **75**, 611–20.
7. Kricka, L. J., Stanley, P. E., Thorpe, G. H. G., and Whitehead, T. P. (1984). *Analytical applications of bioluminescence and chemiluminescence*. Academic, New York.
8. Wood, W. G. (1984). *J. Clin. Chem. Clin. Biochem.*, **22**, 905–18.

9. Gould, S. J. and Subramani, S. (1988). *Anal. Biochem.*, **175**, 5–13.
10. Kricka, L. J. (1988). *Anal. Biochem.*, **175**, 14–21.
11. Hauber, R. and Geiger, R. (1988). *Nucleic Acid Res.*, **16**, 1213.
12. Hauber, R. and Geiger, R. (1989). *J. Clin. Chem. Clin. Biochem.*, **27**, 361–3.
13. Miska, W. and Geiger, R. (1987). *J. Clin. Chem. Clin. Biochem.*, **25**, 23–30.
14. Geiger, R. and Miska, W. (1987). *J. Clin. Chem. Clin. Biochem.*, **25**, 31–8.
15. Berger, J., Hauber, J., Hauber, R., Geiger, R., and Cullen, B. R. (1988). *Gene*, **66**, 1–10.
16. Schneider, E., Gabrijelcic, D., and Geiger, R. (1992). *Eur. J. Clin. Chem. Clin. Biochem.*, **30**, 871–3.
17. Hauber, R. and Geiger, R. (1987). *J. Clin. Chem. Clin. Biochem.*, **26**, 147–8.
18. Hauber, R., Miska, W., Schleinkofer, L., and Geiger, R. (1988). *J. Clin. Chem. Clin. Biochem.*, **26**, 147–8.
19. Geiger, R., Hauber, R., and Miska, W. (1989). *Mol. Cell. Probes*, **3**, 309–28.
20. Geiger, R., Schneider, E., Wallenfels, K., and Miska, W. (1992). *Biol. Chem. Hoppe Seyler*, **373**, 1187–91.

11

Chemiluminescent detection systems for protein blotting

IAN DURRANT and SUE FOWLER

1. Introduction

The immobilization and detection of proteins on membrane supports has become a widely used technique (1, 2). The overall process can be separated into four basic procedures.

(a) transfer and immobilization of the target proteins
(b) blocking of non-specific binding sites on the membrane
(c) binding of specific antibody molecules to target proteins of interest, followed by binding of a second layer of anti-species antibody carrying a label, typically an enzyme
(d) detection of the label by an appropriate enzymic reaction

The process of immobilization, particularly electrophoretic transfer from SDS-polyacrylamide gels (Western blotting (3)), is well documented (4, 5) and will not be dealt with further in this chapter (see Chapters 1–6). Blocking of the membrane is necessary in order to achieve good levels of specific signal against background. From the variety of blocking methods that are known (6) the conditions that are optimal for a particular system can be determined. The detection process, mediated by the label on the second layer of antibody, has undergone a number of changes over the last few years (see *Table 1*).

Traditionally, radiolabels were used for this process, in particular ^{125}I (5). This method gives good sensitivity and a hard copy of the result on X-ray film, but the exposure time is prolonged and there are some reservations about the handling and disposal of radioactive materials. Consequently, efforts focused on the development of non-radioactive techniques for Western blot analysis. Initial procedures concentrated on the use of colorimetric detection in which the final antibody molecule is labelled with an enzyme as a reporter group (7, 8). The presence of the reporter group is then revealed by the precipitation of coloured enzyme substrates. One of the most sensitive methods uses alkaline

Table 1. Comparison of Western blotting detection techniques

	Radiolabel[125]I	Colour alk. phos. NBT/BCIP	Luminescence HRP ECL substrates
Sensitivity	+++	++++	+++++
Economy of antibody usage	++	+++	+++++
Speed of detection	+	+++	+++++
Ease of reprobing	++	++	++++
Ease of quantification	+++++	++	++++
Durability of record	+++++	+++	+++++

phosphatase as the enzyme and nitroblue tetrazolium (NBT) and bromochloroindolyl phosphate (BCIP) as the substrates. This leads to the deposition of a blue colour on the membrane, wherever the enzyme label is present. This technique is more sensitive and quicker than ^{125}I but does not give a permanent hard copy of the result for display and analysis. It is also difficult to reprobe a blot once developed. In order to overcome some of these problems the latest detection systems have concentrated on the use of light emission (luminescence) as an end point for protein detection on membranes.

Substrates that can be triggered to produce light exist for both alkaline phosphatase (9) and horseradish peroxidase (HRP) (10). Utilization of the substrate for alkaline phosphatase does produce a hard copy result of the blot on X-ray film. However, while the overall sensitivity is good, the interpretation of the result can sometimes suffer from problems with high levels of background, resulting from bacterial alkaline phosphatase contamination of buffers. In contrast, the luminescent system available for HRP, in which blue light is generated by the oxidation of luminol, offers excellent signal to noise, is extremely rapid, and is, perhaps, the most sensitive system available.

This technology is available as the ECL™ Western blotting system in which the detection system is based on enhanced chemiluminescence (11, 12). In the basic (non-enhanced) chemiluminescent reaction, HRP is used to oxidize a peracid salt, leading to the formation of a raised oxidation state of the haem group at the centre of HRP itself. This raised state returns to the initial (ground) state in a two-step process (12). At each of these stages a luminol radical is formed, and as this radical decays, light is emitted. In the basic reaction the light emission ceases in a relatively short period of time. However, in the enhanced chemiluminescent reaction an enhancer molecule is added which reacts with the haem group in place of luminol, leading to the formation of enhancer radicals; these radicals in turn react to produce luminol radicals and the light is emitted as before. This reaction is a great deal faster than that for luminol alone, and is sustained for a significant period of time. The presence of the enhancer can lead to an increase in emitted light of more than 1000-fold over the unenhanced reaction. On membranes the light output rises rapidly over the first five minutes and remains at a maximum for another 15 min before steadily decreasing, with a half-life of about 60 min. Typical exposures for the ECL Western blotting system (13–16) are of the order of a few minutes (usually less than 5 min) and may often be in the region of seconds; exposures are possible for 1 h or more if required.

The background is routinely very low and the system has the capacity for multiple re-exposures and multiple re-probing of a blot. The hard copy result obtained on X-ray film can be used to quantify the target by use of densitometry. In addition, the high sensitivity of the system means that expensive antibodies can be used at higher dilutions, leading to significant savings.

2. Basic protocol for ECL Western blotting

2.1 Membrane blocking

The first step is the blocking of the membrane to avoid non-specific binding of antibody molecules to the membrane surface. This is usually performed with a protein-based block. Nitrocellulose and PVDF membranes are used most frequently in this technique; nylon membranes have intrinsically higher binding affinity for proteins and are, therefore, sometimes difficult to block effectively.

A number of compounds have been used to block membranes; the best general-purpose block is that based on detergent and milk proteins (see *Protocol 1*). The level of Tween™ can be varied but concentrations greater than 0.2% should be used with caution as they may lead to removal of target proteins from the membrane and inhibit low-affinity antibodies from binding to the target protein (17). The block can be made in bulk and stored in suitable aliquots at −20 °C. Blocking is performed in containers of a size appropriate to the blot such that the membrane is completely covered in block solution.

Protocol 1. Blocking the membrane

- container for blot
- dried-milk powder
- PBS solution
- Tween 20
- shaking platform

Protocol 1. *Continued*

1. Make up block buffer consisting of 5% (w/v) dried-milk powder, 0.1% (v/v) Tween-20 in PBS (PBS-T).

2. Incubate the blot in block buffer for 1 h at room temperature with gentle agitation.

3. Rinse the blot briefly in two changes of PBS-T buffer (0.1% (v/v) Tween-20 in PBS).

4. Wash the blot in an excess volume of fresh PBS-T buffer for 15 min at room temperature with gentle agitation.

5. Wash the blot twice in fresh PBS-T for 5 min as above. *Do not allow the blot to dry out during or after this blocking process.*

Alternative blocks that have been used successfully in this application include 3% bovine serum albumin (18), 2% polyvinyl pyrrolidone (19), and 1–2% casein (20). These are useful alternatives, particularly for the study of carbohydrate groups on the immobilized targets, as the dried-milk powder-based block may contain significant levels of endogenous carbohydrate.

2.2 Antibody incubations

A typical experimental system utilizes two layers of antibody in the detection procedure (see *Protocol 2*). The first antibody is directed against the target antigen; the antigen may be a ligand on a protein, the protein itself, a specific epitope on a protein or a carbohydrate group. The second antibody is specific for the constant region of the first antibody molecule (anti-species antibody). This second antibody is presented as a conjugate of HRP, the reporter group, for later development with the enhanced chemiluminescence system. Altern-ative approaches may involve three layers of reagents, in which the first specific antibody is detected with a biotinylated anti-species antibody and the third layer is a streptavidin–HRP conjugate. In general such attempts at signal amplification are not required when using the enhanced chemi-luminescent detection system.

However, an important point to note is that because of the sensitivity of the ECL system the immunodetection procedure may need to be re-optimized (see *Protocol 3*). This is a relatively simple task using dot blots of immobilized proteins and antibodies and is well worth the initial effort.

Antibodies are routinely diluted in PBS, although TBS can be easily substituted if desired. Tween-20, or other detergents, are frequently added to the antibody dilution buffer although care must be taken that the detergent does not reduce binding of the antibody to the antigen, particularly for low-affinity antibodies. Occasionally an antibody is found that routinely gives high background with all blocking procedures. This may be overcome by performing the antibody incubation in block buffer.

2.3 Molecular weight estimation

For many experiments identification of targets is aided by the estimation of an approximate molecular weight from reference to size standards placed on the acrylamide gel (Rainbow™ Markers). However, an alternative method is to run biotinylated marker proteins on the gel which can be transferred to the blot and detected simultaneously with the specific target by addition of streptavidin–HRP to the buffer containing the anti-species (HRP-labelled) second antibody. The signal generation process will reveal both the specific target and the molecular weight markers simultaneously.

Protocol 2. Incubation with antibody and antibody washes

- container for blot
- PBS-T buffer (see *Protocol 1*)
- primary antibody stock solution
- secondary antibody–HRP conjugate stock solution
- shaking platform

1. Dilute the primary antibody stock solution as required in PBS-T (see *Protocol 3*).
2. Incubate the blocked blot in diluted primary antibody solution for 1 h at room temperature with gentle agitation.
3. Wash the blot as detailed in *Protocol 1* steps **3–5**.
4. Dilute the secondary antibody–HRP conjugate stock solution as required in PBS-T (see *Protocol 3*).
5. Incubate the blot in the diluted secondary antibody–HRP conjugate solution for 1 h at room temperature with gentle agitation.
6. Wash the blot as detailed in *Protocol 1* steps **3–5**. *Do not allow the blot to dry out during or after these incubations.*

Protocol 3. Optimization of antibody dilutions

- target protein stock solution
- primary antibody stock solution
- secondary antibody–HRP conjugate stock solution

Protocol 3. *Continued*

- nitrocellulose membrane (such as Hybond™-ECL, Amersham)
- PBS-T (see *Protocol 1*)
- block buffer (see *Protocol 1*)
- container for blot
- shaking platform

1. Dilute the target protein to give a quantity appropriate for detection in 2 µl of PBS-T.

2. Apply 2 µl dots of the diluted target protein to the nitrocellulose membrane and allow to air dry.

3. Block the membrane (see *Protocol 1*).

4. Dilute the primary antibody, in PBS-T, across the range 1:100 to 1:5000.

5. Incubate individual blots in the various primary antibody dilutions and wash to remove excess unbound material (see *Protocol 2*).

6. Dilute the secondary antibody–HRP conjugate as required, using the same dilution for all the blots.

7. Incubate all the blots in the diluted secondary antibody–HRP conjugate and wash to remove excess unbound material (see *Protocol 2*).

8. Detect the blots with the enhanced chemiluminescence substrates (see *Protocol 4*) and select the optimum primary antibody dilution based on the level of specific signal and on the level of background obtained.

9. Repeat the above steps using the optimized primary antibody dilution for all blots and incubating individual blots in various concentrations of secondary antibody–HRP conjugate (typically across the range 1:3000 to 1:50 000).

10. After enhanced chemiluminescent detection select the optimum dilution for the secondary antibody–HRP conjugate as in step **8**.

3. Signal generation

3.1 Substrate preparation

The working stock of the substrate is easily formed by simple equivolume mixing of the two components supplied. Solution 1 contains a peracid salt, as a substrate for HRP, and Solution 2 contains both the luminol and the enhancer molecules. The two solutions are kept separate to avoid low levels of chemical decomposition that may occur with prolonged storage. The working solution can be prepared a few hours in advance if necessary and may be kept at 4 °C for up to 24 h if required.

3.2 Development of blots

It is important to have all the required materials to hand and access to the dark-room and X-ray processing facilities assured before starting this procedure; blots can be held in the final antibody wash buffer for up to 30 min before generating the signal. The light reaction begins almost immediately after addition of the substrate and the most quantitative and rapid results are those obtained in the first few minutes after exposure of the HRP to the substrate; delays should be minimized.

The most effective way to develop the blots (see *Protocol 4*) is to lay them out, protein side uppermost, onto a clean, non-absorbent surface, such as Saran-Wrap™, and pipette the ECL working reagent directly on to the membrane. The incubation time is only 1 min and incubation beyond that point offers no advantage. The blots are drained and wrapped in Saran-Wrap to avoid getting any liquid substrate onto the film surface itself whilst in the X-ray cassette. Saran-Wrap is recommended in that it is not prone to static, which can lead to a false signal on the film, and it is known to be transparent to the blue light produced in the reaction. The blots should be placed so that the protein side is against the film. Best results are obtained when the film is in direct contact with the wrapped blots and, in particular, air bubbles should be avoided during the wrapping process. These can be removed by gently smoothing out the trapped air, but it is vital that this is not done too vigorously as this can lead to removal of substrates from the blot surface and so destroy the signal.

3.3 Light capture

Once in the dark-room it is sometimes possible, but not essential, to see the light output directly from the blot with the dark-adapted eye. The light is collected onto blue light-sensitive X-ray film; Hyperfilm™-ECL is recommended as it is optimized for the ECL light output (λmax = 425 nm). Other grey-based films can be used successfully, but lower sensitivity may be seen with some blue-based films. It is recommended, as a guide for new users, and when looking at a new system, that only a 15 s exposure is taken first. Obviously, care must be taken to put the film down quickly and straight, to avoid blurring of the signal. After this time a second film is placed into the cassette and the first is developed using standard X-ray developing chemicals or a suitable automatic film processor. From the result of the first film, and with experience, it is possible to estimate the time required for the second exposure to get the best result. A typical exposure time would be less than 5

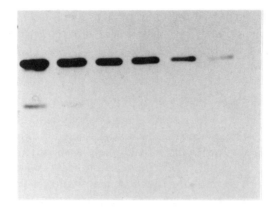

Figure 1. Detection of tubulin in rat brain homogenate. Doubling dilutions of rat brain homogenate (1:100 to 1:3400) were separated by 12% SDS-PAGE and transferred to Hybond-ECL membrane. Immunodetection was performed using mouse monoclonal anti-tubulin (1:1000) and sheep anti-mouse Ig–HRP conjugate (1:3000) followed by addition of ECL detection reagents; 15 sec exposure to Hyperfilm-ECL.

min for most applications (see *Figure 1*). Significant light persists for over 1 h, enabling multiple re-exposures to be performed in order to achieve the optimum result.

Protocol 4. Enhanced chemiluminescent detection reaction

- Saran-Wrap (Dow Chemical Company)
- autoradiography film (Hyperfilm-ECL, Amersham)
- X-ray film cassette (Hypercassette, Amersham)
- dark-room facilities
- X-ray film processing facilities
- ECL detection reagents 1 and 2 (Amersham)

1. Mix equal volumes of detection reagents 1 and 2 to give sufficient working solution to allow 0.125 ml for each cm^2 of membrane.
2. Remove blots from final PBS-T wash buffer, allow to drain briefly, and place protein side up on a clean, non-absorbent surface. Work relatively quickly at this point to avoid the membrane drying out.
3. Add working stock of detection reagent to the surface of the blot and incubate at room temperature for 1 min only.
4. Drain excess detection reagent from the blot and place onto a sheet of Saran-Wrap, protein side down.

---

5. Wrap the blot completely in Saran-Wrap ensuring that air bubbles are not trapped. Place the blots into an X-ray cassette protein side up.

6. Turn off main lights/enter dark-room and place a sheet of X-ray film onto the wrapped blots. Close the cassette and leave the film to expose for 15 sec.

7. Remove the film and replace with a second sheet.

8. Develop the first film and use as a basis for the timing of the second exposure by assessment of signal and background. The second exposure required is typically less than 5 min.

Where it is not possible to obtain suitable dark-room facilities a camera luminometer can be used to capture the light output onto Polaroid™ film (21). This is not as sensitive as X-ray film and exposure times may need to be increased but it will give adequate results in most applications (see *Figure 2*).

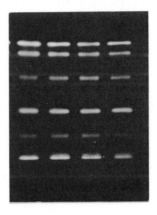

Figure 2. Detection of biotinylated molecular weight markers using a camera lumino-meter. Biotinylated molecular weight markers (Amersham) (phosphorylase b (97.4 kd), bovine serum albumin (68 kd), ovalbumin (46 kd), carbonic anhydrase (31 kd), trypsin inhibitor (20.1 kd), and lysozyme (14.4 kd)) were separated by 12% SDS-PAGE and transferred to Hybond-ECL membrane. The markers were detected using streptavidin–HRP conjugate (1:1500) followed by addition of ECL detection reagents; 1 min exposure to Polaroid 667 film.

3.4 Trouble-shooting

A potential cause of background is rough treatment of the blot itself. Serrated and sharp tweezers should be avoided as physical damage leads to non-specific light reactions located in the area of the damage.

It is possible, occasionally, for the short first exposure to appear overexposed. If this is merely due to excessive levels of signal from the specific target protein then the blots should be left for about 10 min before placing another film into the cassette. If the excess signal appears to be all over the blot then it possible that it has not been sufficiently washed following the second antibody treatment. In this case the blot should be unwrapped and washed again in PBS-T buffer (two 5 min washes) and then redetected with fresh detection reagents. If problems still persist then care should be taken to ensure that the antibody dilutions used are reoptimized correctly for this system or an alternative blocking procedure should be investigated.

4. Quantification of signal

Precise light output values for individual bands on a blot can be obtained from a light-gathering and imaging machine such as a CCD camera. However, as this type of apparatus is not routinely available, an alternative is to use standard X-ray film exposures and a densitometer (22, 23). An increase in linearity of the response of Hyperfilm-ECL to the light output from the ECL reaction can be obtained by pre-flashing the film with a short flash of light to raise the film background by an OD of 0.1 (24). This raises the film to the threshold of response so that the number of photons of light hitting the film is proportional to the number of silver grains converted.

5. Reprobing blots

Luminescence detection does not involve damage to the blot itself. Therefore, it is feasible to reprobe a blot with a second target-specific antibody either with or without stripping off the first signal (see *Protocol 5*). If using the system without stripping then the first signal will probably still give an image. It is only useful therefore where the two signals are known to be well separated on the blot. It is generally better to strip the first set of antibodies off the blot before starting the process over again with fresh blocking and fresh antibodies (25). For certain antibodies it may prove necessary to increase the stripping temperature to as much as 70 °C. The stripping protocol outlined does not significantly affect the target on the membrane but care must be taken to minimize the handling of the blots to avoid physical damage; the cycle can be repeated a number of times.

Protocol 5. Reprobing blots

- container for blot
- PBS-T (see *Protocol 1*)
- block buffer (see *Protocol 1*)

- primary antibody stock solution
- secondary antibody–HRP conjugate stock solution
- 2-mercaptoethanol
- SDS
- Tris–HCl

A. *Reprobing only*

1. Wash previously detected membrane in two changes of PBS-T for 10 min each using a large excess of wash buffer.
2. Block the membrane (see *Protocol 1*), incubate in antibody solutions and wash (see *Protocol 2*), and detect by enhanced chemiluminescence (see *Protocol 4*).

B. *Stripping and reprobing*

1. Submerge the previously detected blot in a large excess of stripping buffer (100 mM 2-mercaptoethanol, 2%(w/v) SDS, 62.5 mM Tris–HCl, pH6.7).
2. Incubate at 50 °C for 30 min with occasional agitation.
3. Wash the stripped blot twice in a large excess of PBS-T for 10 min.
4. Block the membrane (see *Protocol 1*), incubate in antibody solutions and wash (see *Protocol 2*), and detect by enhanced chemiluminescence (see *Protocol 4*).

6. Conclusion

The ECL Western blotting system is, perhaps, the most rapid and sensitive system currently available. The results are obtained in a convenient format that aids both presentation and quantification. In addition, the membranes can be reused, thus saving target, and the usage of antibody may also be reduced, thus saving resources.

References

1. Gershoni, J. M. (1988). In *Methods of biochemical analysis*, (ed. J. M. Gershoni), Vol. 33, pp. 1–58. Wiley, New York.
2. Garfin, D. E. and Bers, G. (1989). In *Protein blotting methodology, research and diagnostic application*, (ed. B. A. Baldo, E. R. Tovey, and N. W. S. St. Leonards), pp. 4–41. Karger, Basel.
3. Burnette, W. N. (1981). *Anal. Biochem.*, **112**, 195.
4. Gershoni, J. M. and Palade, G. E. (1983). *Anal. Biochem.*, **131**, 1.

5. Towbin, H., Staehlin, T., and Gordon, J. (1979). *Proc. Natl. Acad. Sci., USA*, **76**, 4350.
6. Bers, G. and Garfin, D. (1985). *Biotechniques*, **3**, 276.
7. Tsang, V. C. W., Bers, G., and Hancock, K. (1985). In *Enzyme mediated immunoassay*, (ed. T. T. Ngo and H. M. Lenhoff), pp. 389–414. Plenum, New York.
8. Hawkes, R., Niday, E., and Gordon, J. (1982). *Anal. Biochem.*, **119**, 142.
9. Bronstein, I., Edwards, B., and Voyta, J. C. (1989). *J. Biolumin. Chemilumin.*, **4**, 99.
10. Whitehead, T. P., Thorpe, G. H. G., Carter, T. J. N., Groucutt, C., and Kricka, L. J. (1983). *Nature*, **305**, 158.
11. Pollard-Knight, D., Read, C. A., Downes, M. J., Howard, L. A., Leadbetter, M. R., Pheby, S. A., McNaughton, E., Syms, A., and Brady, M. A. W. (1990). *Anal. Biochem.*, **185**, 84.
12. Durrant, I. (1990). *Nature*, **346**, 297.
13. Dalemans, W., Barbry, P., Champigny, G., Jallat, S., Dott, K., Dreyer, D., Crystal, R. G., Pavirani, A., Lecocq, J. P., and Lazdunski, M. (1991). *Nature*, **354**, 526.
14. Oliner, J. D., Kinzler, K. W., Meltzer, P. S., George, D. L., and Vogelstein, B. (1992). *Nature*, **358**, 80.
15. Philpott, A., Leno, G. H., and Laskey, R. A. (1991). *Cell*, **65**, 569.
16. Pendergast, A. M., Muller, A. J., Havlik, M. H., Maru, Y., and Witte, O. N. (1991). *Cell*, **66**, 161.
17. Hoffman, W. L. and Jump, A. A. (1986). *J. Immunol. Methods*, **94**, 191.
18. Wedge, E. and Svenneby, G. (1986). *J. Immunol. Methods*, **88**, 233.
19. Bartles, J. R. and Hubbard, A. L. (1984). *Anal. Biochem.*, **140**, 284.
20. Mandrell, R. E. and Zollinger, W. D. (1984). *J. Immunol. Methods*, **67**, 1.
21. Anon. (1992). *ECL Highlights (Amersham)*, **4**, 17.
22. Seigel, G. M. and Notter, M. F. D. (1992). *Exp. Cell Res.*, **199**, 240.
23. Young, L. T., Li, P. P., Kish, S. J., Siu, K. P., and Warsh, J. J. (1991). *Brain Res.*, **553**, 323.
24. Laskey, R. A. (1992). *Review 23 (Amersham)*. Amersham International.
25. Zeitlin, P. L., Crawford, I., Lu, L., Woel, S., Cohen, M. E., Donowitz, M., Montrose, M. H., Hamosh, A., Cutting, G. R., Gruenert, D., Huganir, R., Maloney, P., and Guggino, W. B. (1992). *Proc. Natl. Acad. Sci, USA.*, **89**, 344.

SECTION 4

Applications of Protein Blotting

12

Detection and characterization of glycoprotein carbohydrate chains after electrophoretic separation

TATSURO IRIMURA and HIROTO KAWASHIMA

1. Introduction

Lectins and carbohydrate-specific antibodies are often used for the detection of carbohydrate chains after electrophoretic separation of glycoproteins. Lectin blotting and antibody blotting can be applied before or after electrophoretic transfer of the glycoproteins to nitrocellulose membranes (1). The structural information from these blotting experiments is based on the carbohydrate binding specificity of the immunochemical agents applied. The information can be substantiated by partial modification of the glycoprotein carbohydrate chains prior to the reaction with immunochemical agents (2). To further elucidate the carbohydrate structures of electrophoretically separated glycoproteins, a simple method for the release of oligosaccharides from glycoproteins has also been developed (3). In this method, glycoproteins are electroblotted onto Immobilon transfer membranes. A small piece of the membrane with a glycoprotein band is cut out, dried in a desiccator and subjected to gas-phase hydrazinolysis. The released oligosaccharides, after re-N-acetylation, can be characterized by lectin affinity chromatography, gel permiation chromatography, and other means of oligosaccharide analysis.

2. Lectin staining of electrophoretically separated glycoproteins with in situ chemical modification of carbohydrate chains

Glycoproteins may be electrophoretically transferred onto nitrocellulose membranes prior to the incubation with lectins and antibodies. All the staining and washing steps can be shortened when the samples are transferred onto nitrocellulose membranes. Rapid washing is necessary when luminescent substrates such as ECL (Amersham) are used. However, the efficiency of electrophoretic transfer of high-M_r glycoproteins is low and inconsistent. Chemical modification methods shown below can be applied to glycoproteins in polyacrylamide gels as well as those blotted onto membranes.

Protocol 1. Staining of glycoproteins and polyacrylamide gels

A. *Lectin staining of glycoproteins on polyacrylamide gels with ^{125}I-labelled lectins*

Reagents

- TBS + NaN$_3$: 25 mM Tris–HCl buffer pH 7.4 containing 0.12 M NaCl containing 0.01% NaN$_3$
- ^{125}I-Iodinated lectin: diluted 5–10 μg/ml in TBS + NaN$_3$ containing 1% BSA. Diluted iodinated lectin should be filtered through 0.3 or 0.45 μm Millipore filter. The solution may be reused four or five times

Method

1. (day 0–1) Stain polyacrylamide gels with Coomassie Brilliant Blue in 25% isopropanol and 10% acetic acid. Destain with 10% acetic acid.

2. (day 1–day 3) Neutralize and wash at room temperature with TBS + NaN$_3$ with occasional changes.

3. (day 3) Stain with ^{125}I-lectins (approximately 5 μg/ml) at room temperature for 1–2 h.

4. (day 3–day 5) Wash at room temperature for 48 h with TBS +NaN$_3$ with occasional changes.

5. (day 5) Dry gels and perform autoradiography.

B. *Staining of polyacrylamide gels with biotinylated lectins*

Reagents

- TBS: 25 mM Tris–HCl buffer pH 7.4 containing 0.12 M NaCl
- biotinylated lectin: 10 μg/ml in TBS
- Vectastain ABC or avidine-peroxidase: Vectastain reagent must stand for 30 min after preparation before it can be used. Two drops each A and B/10 ml TBS
- peroxidase substrate: mix 3 ml of 4-chloro-1-naphthol (3 mg/ml in EtOH store at −20 °C), 21 ml of DI H$_2$O, 120 μl of 1 M Tris–HCl buffer pH 7.4, and 16 μl of 30% H$_2$O$_2$

Method

1. Fix in 25% isopropanol 10% acetic acid for 4 h.

---

2. Neutralize in TBS, overnight, several changes.

3. Add biotinylated lectins 10 µg/ml in TBS (minimum volume to cover the entire gel) and incubate for 4 h.

4. Wash in TBS, overnight, several changes.

5. Add 30 ml Vectastain ABC reagent, 4 h.

6. Wash in TBS, three changes, 2 h.

7. Wash in DI water, five immediate changes.

8. Add 25 ml peroxidase substrate, 15 min.

9. Aspirate and add DI water.

Note: (a) Times given are for gels bound to Gelbond PAG. Gels not bound to gelbond or nitrocellulose membranes require about half of the incubation times.
(b) In place of Vectastain ABC reagent, avidin peroxidase (1:1000 dilution in TBS of 5 mg/ml solution) can be used.
(c) The same method can be applied to nitrocellulose membranes.

These are few examples of the protocols used in our laboratory. The detection of bound lectin or antibody can be achieved by any variation of protein blotting methods. Skim milk should be avoided for the blocking agent because it contains a variety of carbohydrate chains. It is highly recommended to include standard glycoproteins with known carbohydrate chain structures on the same gels. For example, hen ovalbumin is useful as a standard glycoprotein containing high mannose- and hybrid-type carbohydrate chains. Bovine fetuin contains triantennary-complex-type carbohydrate chains and O-linked tetrasaccharides [NeuAc2—3Gal1—3 (NeuAc2—6)GalNAc-R]. Also, inhibition of the lectin binding by prior incubation of lectins with appropriate inhibitory sugars needs to be demonstrated. For this purpose, monosaccharides can be used for many lectins. It should be reminded that these inhibitions by monosaccharides do not necessarily indicate the presence of the same monosaccharides at the non-reducing terminal of carbohydrate chains in the glycoproteins detected by lectin binding. Many cell surface glycoproteins contain sialic acid at the non-reducing terminal of their carbohydrate chains. Some lectins preferentially bind sialylated carbohydrate chains. Some lectins preferentially bind carbohydrate residues penultimate to sialic acid, after sialic acid is removed. For these lectins the comparison between intact and desialysed glycoproteins provides additional information. *In situ* mild acid hydrolysis is an easy method by which to achieve complete removal of sialic acid (2). Smith degradation is applied to remove peripheral carbohydrates after removal of sialic acid (2).

Protocol 2. Mild acid hydrolysis of sialylglycosides in
polyacrylamide gels

Reagents

- 50 mM H_2SO_4: mix 100 ml 1 N H_2SO_4 with 900 ml H_2O. (1 N H_2SO_4: mix
  10 ml conc. H_2SO_4 with 350 ml H_2O)
- TBS: (150 mM NaCl, 25 mM Tris–HCl pH 7.3): 35 g NaCl, 100 ml 1 M
  Tris–HCl pH 7.3, add H_2O to make 4 litre

Method

1. Heat 50 mM H_2SO_4 up to 80 °C $\pm$ 5 °C.
2. Cook gels or membranes for 1 h in 50 mM H_2SO_4.
3. Discard the solution and rinse the gels or membranes in TBS.

Protocol 3. Smith degradation of glycoprotein carbohydrate
chains in polyacrylamide gels

Reagents

- 75 mM $NaIO_4$ in 50 mM sodium acetate buffer, pH 4.0: 1.6 g of $NaIO_4$
  (anhydrous, mol. wt. 213.9)/100 ml
- 0.1 M NaBorate buffer: dissolve H_3BO_3 3.09 g, $Na_2B_4O_7$ 4.76 *g*, make up
  to 1 litre with water. The pH of this solution should be approximately 8.6
- 0.1 M $NaBH_4$, 0.1 M NaBorate buffer: $NaBH_4$ molecular weight 37.85
  (anhydrous) 0.38 g/100 ml

Method

1. (day 1) Prepare the running gel.
2. (day 2) Perform electrophoresis (and transblot).
3. Fix and stain (Coomassie Brilliant Blue in 25% isopropanol and 10%
   acetic acid).
4. (day 3) Destain and wash with 10% acetic acid at room temperature
   for 3 h.
5. (day 3–day 5) Carry out periodate treatment at 4 °C for 48 h with 75
   mM sodium periodate, 50 mM sodium acetate buffer, pH 4.0 in the
   dark.
6. (day 5) Wash with 1% ethyleneglycol, at room temperature for 2 h.

7. (day 5) Reduce with 0.1 M NaBH$_4$ in 0.1 M NaBorate buffer, pH 8.0 at room temperature for 4 h.

8. Wash with DI water at room temperature for 1 h.

9. (day 5–6) Re-stain with Coomassie Brilliant Blue in 25% isopropanol and 10% acetic acid, and destain with 10% acetic acid.

10. Hydrolyse in mild acid at 80 °C for 1 h.

11. (day 6–day 7) Neutralize and wash at room temperature.

3. Release of oligosaccharides from electro-phoretically separated glycoproteins

The binding of lectins and carbohydrate-specific antibodies to glycoproteins is influenced by a variety of factors other than the carbohydrate structures. In particular the spatial arrangement of the carbohydrate chains on a glyco-protein seems to play a significant role. A single glycoprotein may contain heterogeneous carbohydrate chains, making the interpretation of binding data difficult. Analysis of released oligosaccharides from each glycoprotein band provides additional structural information. Hydrazinolysis of glyco-proteins is a useful technique to release Asn-linked oligosaccharides from glycoproteins (4, 5). This method has recently been applied to electro-phoretically separated glycoproteins in our laboratory (3). The approach is still in its developmental stage. So far we have applied this method to purified glycoproteins. For example, we used desialylated α_1-acid glycoprotein labelled by the galactose oxidase treatment and reduction with NaB^{3}H$_4$ as a model compound. Glycoprotein samples were subjected to SDS-poly-acrylamide gel electrophoresis (SDS–PAGE) in 1 mm thick slab gels according to the method of Laemmli.

Protocol 4. Hydrazinolysis

A. *In situ hydrazinolysis of glycoproteins in slab gels*

Reagents

- Anhydrous hydrazine: this reagent is provided with 'Hydraclub' (Hohnen Oil Co. Ltd, Tokyo, Japan). The reagent is also available from Pierce, Lockland, Il, USA

- Saturated sodium bicarbonate solution

- Acetic anhydride: this reagent needs to avoid contact with moisture

Protocol 4. *Continued*

Method

1. After electrophoresis, stain the gel with Coomassie Blue and then destain.

2. Cut out a portion of the gel containing a band corresponding to the required glycoprotein and mash with a microspatula.

3. Transfer the mashed gel to glass vials (8 × 50 mm) and dry under vacuum in a P_2O_5 desiccator at 60 °C for 4 h.

4. Place the vials in gas-phase hydrazinolysis apparatus 'Hydraclub' (Hohnen Oil Co. Ltd, Tokyo, Japan). Perform hydrazinolysis.

5. After hydrazinolysis and complete removal of hydrazine add 600 μl of distilled water to each vial. Alternatively, add saturated sodium bicarbonate solution (600 μl) and acetic anhydride (60 μl) to each vial in order to obtain N-acetylated oligosaccharides.

B. *Hydrazinolysis of electroblotted glycoproteins*

Reagents

● Immobilon transfer membranes: Millipore Co. (Bedford, MA, USA) Other reagents are the same as *Protocol 4A*

Method

1. Carry out electrophoresis of glycoproteins in a 1 mm thick slab gel according to the method of Laemmli. After electrophoresis electroblot the glycoprotein onto an Immobilon transfer membrane.

2. Locate glycoproteins after staining with Coomassie Blue, and cut out the appropriate portion of the Immobilon transfer membrane. Transfer pieces of the membrane to hydrazinolysis vials (8 × 50 mm) and dry in a P_2O_5 desiccator at 80 °C for 4 h.

3. Perform hydrazinolysis with 'Hydraclub' apparatus.

4. After hydrazinolysis recover the radioactivity by the same procedures as in step **5** above.

These two methods (*Protocols 4A* and *4B*) give similar results. The gas-phase hydrazinolysis apparatus was very useful for this purpose, because anhydrous hydrazine was easily removed form the gel after hydrazinolysis. The obtained oligosaccharides can be labelled with fluorescence compounds or radioactive compounds. The resultant labelled oligosaccharides are ready to be characterized by gel permeation chromatography, high-performance liquid chromatography, or lectin affinity chromatography.

References

1. Burridge, K. (1978). *Methods Enzymol.*, **50**, 54.
2. Irimura, T. and Nicolson, G. L. (1983). *Carbohydr. Res.*, **115**, 209.
3. Kawashima, H., Murata, T., Yamamoto, K., Tateishi, A., Irimura, T., and Osawa, T. (1992). *J. Biochem.*, **111**, 620.
4. Fukuda, M., Kondo, T., and Osawa, T. (1976). *J. Biochem.*, **80**, 1223.
5. Takasaki, S., Mizuochi, T., and Kobata, A. (1982). *Methods Enzymol.*, **83**, 263.

13

DNA binding of immobilized proteins

CONSTANTIN N. FLYTZANIS

1. Introduction

The identification of proteins which have affinity for specific DNA sequences has greatly contributed to our understanding of the transcriptional control of gene expression. A plethora of transcription factors have been purified and characterized by techniques that take advantage of the specificity of recognition that such nuclear proteins exhibit towards relatively small sequences of DNA. In theory at least, having a DNA element guarantees the isolation of the protein which binds to it *in vitro*, and vice versa. Techniques which involve the interaction of immobilized proteins on membrane supports to labelled DNA probes are often referred to as 'Southwestern'. In this category belong the screening of cDNA expression libraries and protein blots, with which we will deal in this chapter. The basic technique involves four steps:

(a) immobilization of proteins on solid support
(b) blocking of undesired reactive groups on the supportive membrane
(c) binding of DNA to the protein
(d) detection of bound DNA

In the following I will concentrate mostly on the specific binding of DNA probes to immobilized proteins, since the other chapters in this book deal extensively with the other procedures and mention only important deviations from well established protocols. This chapter is divided into two sections, the screening of expression libraries with specific DNA sites and the binding of such elements to immobilized proteins on nitrocellulose filters.

2. Screening of bacteriophage expression libraries

A strategy for the isolation of genes encoding DNA-binding proteins by direct screening of cDNA expression libraries with a specific recognition site as a probe was developed to by-pass tedious biochemical purification schemes of the protein in question (1, 2). The advantage of this technique is that in a relatively short time, and with limited resources, at least the DNA-binding domain of a fusion protein can be isolated. About 10^6 recombinant clones is usually an adequate number to screen, but even for the best cDNA libraries this number may vary considerably depending on the prevalence of the corresponding mRNA. Thus, the quantity of a protein in nuclear extracts and its estimated binding constant often have no bearing on the number of clones needing to be screened. One must keep in mind that this technique does not work for every DNA-binding protein and must thus limit the extent of such screenings (the successful completion of positive controls is of course a must). Disadvantages of the technique include the possible loss of positive signals during the washes owing to low binding constants of some proteins, inability of some fusion proteins to bind to DNA, the need for dimerization domains that may not be included in the cDNA cloned or may not be functional in a fusion protein, and the binding of some proteins only in a heterodimeric form with another protein. All the above assume of course that the protein binding domain will be functional after being expressed in bacteria (which is true for the majority of the cases) and no eucaryotic cell modifications are needed. The basic protocol involves lifting the phage plaques onto nitrocellulose, renaturation of the fusion proteins *in situ*, blocking of the nitrocellulose reacting sites, incubation with the radioactively labelled DNA probe, and washes of the unbound material.

Protocol 1. Screening of bacteriophage expression libraries

1. Infect bacteria with the expression library to be screened and incubate on agar plates at 42 °C until very small plaques become visible.

2. Overlay the plates with nitrocellulose filters which have been pre-soaked in 10 mM IPTG and air dried to facilitate induction of the fusion proteins. After additional incubation for 4–6 h at 37 °C mark the filter position on the plates and remove the filters.

3. To block active sites on the nitrocellulose incubate the filters in blocking solution (5% non-fat milk powder in 50 mM Tris, pH 7.5, 50 mM NaCL, 1 mM EDTA, 1 mM DTT) for 1 h at room temperature. Subsequently remove the blocking solution by washing the filters in the binding buffer (10 mM Tris, pH 7.5, 50 mM NaCL, 1 mM EDTA, 1 mM DTT), three times for a few minutes each. Filters can be stored in the binding buffer at 4 °C for up to 1 day before incubation with the DNA probe (see below for preparation of the probe).

4. Incubate the filters for about 1 h at room temperature in binding buffer containing about (1–2) × 10^6 c.p.m. of ^{32}P-labelled DNA probe and 10 µg of non-specific carrier DNA per ml. Poly[dI-dC] (1) or denatured calf

---

thymus DNA (3) can be used as the carrier. Completely immerse the filters in the binding buffer (at least 5 ml per filter) and gently shake.

5. Although the duration of the washes should be empirically determined four changes of the binding buffer for about 5 min each should be adequate. Use at least 10 ml of binding buffer per filter for each wash.

6. After the washing cycles air dry the filters and expose them to X-ray film with the aid of an intensifying screen. Pick (presumably) positive plaques from the plates, replate prepared stocks (4) and screen again in order to purify single positive plaques. It is recommended that duplicate filters be screened with both the specific DNA probe which binds to the protein and a mutant DNA probe that is not specifically recognized by it. This procedure will help identify the true positives from the false positives. Finally identify the clones by isolating bacterial cell extracts containing the fusion protein and then perform either footprinting (5) or mobility shift assays (6).

2.1 Preparation of the DNA probe

It has been demonstrated that the use of oligomerized DNA recognition sites strongly enhances the signal obtained by the nitrocellulose bound proteins (2, 3). Such multimers are either obtained by subcloning ligated DNA fragments or by the ligation of synthetic oligonucleotides containing the protein recognition sequence. Selection of oligomers (8–10mers) can be achieved by column chromatograph using G-200 Sephadex. The selected oligomers can be subsequently either homogeneously labelled with ^{32}P by nick-translation (4) or end-labelled using polynucleotide kinase or Klenow's DNA polymerase to fill in 5' protruding ends.

2.2 Other considerations

A helpful modification of the above protocol has been introduced by Vinson *et al.* (2), in which the filter-bound proteins were denatured and then allowed to renature before reacting to the DNA probe. This denaturation/renaturation procedure increases the sensitivity of detection, perhaps by allowing a larger amount of the protein to participate in the reaction, which otherwise may remain bound on the filter in an inactive or inaccessible form. This procedure involves the incubation of the filters, after lifting them from the plates and air drying them, in denaturation solution (6 M guanidine hydrochloride in 25 mM Hepes, pH 7.9, 25 mM NaCl, 5 mM MgCl$_2$, 0.5 mM DTT) for 15 min in the cold-room. This step in 6 M guanidine hydrochloride is repeated twice and then the filters are incubated in same buffer but with sequentially (by a factor of 2) decreasing concentrations of guanidine hydrochloride for 10 min each in the cold-room. After five such serial dilutions (when the concentration of guanidine hydrochloride reaches 0.1–0.2 M) the filters are incubated in binding buffer without any guanidine hydrochloride, twice for 10 min each in the cold-room. After these renaturation steps are completed the filters are immersed in the blocking solution (see step **3**, *Protocol 1* and subsequently treated as described in *Protocol 1*.

3. Detection of DNA-binding proteins blotted onto nitrocellulose

This technique, often called 'Southwestern', is a quick and easy way of identifying a DNA-binding protein after separation by gel electrophoresis (7). The advantage of this technique is that knowledge of the approximate molecular weight of the protein allows for the appropriate isolation strategy to be followed and can be used as an assay of purity and function during the isolation steps. As for the screening procedure, if the high-affinity protein complex that binds the DNA is composed by heterodimers, then this method will not detect the specific binder. If though, one of the proteins is still able to bind alone the specific sequence with above-background affinity this technique will be adequate to detect it. A modification of the 'Southwestern' procedure was reported by Matsuno *et al.* (8) in order to detect protein–DNA complexes on nitrocellulose filters that involve both protein–DNA and protein–protein interactions. This modified protocol allows first the DNA probe to interact with total or fractionated nuclear extract and then these preformed complexes are incubated according to the basic procedure with the nitrocellulose blotted proteins. Using both one- and two-dimensional gel electrophoresis as well as various denaturing and native conditions Moreland *et al.* (9) have extensively used the 'Southwestern' procedure to characterize the DNA-binding properties of the polyomavirus capsid protein VP1, demonstrating the usefulness of the technique with cloned recombinant proteins as well.

The DNA probes used in 'Southwesterns' can be either known and characterized *cis*-acting elements or molecules which can be designed accordingly in order to search for a DNA-binding protein with desired properties. Thus, Yee *et al.* (10) reported the identification of a group of specific single-stranded $d(TC)_n$ binding proteins in various species using the 'Southwestern' analysis. In some cases specific DNA-binding proteins have being isolated without previous knowledge of their corresponding recognition sites. Keller and Maniatis (11) have described a preparative 'Southwestern' method to select DNA sequences which are specifically recognized by a DNA-binding protein. This method involves the construction of a random oligonucleotide (15mer) library which is screened with the recombinant protein immobilized on nitrocellulose by repeated cycles of binding and rescue of the oligonucleotides. Thus, the 'Southwestern' technique can be used either to identify a protein which binds a known *cis*-acting element or to specifically select the corresponding site(s) to a previously isolated DNA-binding protein.

Protocol 2. Detection of DNA-binding proteins (7)

1. Perform gel electrophoresis of the protein sample (SDS/PAGE as described by Laemmli (12) is the separation method of choice). It is recommended to determine the conditions under which the sample is prepared empirically. In some cases the reducing agent should be omitted from the sample buffer and in others the SDS concentration should be lowered to 0.5% (13). It is also important not to boil the protein samples before loading on the gels.

2. Blot the proteins to nitrocellulose according to the method of Towbin *et al.* (14), with the exception that the transfer buffer should not contain methanol.

3. Block the nitrocellulose filter by incubation in 5% (w/v) non-fat dried milk (15) in 10 mM Hepes pH 8.0, for 1 h at room temperature.

4. Incubate the blots with the radioactive DNA probe (1×10^6 c.p.m./ml) in binding buffer (10 mM hepes pH 8.0, 50 mM NaCl, 10 mM $MgCl_2$, 0.1 mM EDTA, 1 mM DTT, 0.25% non-fat dried milk) for 1 h at room temperature. Prepare the probe as in *Protocol 1*.

5. Wash the filters in three to four changes of the binding buffer for 10 min each at room temperature. To decrease possible low-specificity complexes, the washes can be done in binding buffer with higher salt concentration (determined empirically).

6. Air dry the nitrocellulose blots and expose them to X-ray film for autoradiography.

3.1 Other considerations

The diversity of properties characteristic of DNA-binding proteins makes it difficult to follow the same 'Southwestern' protocol without modification for every protein in question. Thus, some proteins will withstand the sample boiling, or the reducing agents of gel electrophoresis, for some proteins transfer onto nitrocellulose in the presence of methanol does not cause a problem, etc. Often the denaturation/renaturation procedure (2) described in section 2 is necessary for efficient binding, and other investigators have renatured the proteins after transfer in a detergent-containing solution (9). It is also important in some cases to supplement the binding buffer with $ZnSO_4$

if the protein is known to contain zinc finger domains, to adjust the salt and the $MgCl_2$ concentration, and to omit the reducing agent (DTT).

It is strongly recommended to use a mutated DNA probe, with specific changes in the recognition sequence that abolish binding, as a negative control. Often the addition to the binding buffer of non-specific DNA (double and/or single stranded) is necessary to reveal only the specific complexes and the addition of unlabelled probe as a specific competitor ensures the identity of the specific protein. The nature and concentration of such competitors (molar ratio to the probe) should be previously determined by a mobility shift assay (5).

Although the presence of many specific and non-specific DNA-binding proteins in nuclear extracts may hold some surprises and can lead to artifacts in a 'Southwestern' assay, careful optimization of the technique for each protein in question allows one to employ an easy assay for its identification during various purification steps, as well as to study its biochemical properties.

References

1. Singh, H., LeBowitz, J. H., Baldwin, A. S. jun., and Sharp, P. A. (1988). *Cell*, **52**, 415.
2. Vinson, C. R., LaMarco, K. L., Johnson, P. F., Landschulz, W. H., and McKnight, S. L. (1988). *Genes Devel.*, **2**, 801.
3. Staudt, L. M., Clerc, R. G., Singh, H., LeBowitz, J. H., Sharp, P. A., and Baltimore, D. (1988). *Science*, **241**, 577.
4. Maniatis, T., Fritsch, E. F., and Sambrook, J. (1982). *Molecular cloning: a laboratory manual*. Cold Spring Harbor Laboratory Press, Cold Spring Harbor, NY.
5. Fried, M. and Crothers, D. (1981). *Nucleic Acids Res.*, **9**, 6505.
6. Galas, D. and Schmitz, A. (1978). *Nucleic Acids Res.*, **5**, 3157.
7. Miskimins, W. K., Roberts, M. P., McClelland, A., and Ruddle, F. H. (1985). *Proc. Natl. Acad. Sci., USA*, **82**, 6741.
8. Matsuno, K., Suzuki, T., Takiya, S., and Suzuki, Y. (1989). *J. Biol. Chem.*, **264**, 4599.
9. Moreland, R. B., Montross, L., and Garcea, R. L. (1991). *J. Virol.*, **65**, 1168.
10. Yee, H. A., Wong, A. K. C., van de Sande, J. H., and Rattner, J. B. (1991). *Nucleic Acids Res.*, **19**, 949.
11. Keller, A. D. and Maniatis, T. (1991). *Nucleic Acids Res.*, **19**, 4675.
12. Laemmli, U. K. (1970). *Nature*, **227**, 680.
13. DiMario, P. J., Bromley, S. E., and Gall, J. G. (1989). *Chromosoma*, **97**, 413.
14. Towbin, H., Staehelin, T., and Gordon, J. (1979). *Proc. Natl. Acad. Sci., USA*, **76**, 4350.
15. Johnson, D. A., Gautsch, J. W., Sportsman, J. R., and Elder, J. H. (1984). *Gene Anal. Tech.*, **3**, 3.

Use of peptide ligands for the detection of binding proteins by Western blotting

PAUL HOSSENLOPP and MICHEL BINOUX

1. Introduction

Western ligand blotting is a variation of the method of protein analysis first described by Towbin (1) in a pioneering article, 'Electrophoretic transfer of proteins from polyacrylamide gels to nitrocellulose sheets', and subsequently referred to as 'Western blotting'. The technique involves electrophoretic separation of proteins which are then transferred to a nitrocellulose or equivalent membrane where they are recognized either by an antibody (this was the method reported by Towbin, known as immunoblotting) or by a specific ligand (known as ligand blotting).

Towbin had foreseen the use of ligands, since in the conclusion to his article he predicted that his technique would become applicable not only to identification of proteins by antibodies, but, more generally, to analysis of any specific interaction between a protein and its ligand (nucleic acid, nucleotide, hormone, or another protein).

Volumes of literature have since proved him right. The reviews by Gershoni and Palade (2) and Beisiegel (3) describe the first studies done using ligand-specific recognition of binding proteins (BPs), in the broad sense of the term. Specific ligands include DNA or RNA (4), heparin (5), LDL (6), a toxin (2), a hormone (GH), (7), a growth factor (EGF), (8), or another protein like calmodulin (2), fibronectin (9), and a histone (4), or quite simply, calcium (10).

Numerous BPs have now been analysed by Western ligand blotting (WLB). Application of this technique to membrane receptors was described by Soutar and Wade in an earlier volume of this series (*Protein function: a practical approach* (1989)). *Table 1* gives a non-exhaustive list of BPs or binding sites investigated in this way, along with their protein or peptide ligands which essentially are the ones of interest in this chapter.

Table 1. Binding proteins investigated by Western ligand blotting

Binding protein	Ligand	Label	References
EGF receptor	EGF	Anti-EGF[a]	8
EGF receptor	EGF	^{125}I[b]	11
Collagenous proteins	Fibronectin fragments	Peroxydase[c]	9
Acetylcholine receptor	α-bungarotoxin	^{125}I[b]	2, 12
Lipoprotein receptor	LDL	Anti-LDL[a]	6
LDL receptor-related protein	ßVLDL	Biotinylated[d]	13
GH membrane BP	GH	^{125}I[b]	7
Calmodulin BP	Calmodulin	^{125}I[b]	2, 14
IGFBPs	IGF-I and -II	^{125}I[b]	15
M6-P/IGF-II receptor	IGF-II	^{125}I[b]	16
M6-P/IGF-II receptor	Cathepsin D	^{125}I[b]	16
Laminin B	Vimentin	^{125}I[b]	17
Laminin B	Desmin derivatives	^{125}I[b]	17
Filensin	Vimentin	^{125}I[b]	18
LH receptor	hCG	^{125}I[b]	19
IL-1 receptor	IL-1 α	^{125}I[b]	20
Albumin BP	Albumin	^{125}I[b] or gold[e]	21
Vitellogenin receptor	Vitellogenin	^{125}I[b]	22
Nuclear localization sequence BP	Nuclear localization sequence	^{14}C[b]	23
TNF receptor	TNF	^{125}I[b]	24
Activin BP (follistatin)	Activin	^{125}I[b]	25
G-CSF receptor	CSF	^{125}I[b]	26
t-PA membrane BP	t-PA	^{125}I[b] or anti-t-PA[a]	27
u-PA membrane BP	u-PA	^{125}I[b]-or anti-u-PA[a]	27
u-PA membrane BP	u-PA	Biotinylated[d]	28
Mannose receptor	t-PA	Anti-t-PA[a]	29
Vitronectin	PA-I	Anti-PA-I[a]	30
Plasminogen membrane BP	Plasminogen	^{125}I[b]	31
Neurite outgrowth factor BP	NOF	Anti-NOF[a]	32
Angiogenin receptor	Angiogenin	^{125}I[b]	33

[a] The ligand is recognized by an antibody which is identified by immunoblotting.
[b] The ligand is radiolabelled.
[c] The ligand is coupled to an enzyme whose activity is assayed.
[d] The ligand is biotinylated.
[e] The ligand is coupled to gold.

2. Western ligand blotting

2.1 General precautions to be taken

Some proteins are thermolabile and fail to renature sufficiently after transfer still to bind the ligand. Any heating should therefore be avoided and, as far as possible, all manipulations should be done at low temperatures (cold table, cooled electrophoresis, etc.).

In general it is advisable, but sometimes it is essential, to de-gas the water used for buffers, especially the transfer buffer, to prevent formation of bubbles.

2.2 SDS polyacrylamide gel electrophoresis (SDS-PAGE)

This is the classical denaturing electrophoresis described by Laemmli (34), with the important difference that it should be run in the absence of reducing agent, since reduction of disulphide bridges in proteins generally results in loss of binding ability. Nevertheless, cases have been reported where treatment with reducing agents does not prevent the protein from binding its ligand (for example vimentin or desmin membrane-binding proteins (17), t-PA membrane-binding protein (27), or plasminogen membrane-binding protein (31)). Specially mild conditions of dissociation and resolution have been described (35), where detergent was omitted from both the separating and stacking gels, the sample buffer contained 1% lithium dodecyl sulphate, and the upper electrode buffer contained 0.1% of the same detergent.

For binding proteins of similar molecular weight, homogenous gels may be used (12.5%, for example, for insulin-like growth factor binding proteins (IGFBPs) of M_r 20 000 to 40 000 (15)). Where molecular weights are very different, acrylamide gel gradients should be used (5% to 17.5% for binding proteins of M_r 20 000 to 200 000).

The description below is of the electrophoresis routinely used in our laboratory to study IGFBPs, essentially according to Laemmli (without reducing agent), on $16 \times 18 \times 0.15$ cm gels. Mini-gels can also be used, which means smaller samples are applied, saving time and reagents, but, in our hands, these yield slightly poorer resolution.

For details on PAGE techniques, the interested reader is referred to earlier volumes in this series (36, 37).

2.2.1 Preparation of samples and reference proteins

The sample buffer (SB) should be prepared as follows:

- 10% glycerol
- 62.5 mM Tris–HCl, pH 6.8
- 2.5% SDS
- 0.001% bromophenol blue
- without reducing agent for the samples, with 25 mM dithiothreitol, or 5% β-mercaptoethanol for marker proteins (or known molecular mass).

Samples (lyophilized or native) are added to a given volume of SB, but it is sometimes necessary to use 5 × concentrated SB for larger samples. Ionic strength should be low, or at least similar from one sample to another. Adjustments may be made by addition of concentrated saline or desalting by dialysis or gel filtration (PD 10 Pharmacia, for example) using a volatile buffer (such as ammonium acetate) and then lyophilization.

In some cases (identification, isolation from an excessively concentrated protein sample), the proteins under study may first be precipitated using a specific antibody, as described in another volume of this series (38). We have had success with an immunoprecipitation technique involving antibody covalently bound to a Protein A–Sepharose 4B matrix, from which immuno-globulin-free protein can be recovered before electrophoresis (39).

Reference proteins may be either standard molecular mass markers or a mixture of known proteins of the same type as the BP under study. For the IGFBPs, we use a pool of either hypopituitary human or fetal calf serum in which most of the known IGFBPs are clearly defined, with molecular masses previously determined from standards.

In order to maximize denaturation by SDS, samples should be heated at either 100 °C for at least 2 min or at 60 °C for 15 min before electrophoresis, but in some cases denaturing conditions need to be less harsh and heating either reduced or omitted (35). Nevertheless, insufficient heating can result in incomplete dissociation of the complexes (40).

With long-term electrophoresis (overnight or longer) of BPs with activity that is sensitive to reduction, reducing agent (accompanying the markers) may diffuse into the adjacent lane and alter the BPs. It is therefore good practice to leave this lane empty.

2.3 Transfer

The protocol below is one that we use routinely to analyse IGFBPs, transfer being carried out in liquid medium. Modifications of this are possible, and may be necessary, depending on the type of binding protein under study (see Section 2.3.1).

Protocol 1. Analysis of IGFBPs

Materials

- nitrocellulose (Schleicher and Schull BA 85, 45 μm pore size)
- Whatman 3 MM or 17 Chr filter paper
- transfer chamber with plate electrodes and a magnetic stirrer at the bottom and an effective cooling system, or semi-dry transfer apparatus
- holders containing two plastic grids and Scotch-Brite pads to sandwich the nitrocellulose/gel assembly firmly. Pads should be thoroughly washed after use
- buffers
  - transfer buffer (TB): 15 mM Tris, 120 mM glycine, pH 8.3, 15% methanol
  - TBS buffer: 10 mM Tris–HCl, pH 7.4, 150 mM NaCl

- quenching buffer: TBS, 0.5% ligand- and BP-free BSA, 0.1% Tween-20
- incubation buffer: TBS, 1 mg/ml ligand-free BSA, labelled ligand. It is recommended that 0.5 mg/ml sodium azide be added for long-term incubations
- washing buffer: TBS with/without 0.1% Tween-20
- plastic bags or double sheets to be sealed for incubation with the labelled ligand
- large Petri dishes (20 cm diameter) or equivalent for various steps of membrane treatment
- large container for sandwich assembly

A. *Pre-transfer*

1. As a general rule wear gloves to avoid touching the membranes.
2. Cut the nitrocellulose membrane and filter paper to the size of the gel or portion of the gel to be transferred. Cut off one corner as a guide mark.
3. Place the membrane on the surface of transfer buffer in a Petri dish, allow buffer to penetrate the membrane completely by capillary force, then cover it with TB for 15 min. Soak the filters in the same buffer.
4. Soak the Scotch-Brite pads for a few minutes in a container about one-third full of TB and remove bubbles by squashing them against the bottom of the container.
5. Fill the transfer apparatus with cold TB and begin cooling so as to maintain a temperature of 15–20 °C.

B. *Transfer*

1. At the end of electrophoresis remove the gel, cut off one corner as a guide mark, remove useless portions and soak the gel in TB for 10 min.
2. Building up the sandwich: perform the following steps under buffer in a container one-third filled with TB.
3. Lay the first sheet of filter paper on a Scotch-Brite pad already placed on a open grid.
4. Layer the gel on the filter paper.
5. Following the guide marks, place the membrane on the gel.
6. Layer one 17 Chr, or two or three 3 MM filter papers onto the membrane so as to obtain a tightly fitting assembly.

Protocol 1. *Continued*

7. Check for maximum contact between the layers and remove air bubbles by rolling over the paper with fingers and/or a large-calibre pipette (5 ml).

8. Close up the holder containing the sandwich.

9. Rapidly mount the holder into the transfer chamber with the membrane side towards the anode. Remove any bubbles that may have appeared.

10. Turn on the magnetic stirrer.

11. Start transfer by applying current: 130 V 0.6 A (constant), 1 h.

C. *Post-transfer*

1. Remove the membrane, air dry for a few minutes, and stain the gel (classical methods) to ensure effective transfer.

2. All subsequent treatment of the membrane to be carried out at 4 °C in Petri dishes and with gentle stirring (except for incubation with ligand).

3. Incubate the membrane with 100–150 ml quenching buffer for 45 min.

4. Prepare a double sheet of plastic larger than the membrane. Seal one side and totally open one sheet along the seal.

5. Rinse the membrane in TBS twice for 1 min, then layer it on the inner surface of the double sheet of plastic, along the seal.

6. Close up the plastic sheet and smooth it to remove bubbles.

7. Seal two sides completely, and the last to three-quarters its length.

8. Through the opening, introduce 2–3 ml incubation buffer (for a nitrocellulose membrane of 11 × 15.5 cm) containing 300 000 c.p.m. ^{125}I-labelled ligand.

9. Seal the plastic bag after removing air bubbles.

10. Massage the bag so as to distribute the mixture evenly and leave it lying flat (preferably on filter paper in case of leakage) overnight or for 36 h at 4 °C.

11. Wash successively in 100–150 ml buffer: 10 min in TBS, 0.1% Tween-20, then 5 × 10 min in TBS changing containers after the first two washes.

12. Dry the nitrocellulose membrane and sandwich it between two Chronex Lightning Plus enhancing screens (E.I. Dupont) and X-ray film (Amersham) in the autoradiography cassette and expose at −70 °C (see Chapter 9).

2.3.1 Comments

Many of these also apply to Western blotting in general (see reviews in (2) and (3) and other chapters in this volume).

i. Transfer efficiency

During set-up for a given type of BP, it is advisable to test different buffers and to work with two types of membrane on the anode side (G. Peltre, personal communication), so as to find the conditions yielding transfer of the majority of proteins under study to the first membrane. It is also wise to check that no (particularly basic) proteins have been transferred to the cathode side.

In testing for transfer efficiency, the proteins remaining on the gel are compared with those transferred onto the membrane. Several methods are possible:

(a) Stain both the gel and the membrane, with Amido Black 10 B or Ponceau S, for example.

(b) Monitor with stained marker proteins (commercially available).

(c) Monitor with radiolabelled marker proteins (commercially available, or laboratory labelled). Autoradiographs of the dried gel are compared with those of the membrane with or without quenching. For more accurate quantification, run a single labelled protein per lane during electrophoresis, identify it by autoradiography and measure the density of the bands by densitometric scanner, or cut out and count in a spectrometer. It has now become possible to quantify by direct radioactivity measurement using an autoradiographic scanner.)

Transfer efficiency may vary from one protein to another, depending especially on its size and charge and the concentration of polyacrylamide gel used. Several parameters may be modified to increase the efficiency of transfer: polyacrylamide gel concentration, the composition of the transfer buffer, the type and porosity of the membrane, and duration and electrical conditions of transfer.

A number of authors have reported diminished transfer efficiency with larger proteins and higher concentrations of gel. When investigating molecules with very different, and particularly, high, molecular weights, gel gradients are advisable, because the loss of efficiency linked to molecule size may be compensated for by the lower gel concentration in the zones where high-M_r proteins migrate (11).

As regards buffer, pH is important. After SDS-PAGE, the SDS-protein complexes migrate towards the anode at high pH. Addition of SDS may facilitate elution of the proteins from the gel matrix, but may also weaken their binding to the membrane. If transfer is required from a non-denaturing gel, a more acid pH should be used to transfer basic proteins. Methanol is known to reduce the efficiency of elution by denaturing and fixing proteins to the gel, but to enhance the binding capacity of the nitrocellulose membrane by strengthening hydrophobic interactions. For high molecular weight molecules, methanol concentrations can therefore be reduced so as to promote elution, but for smaller molecules they are increased to facilitate binding to the membrane. Methanol also stabilizes the geometrical arrangement of the gel during transfer. If lower concentrations of methanol are used, or if maximum amounts of SDS need to be removed, longer periods of gel equilibration in TB are necessary before transfer.

Nitrocellulose membranes of smaller pore size and higher binding capacity (0.2 µm seems to be optimal) may be appropriate, or other types of membrane, such as polyvinylidene difluoride (Immobilion PVDF), nylon, etc.

ii. Semi-dry transfer
Transfer may also be carried out under semi-dry conditions, with some modifications to the above. In our hands, this has proved less reproducible for large gels (16 × 18 × 0.15 cm) because: uniform transfer over the whole gel is difficult to obtain; the speed of transfer in some cases differs more from one protein to another; and the liquid phase may become highly acidic, which could harm certain proteins.

We have successfully used semi-dry transfer for mini-gels (6 × 8 × 0.15 cm), however, with the following adaptations:

(a) equilibration of the gels in TB for a least 20 min prior to transfer

(b) addition of three 3 MM or one 17 Chr filter paper on either side of the gel in the sandwich

(c) transfer for 45 min at 24 V (constant voltage) and maximum amperage of 5.5 A/cm^2

iii. Quenching
The purpose of quenching is to saturate all potential ligand binding sites on the membrane itself and to achieve maximum renaturation of the protein so that it may bind the ligand. A wide variety of reagents serve one or both of these purposes (detergents, proteins, divalent cations, reducing agents).

Whether it concerns reagents or incubation conditions, quenching always aims to provide maximum signal with minimum background. One way of determining optimal conditions is to deposit the proteins under study directly onto the nitrocellulose membrane, to apply different quenching procedures and then to test with the ligand. However, this may be misleading, since in some cases these may not be the optimal conditions for transferred BPs (41).

Non-ionic detergents
The action of non-ionic detergents, like Tween, NP-40 and Triton, appears to involve reduction of BP binding to the nitrocellulose (14, 42, and this volume). For proteins bound to the membrane (transferred proteins) there are two effects, one helpful and the other not. Either the proteins are partially

detached from the membrane, and hence renature more easily, or else the protein is lost. For proteins that are not bound to the membrane, like the ligand, detergent will reduce non-specific binding and therefore background.

Proteins

Quenching with proteins is widely used, but not always essential. Examples include BSA, gelatin, haemoglobin, skimmed milk or casein, ovalbumin and IgG. Haemoglobin has the advantage of staining the nitrocellulose, which means that the protein bands appear more clearly and can be easily cut out, if necessary (11). Bovine IgG has been used to study albumin-binding proteins (21), where albumin could obviously not be applied for quenching.

The quenching agents must contain neither ligand nor the BP under study. Particular care should be taken when a protein is used that has been extracted from a biological fluid. In our studies of IGFBPs, IGF- and IGFBP-free preparations of BSA were difficult to find, since serum contains large amounts of both. For the same reasons, skimmed milk, which is frequently used in classical Western blotting, is not advisable when studying IGFBPs.

Other agents

Use of salmon sperm DNA has been reported (11), and, in addition to proteins, dithiothreitol (for proteins whose binding activity is unchanged by reduction), magnesium, and PMSF (17).

iv. Sheet storage after transfer

Nitrocellulose can be stored dried in sealed bags for at least a week at either 4 °C (11) or −20 °C (our unpublished results) before being incubated with ligand. Similarly, it can be stored after ligand blotting for further analysis by immunoblotting (see Section 4.1.1).

v. Incubation with the ligand
Type and quality of ligand

Table 1 lists some ligands and the type of labelling used. Specificity must be checked in each case.

(a) *Radiolabelled ligands.* This is the simplest method, where binding specificity can easily be tested by incubating with and without excess unlabelled ligand. Visualization is by autoradiography or using an autoradiographic scanner.

The quality of the labelled ligand, by which the binding sites are revealed, is pivotal, and should be the first suspect if poor signals are obtained. In the case of our IGFBPs, a drop in tracer quality is seen in ligand blotting before it becomes evident in RIA. We have always used a mixture of radiolabelled IGF-I and IGF-II in detecting IGFBPs, since they recognize both IGFs, but this facilitates visualization of IGFBPs with a preferential affinity for IGF-II, such as IGFBP-2 and especially IGFBP-6 (43).

177

(b) *Biotinylated ligands.* Here, classical methods are used to recognize the biotin radical.

(c) *Ligands bound to enzymes.* Assay of the enzymatic activity is used to detect the ligand and hence the BP.

(d) *Stained ligands.* The ligand may be coupled, for example, to gold.

(e) *Anti-ligand antibodies.* Unlabelled ligand may be detected through an anti-ligand antibody revealed by classical immunoblotting.

Incubation buffer and ligand concentration

Signal intensity is directly related to ligand concentration. With labelled ligands, if quantities are not limited, one may increase either concentration (10^6 c.p.m. is standard for many authors) in order to reduce incubation time, or volume (1.5×10^6 c.p.m. in 15 to 20 ml) in order to incubate in a Petri dish with stirring (P. Monget, personal communication). For our part, with relatively small amounts of tracer (300 000 c.p.m.), the latter has proved less efficient than in incubation in a sealed bag.

In order to prevent loss or denaturation of the tracer, the buffer should contain proteins, either 1 mg/ml BSA, or 0.25 mg/ml gelatin (maximum concentration when incubating at 4 °C), or 0.2 mg/ml protamine sulphate (P. Monget).

Non-ionic detergents may also enhance binding of the ligand to the membrane-bound protein (11).

Other elements are sometimes essential, like calcium in the case of lipoprotein binding to LDL receptors (13) or t-PA binding to the mannose receptor (29) or calmodulin to its BP (2, 14). Mg is used for the mannose-6-phosphate/IGF-II receptor (16) and Mg plus dithiothreitol for vimentin membrane BPs (17).

Incubation time

Time-course studies should be done under the incubation conditions chosen in order to determine optimum incubation time.

vi. Washing

This should not be for too long, as the ligand may be released during prolonged washing (27).

3. Quantitative analysis of transferred binding proteins

3.1 Quantification of the blots

3.1.1 Cutting out of the blots and counting (^{125}I-labelled ligands)

i. *Varying BP and constant radioligand concentrations*

After electrophoresis of the BPs, transfer to nitrocellulose, incubation with labelled ligand, and autoradiography, the nitrocellulose membrane and the autoradiogram are aligned so as to pencil in on the membrane the positions of the bands revealed by autoradiography. The pencil-marked bands are then cut out and counted in a gamma spectrometer. This was the methodology used to quantify the changes in serum IGFBPs in a subject after IGF administration (44).

ii. Constant BP and varying radioligand concentrations

An alternative method is to deposit the BP-containing sample across the width of the electrophoretic gel. After transfer to nitrocellulose, the membrane is cut longitudinally in 1-cm strips which are then incubated with increasing concentrations of labelled ligand. Non-specific binding is determined by incubating one strip with labelled and an excess of cold ligand. The washed strips are then autoradiographed. Finally the blots corresponding to the bands are cut out and counted in a gamma spectrometer. This technique has been used for the acetylcholine (12) and IL-1 (20) receptors.

3.1.2 Scanning

Laser densitometry and image analysis are the most commonly used means of scanning. In our experience of densitometry, with identical samples placed on the same gel minor variations occur from one lane to another, leading to a large margin of error in the estimations if the total surface of a band is measured. We have obtained the most accurate measurements by scanning two zones of the central portion of each band. Direct radioactivity measurement is also possible using an autoradiographic scanner.

3.2 Competitive binding studies

3.2.1 Cutting out of the blots and incubation

As described above (Section 3.1.1 (*i*)) the BP sample is layered across the width of the gel and, after transfer, the nitrocellulose is cut longitudinally in 1-cm wide strips which are incubated with a constant concentration of radiolabelled, and increasing concentrations of unlabelled, ligand, then washed and autoradiographed. The bands thus revealed can either be cut out and counted in a gamma spectrometer (12) or the autoradiographs scanned (20).

Details of our method for IGFBPs have been published elsewhere (45). Briefly:

(a) The sample is deposited across the width of the gel.

(b) After electrophoresis, proteins are transferred onto two superimposed membranes.

(c) Following quenching, the lateral portions of the first membrane and all of the second membrane are incubated with radiolabelled IGF.

(d) Through autoradiography of the lateral portions and of the second membrane the positions of the BPs can be identified on the central portion of the first membrane.

(e) This central portion is then cut into transverse bands, each containing one type of BP.

(f) The bands are cut into 5 × 5 mm pieces.

(g) The pieces are then incubated in phosphate buffer with a fixed concentration of ^{125}I-IGF-I or -II (the number of pieces per tube should yield a B/T of $\geq$ 10%) and increasing concentrations of unlabelled IGF.

(h) Once washed, the tubes are counted in a gamma spectrometer.

In this manner, the preferential affinities for either IGF-I or IGF-II of several IGFBPs could be determined, before being purified (45). We also showed that the two differently glycosylated forms of IGFBP-3 have different relative affinities for both IGF-I and IGF-II, this being corroborated by another, non-denaturing technique (45).

3.2.2 Multiple screening

With the latest types of commercially available apparatus, sealed mini-incubation cells can be established on the transfer membrane, which correspond to the lanes of the gel. This means that individual sample lanes can be screened without slicing the membrane into strips. This material is designed for simultaneous use of different detection methods or antibodies side by side, and will also be appropriate for competitive binding experiments to determine the affinities for their ligands of BPs separated electrophoretically and then transferred to a membrane.

4. Uses and limitations

4.1 Uses

In Western ligand blotting (WLB), which involves denaturing electrophoresis and hence dissociation of the BP from its endogenous ligand, BPs are identified with the use of purified or recombinant ligands.

4.1.1 Identification of ligand-specific proteins

Primarily, WLB is used to detect, in a mixture of known or unknown proteins (like a crude extract), those which specifically bind a given ligand. Identification of a binding protein is therefore possible before a protein has been purified and its antibody has become available.

A single ligand may recognize different proteins providing they possess some structural homology. This feature has proved useful in the case of the IGFBPs, all six of which may be identified in any biological fluid or culture medium (*Figures 1* and *2*), as well as in the fractions obtained in the course of purification, thereby significantly facilitating isolation. Also, IGFBPs from species as different as man, bovines, murines, the chicken, and some fishes have been identified using a single labelled ligand, human IGF (our unpublished results and 46). This convenient characteristic of the IGFs is, however, not true of all ligands. Mouse u-PA binds the mouse u-PA receptor, but fails to recognize its human homologue and *vice versa* (28).

With WLB, the precise binding sequence of a proteolysed BP can be pinpointed, a technique which is now being employed in the analysis of bacterially expressed ligand binding sites (35).

Another aspect is the possibility of reusing the membrane, from which the ligand may or may not have been detached (2), for further analysis by immunoblotting. This is time-saving, reduces the quantities of reagent needed and, in addition, allows rigorous comparisons to be made of the results of the two methods, since the patterns obtained can be directly superimposed. In our laboratory this has proved particularly useful when the immuno-complexes are revealed by chemiluminescence, where sensitivity is much higher than in staining techniques.

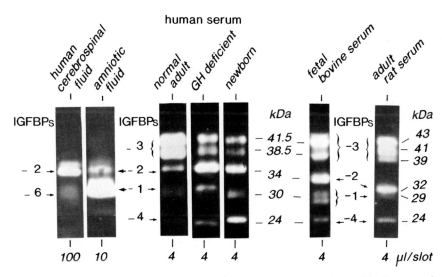

Figure 1. Western ligand blot analysis of insulin-like growth factor binding proteins (IGFBPs) in different biological fluids. Following SDS-PAGE under non-reducing conditions, the proteins were electroblotted onto nitrocellulose, incubated with a mixture of human ^{125}I-IGF-I and -II, and the IGFBPs revealed by autoradiography. Binding specificity was demonstrated by incubating part of the nitrocellulose with excess unlabelled IGF.

The IGFBPs are indicated in this figure according to their international nomenclature (IGFBP-1 to -6). Comparison of their electrophoretic profiles, which are characteristic of the biological fluids analysed, shows:

(a) the remarkable interspecies similarity between the different molecular forms of IGFBP (man, bovine, rat)

(b) the tissue-specific differences in IGFBP expression: serum (which reflects hepatic production), cerebrospinal fluid, amniotic fluid and

(c) in serum, the differences in expression as related to stage of development (newborn versus adult) and hormonal status (normal versus GH-deficient subjects).

Detecting binding proteins by Western blotting

human liver culture medium

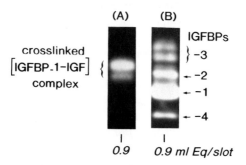

Figure 2. Western blot analysis of IGFBPs: data obtained by prior crosslinking to labelled IGF compared with those obtained by ligand blotting. Two aliquots, (A) and (B), of the same culture medium were run simultaneously in SDS-PAGE. Sample A had first been incubated with ^{125}I-IGF-I and -II and treated with dimethylsuberimidate to ensure covalent binding of the IGFs and IGFBPs.

The electrophoretically separated proteins were transferred to nitrocellulose which was then cut in two. The portion containing Sample A proteins was autoradiographed and the one containing Sample B proteins was first incubated with ^{125}I-IGF-I and -II, then autoradiographed. The ligand blot (B) revealed IGFBPs-1 to 4. The molecular mass of IGFBP-1 was estimated at 30 kDa. Here, only IGFBP-1 was detectable in Sample A, appearing as a 37-34-kDa doublet corresponding to the crosslinked [IGFBP-1-^{125}I-IGF] complex.

i. Western ligand blotting versus crosslinking

WLB has several advantages over crosslinking of a labelled ligand to its BP:

(a) The molecular weight measured for a visualized protein is that of the protein itself, as opposed to the protein–ligand complex; however, when electrophoresis is run without a reducing agent, and if the protein has one or more disulphide bridges, the molecular weight as measured may be imprecise.

(b) Since electrophoresis is run under denaturing conditions, the binding sites are freed of endogenous ligand and there is no competition for tracer binding.

(c) In some cases, WLB reveals BPs that are undetectable after crosslinking (47), as occurs for IGFBPs released in liver culture media (*Figure 2*); in other cases, however, the opposite may be true (see Section 4.2);

(d) When analysing serum, artefacts may appear through crosslinking to non-specific proteins (for example albumin), which does not occur in WLB.

ii. Western ligand blotting and gel overlay

WLB is quicker than gel overlay (14), but the latter can be useful when

182

working with ultra-thin gels. Using the PhastSystem (Pharmacia), we have obtained similar results for IGFBPs revealed either following transfer to a membrane or directly incubating the gel with labelled IGF tracer, although the second method yields slightly poorer resolution (unpublished results).

4.1.2 Structural and functional studies

WLB may be used to test binding specificity. For instance, excess cold IL-1 has been shown to inhibit the binding of labelled IL-1 to the IL-1 receptor, whereas IL-2, TNFα and interferon γ do not (20). Comparative studies have also been done between the native and mutated binding sequences of a protein ligand to a membrane protein (23).

Quantitative blot analyses have made it possible to determine the affinities of complexes formed on the filter (12, 20, 35). It has been possible in some cases to identify binding sites with different affinities for the same ligand or for two structurally related ligands. Amongst the IGFBPs, IGFBP-6's weak signal with IGF-I compared with IGF-II reflects its strongly preferential affinity for IGF-II (see Section 3.2). Low-affinity monomeric, and high-affinity oligomeric, CSF receptors have been detected before confirmation by sucrose gradient centrifugation (26).

The presence or absence of carbohydrate units have been detected in certain BPs by glycanase treatment either of the samples prior to electrophoresis (48) or of the proteins bound to the membrane (2). In the case of an acetylcholine receptor subunit, the deglycosylated form has been found to be equally capable of ligand binding as the mature subunit (35).

Results of WLB analyses yield information on the domains of interaction between the ligand and the BP:

(a) Lysine has been seen to prevent the binding of plasminogen to its specific membrane-binding sites (31).

(b) Reduced or alkylated forms of t-PA and u-PA no longer bind their respective membrane BPs (27).

(c) t-PA and u-PA inhibitors (at the plasmonigen activator site) fail to inhibit t-PA and u-PA binding to their respective membrane BPs, indicating that active sites are not involved in the interactions with membrane-binding sites (27).

(d) Anti-NOF BP antibody prevents both binding of NOF and its biological action (32).

The possible influence of effector molecules in ligand-to-BP binding have been studied by WLB. ApoE was shown to increase VLDL binding to the LDL receptor-related protein, and ApoC, but not ApoAI or ApoAII, to inhibit this effect (13).

Finally, BPs may be more precisely characterized by two-dimensional polyacrylamide gel electrophoresis and ligand blot analysis (49).

4.1.3 Clinical investigation

i. Qualitative analyses

Unlike RIA, WLB yields qualitative, or at best semi-quantitative, results. Nevertheless, for the IGFBPs, WLB in a single experiment gives an overall view of the various molecular forms and their relative proportions in a given medium. Such a picture can be useful in diagnostics and clinical investigation (50). Ideally, samples should always be studied at a minimum of two concentrations and compared with reference samples.

ii. Western ligand blotting versus RIA

Contradictory findings have been reported for IGFBP-3. With RIA, serum levels of IGFBP-3 appear elevated in women at the end of pregnancy (51).

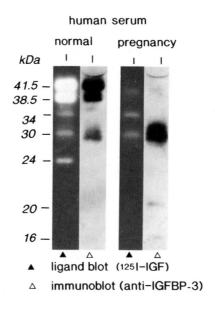

▲   ligand blot (125I–IGF)

△   immunoblot (anti-IGFBP-3)

Figure 3. Western blot analysis of IGFBPs in pools of sera from normal adults and pregnant women (23–39 weeks). Following SDS-PAGE (4 µl per slot) and transfer to nitrocellulose, the nitrocellulose was incubated first with ^{125}I-IGF-I and -II to detect the IGFBPs, then with a specific anti-IGFBP-3 antibody to identify IGFBP-3 and its fragments.

During pregnancy, one or more serine proteases are responsible for limited proteolysis of certain IGFBPs, IGFBP-3 in particular, resulting in easier dissociation of the IGFs, hence increasing their bioavailability. This proteolysis results in an alteration of the electrophoretic migration of IGFBP-3, which normally appears as a 41.5–38.5 kDa doublet, and of its binding activity. With immunoblotting, the anti-IGFBP-3 antibody detects several proteolytical fragments, the major one being at 30 kDa, which is undetectable by ligand blotting. In the serum of normal adults, immunoblotting shows that IGFBP-3 proteolysis occurs in the normal state, although to a much lesser extent than during pregnancy.

With WLB, by contrast, IGFBP-3 is no longer visible at this stage (52, 53). The discrepancy is explained by the fact that proteolytic activity appears in the serum of pregnant women, which specifically causes partial degradation of IGFBP-3. The resulting fragment migrates at 30 kDa, as opposed to the 38.5–41.5 kDa of the native protein, and is recognizable by immunoblotting, but barely so by ligand blotting (52; *Figure 3*). Classical radio-competition experiments showed that the proteolysed IGFBP-3's affinity for IGFs is much weaker than that of the intact BP, which explains its almost negligible ability to bind tracer in WLB (52). In this instance, WLB yields a picture which is closer to physiological reality than does RIA.

4.2 Limitations

Not all binding sites are recognizable by WLB.

The sites need either to be unsaturated or dissociated from their endogenous ligand during denaturing electrophoresis. Denaturation can prevent detection of oligomeric complexes of which BPs are a component (as in the ternary IGF/IGFBP-3/α-subunit complex). For this reason, WLB analysis of the Type-I IGF receptor (an oligomeric structure) has proved impossible, whereas that of the mannose-6-phosphate/IGF-II receptor (a monomeric structure) has been done with success (16). Nevertheless, oligomers of IGFBP-1, which are probably linked by disulphide bridges, have proved to be detectable (54). It should also be borne in mind that if IGFBPs are to be quantified after ligand blotting, the ligand must be totally dissociated from the IGFBP (40). Finally, ligand blotting can essentially not be applied to studies of interactions which cannot be dissociated by SDS (as in the case of certain proteases bound to their inhibitors (55)).

Renaturation of the binding site after transfer needs to be sufficient for ligand binding to take place. (Renaturation of proteins is discussed in Chapter 17.) An initially weak affinity may be even weaker in the renatured protein. The proteolysed IGFBP-3 in pregnancy serum described above is an example of such a loss of affinity leading to lack of detectability after transfer. Incomplete renaturation probably also accounts for the lower affinity for the ligand obtained by Western blotting than that measured in solution, as in the case of IGFBP-2 (43, 45) and the IL-1 receptor (20). It is also possible that the weaker binding seen on the membrane may, in the case of an oligomeric receptor, reflect a weaker affinity of the isolated subunit than the native oligomer (12).

In some media, IGFBPs have proved detectable by affinity labelling, but not by WLB, even after extensive modification of transfer conditions (41).

When disulphide bridges are present, the molecular weights estimated after electrophoresis without reducing agent may be erroneous. However, reducing agents may prevent the protein from recovering its shape and binding its ligand. It is nevertheless noteworthy that reduction can be reversed in some IGFBPs after transfer. Glutathion treatment of the blots has been found to restore the IGFBP's binding activity. (S. Hardouin and M. Binoux, unpublished results).

Despite these limitations, Western ligand blotting is a simple method which, with minor case-by-case adaptions, is successfully applicable to the detection of a wide variety of binding proteins and, to a certain degree, to analysis of their structures and functions.

Acknowledgements

We are grateful to Drs J. C. Courvalin and G. Peltre for helpful discussions and to Dr C. Lalou and B. Segovia for some of the studies on IGFBPs reported here. This work was supported by the Institut National de la Santé et de la Recherche Médicale. P.H. is Chargé de Recherches au Centre National de la Recherche Scientifique.

References

1. Towbin, H., Staehelin, T., and Gordon, J. (1979). *Proc. Natl. Acad. Sci., USA*, **76**, 4350.
2. Gershoni, J. M. and Palade, G. E. (1983). *Anal. Biochem.*, **131**, 1.
3. Beisiegel, U. (1986). *Electrophoresis*, **7**, 1.
4. Bowen, B., Steinberg, J., Laemmli, U. K., and Weintraub, H. (1980). *Nucleic Acids Res.*, **8**, 1.
5. Cardin, A. D., Witt, K. R., and Jackson, R. L. (1984). *Anal. Biochem.*, **137**, 368.
6. Daniel, T. O., Schneider, W. J., Goldstein, J. L., and Brown, M. S. (1983). *J. Biol. Chem.*, **258**, 4606.
7. Haeuptle, M. T., Aubert, M. L., Djiane, J., and Kraehenbuhl, J. P. (1983). *J. Biol. Chem.*, **258**, 305.
8. Fernandez-Pol, J. A. (1982). *FEBS Lett.*, **143**, 86.
9. Bell, M. L. and Engvall, E. (1982). *Anal. Biochem.*, **123**, 329.
10. Maruyama, K., Mikawa, T., and Ebashi, S. (1984). *J. Biochem.*, **95**, 511.
11. Lin, P. H., Selinfreund, R., and Wharton, W. (1987). *Anal. Biochem.*, **167**, 128.
12. Oblas, B., Boyd, N. D., and Singer, R. H. (1983). *Anal. Biochem.*, **130**, 1.
13. Kowal, R. C., Herz, J., Weisgraber, K. H., Mahley, R. W., Brown, M. S., and Goldstein, J. L. (1990). *J. Biol. Chem.*, **265**, 10771.
14. Flanagan, S. D. and Beverly, Y. (1984). *Anal. Biochem.*, **140**, 510.
15. Hossenlopp, P., Seurin, D., Segovia-Quinson, B., Hardouin, S., and Binoux, M. (1986). *Anal. Biochem.*, **154**, 138.
16. Mathieu, M., Rochefort, H., Barenton, B., Prebois, C., and Vignon, F. (1990). *Mol. Endocrinol.*, **4**, 1327.
17. Georgatos, S. D., Weber, K., Geisler, N., and Blobel, G. (1987). *Proc. Natl. Acad. Sci., USA*, **84**, 6780.
18. Merdes, A., Brunkener, M., Horstmann, H., and Georgatos, S. D. (1991). *J. Cell. Biol.*, **115**, 397.

19. Keinanen, K. P., Kellokumpu, S., Metsikko, M. K., and Rajaniemi, H. J. (1987). *J. Biol. Chem.*, **262**, 7920.
20. Bird, T. A., Gearing, A. J. H., and Saklatvala, J. (1988). *J. Biol. Chem.*, **263**, 12063.
21. Ghinea, N., Fixman, A., Alexandru, D., Popov, D., Hasu, M., Ghitescu, L., Eskenasy, M., Simionescu, M., and Simionescu, N. (1988). *J. Cell. Biol.*, **107**, 231.
22. Stifani, S., George, R., and Schneider, W. J. (1988). *Biochem. J.*, **250**, 467.
23. Lee, W. C. and Melese, T. (1989). *Proc. Natl. Acad. Sci., USA*, **86**, 8808.
24. Smith, R. A. and Baglioni, C. (1989). *J. Biol. Chem.*, **264**, 14646.
25. Nakamura, T., Takio, K., Eto, Y., Shibai, H., Titani, K., and Sugino, H. (1990). *Science*, **247**, 836.
26. Fukunaga, R., Ishizaka-Ikeda, E., and Shigekazu, N. (1990). *J. Biol. Chem.*, **265**, 14008.
27. Hajjar, K. A. and Hamel, N. M. (1990). *J. Biol. Chem.*, **265**, 2908.
28. Solberg, H., Lober, D., Eriksen, J., Ploug, M., Ronne, E., Behrendt, N., Dano, K., and Hoyer-Hansen, G. (1992). *Eur. J. Biochem.*, **205**, 451.
29. Otter, M., Barrett-Bergshoeff, M. M., and Rijken, D. C. (1991). *J. Biol. Chem.*, **266**, 13931.
30. Preissner, K. T., Grulich-Henn, J., Ehrlich, H. J., Declerck, P., Justus, C., Collen, D., Pannelock, H., and Muller-Berghaus, G. (1990). *J. Biol. Chem.*, **265**, 18490.
31. Dudani, A. K., Hashemi,S., Aye, M. T., and Ganz, P. R. (1991). *Mol. Cell. Biochem.*, **108**, 133.
32. Taniura, H., Kuo, C. H., Hayashi, Y., and Miki, N. (1991). *J. Cell. Biol.*, **112**, 313.
33. Chamoux, M., Dehouck, M. P., Fruchart, J. C., Spik, G., Montreuil, J., and Cecchelli, R. (1991). *Biochem. Biophys. Res. Commun.*, **176**, 833.
34. Laemmli, U. K. (1970). *Nature*, **227**, 680.
35. Gershoni, J. M. (1987). *Electrophoresis*, **8**, 428.
36. Hames, B. D. and Rickwood, D. (eds.) (1981). *Gel electrophoresis of proteins: a practical approach* IRL, Oxford.
37. See, Y. P. and Jackowski, G. (1989). In *Protein structure: a practical approach*, (ed. T. E. Creighton), p. 1. IRL, Oxford.
38. Scheidtmann, K. H. (1989). In *Protein structure: a practical approach*, (ed. T. E. Creighton), p. 93. IRL, Oxford.
39. Schneider, C., Newman, R. A., Sutherland, D. R., Asser, U., and Greaves, M. F. (1982). *J. Biol. Chem.*, **257**, 10766.
40. Bicsak, T. A., Nakatani, A., Shimonaka, M., Malkowski, M., and Ling, N. (1990). *Anal. Biochem.*, **191**, 75.
41. Ocrant, I., Fay, C. T., Pham, H., and Rosenfeld, R. G. (1992). *Endocrinology*, **131**, 221.
42. Lin, W. and Kasamatsu, H. (1983). *Anal. Biochem.*, **128**, 302.
43. Roghani, M., Lassarre, C., Zapf, J., Povoa, G., and Binoux, M. (1991). *J. Clin. Endocrinol. Metab.*, **73**, 658.
44. Zapf, J., Schmid, C., Guler, H. P., Waldvogel, M., Hauri, C., Futo, E., Hossenlopp, P., Binoux, M., and Froesch, E. R. (1990). *J. Clin. Invest.*, **86**, 952.

45. Hardouin, S., Hossenlopp, P., Segovia, B., Seurin, D., Portolan, G., Lassarre, C., and Binoux, M. (1987). *Eur. J. Biochem.*, **170**, 121.
46. Upton, Z., Chan, S. J., Steiner, D. F., Wallace, J. C., and Ballard, F. J. (1993). *Growth Regulation*, **3**, 29.
47. Hossenlopp, P., Seurin, D., Segovia, B., Portolan, G., and Binoux, M. (1987). *Eur. J. Biochem.*, **170**, 133.
48. Lamson, G., Oh, Y., Pham, H., Guidice, L. C., and Rosenfeld, R. G. (1989). *J. Clin. Endocrinol. Metab.*, **69**, 852.
49. Fazleabas, A. T. and Donnelly, K. M. (1992). *Anal. Biochem.*, **202**, 40.
50. Hardouin, S., Gourmelen, M., Noguiez, P., Seurin, D., Roghani, M., Le Bouc, Y., Povoa, G., Merimee, T. J., Hossenlopp, P., and Binoux, M. (1989). *J. Clin. Endocrinol. Metab.*, **69**, 1291.
51. Baxter, R. C. and Martin, J. L. (1986). *J. Clin. Invest.*, **78**, 1504.
52. Hossenlopp, P., Segovia, B., Lassarre, C., Roghani, M., Bredon, M., and Binoux, M. (1990). *J. Clin. Endocrinol. Metab.*, **71**, 797.
53. Giudice, L. C., Farrell, E. M., Pham, H., Lamson, G., and Rosenfeld, R. G. (1990). *J. Clin. Endocrinol. Metab.*, **71**, 806.
54. Busby, W. H., Hossenlopp, P., Binoux, M., and Clemmons, D. R. (1989). *Endocrinology*, **125**, 773.
55. Levin, E. G. (1983). *Proc. Natl. Acad. Sci., USA*, **80**, 6804.

15

Use of blotted proteins as immunogens

BOGUSLAW SZEWCZYK and DAVID R. HARPER

1. Introduction

In the past a considerable amount of effort has been directed at recovering proteins resolved by sodium dodecyl sulphate polyacrylamide gel electro-phoresis (SDS-PAGE) and using them as immunogens. Typically, proteins have been recovered from polyacrylamide gels by either diffusion or electroelution procedures. However, in spite of the numerous variations in these procedures, none of the available methods is entirely satisfactory. Some of the methods require complicated manipulations or specialized equipment, while others lead to poor recovery. To overcome the limitations of elution of proteins from polyacrylamide gels, Parekh et al. (1) attempted to elute proteins from nitrocellulose replicas of SDS-PAGE gels. In most cases the maximum elution of proteins and minimum solubilization of nitrocellulose was achieved with acetonitrile or pyridine (concentration range 20–50%) in 0.1 M ammonium acetate, pH 8.9. One of the difficulties with this elution procedure is the limited degradation of the nitrocellulose membrane in organic eluents (2). Anderson (3) removed proteins from nitrocellulose replicas of SDS-PAGE gels by solubilization of the nitrocellulose with acetone followed by precipitation of the protein in the presence of a carrier such as Polybrene. The protein-bearing nitrocellulose can be also solubilized with dimethyl sulphoxide, mixed with Freund's adjuvant and used as an immunogen in rabbits (4). Dimethyl sulphoxide is tolerated by rabbits but not by mice, so the method is unsuitable for raising murine monoclonal antibodies. Diano et al. (5) proposed a different approach for raising antibodies to nitrocellulose-bound proteins. The spot corresponding to the antigenic protein was excised from the nitrocellulose replica of the SDS-PAGE gel and cut into very small pieces with scissors. The pieces were further macerated by sonication and the suspension was injected sub-cutaneously into at least 20 sites on a rabbit.

In 1986 the Millipore Corporation introduced polyvinylidene fluoride (PVDF) membrane for protein blotting applications. This membrane (described in detail in Chapter 4 of this text) has been used extensively for elution of proteins from electroblotted replicas of SDS-PAGE gels and subsequent use of the eluted proteins as immunogens. In contrast to nitrocellulose, PVDF membrane is practically inert to the majority of eluants, therefore the eluted protein does not contain any extraneous material from the matrix. The eluents used for the recovery of proteins from PVDF blots can be roughly divided into two main groups: aqueous/organic solvent mixtures, and detergent-based solutions. The latter group of eluants leads to the more complete elution for most PVDF-bound proteins, therefore the majority of methods described in this chapter refer to the use of detergent mixtures for eluting proteins from the PVDF blots.

2. Preparation of PVDF replicas of SDS-PAGE gels

2.1 SDS-PAGE and transfer to PVDF membranes

A description of SDS-PAGE is not appropriate for this chapter, and the reader is referred to an earlier volume of this series (7) for the details on gel preparation. A mixture of proteins containing an immunogen to be purified is applied to an SDS-PAGE gel and run until the dye-front reaches the end of the gel. The resolved proteins are then transferred to a PVDF membrane either by semi-dry blotting or tank blotting. The details of the equipment used for transfer are described in Chapters 2 and 5 of this volume. *Protocol 1* is for tank blotting but semi-dry blotting yields essentially the same results. Some important points are to be kept in mind when planning a transfer for subsequent elution:

(a) Transfer of proteins should not be done at elevated temperatures (above 30 °C) as the force of protein binding to PVDF membranes apparently increases with temperature. It is advisable to perform transfers at 4 °C or use pre-cooled transfer buffer.

(b) The PVDF membrane should not be overloaded with protein to prevent deep penetration of proteins into the membrane. The band to be excised should not contain more than 20 µg of a protein per single electrophoretic lane (1 cm in width).

(c) Throughout the procedure disposable gloves should be used. This avoids cytokeratin fingerprints on the membrane.

(d) Protein molecular weight standards should be included in one of the lanes of SDS-PAGE gel. To assess the quality of transfer it is advisable to include pre-stained molecular weight standards (these can be purchased from Sigma, Amersham, Bio-Rad, and many other companies).

Protocol 1. Transfer of proteins from SDS-PAGE gels to PVDF membranes

Equipment

- a blotting apparatus (for example Trans Blot Cell from Bio-Rad Laboratories, Richmond, CA, USA)
- a power supply capable of delivering the required current
- glass vessels with flat bottom (for example, Pyrex baking dishes)
- a rocker platform
- scissors

Materials

- methanol
- transfer buffer: Tris–glycine (25 mM Tris-base/192 mM glycine) pH 8.3
- PVDF membrane (e.g. Immobilon-P fom Millipore Corp., Bedford, MA, USA)
- Whatman 3MM filter paper
- Scotch-Brite pads
- disposable gloves

Method

1. During the running of the SDS-PAGE gel prepare the transfer buffer (about 4 litre for a Bio-Rad Trans Blot Cell). Dissolve 3 g of Tris-base and 14.4 g of glycine in 1 litre of distilled water (or dilute from 10 × stock stored at 4 °C). Do not adjust the pH, it should be approximately equal to 8.3 (small variations in pH are not critical for the quality of transfer). Keep the buffer at 4 °C.

2. Pour methanol (about 50 ml) to one of the glass dishes and at least 200 ml of the transfer buffer to each of four other dishes. One of the glass dishes should be large enough to accommodate a gel holder.

3. Place the gel holder and Scotch-Brite pads in the biggest dish, and four sheets of Whatman paper in another dish. The Whatman sheets should be slightly smaller than the Scotch-Brite pads.

4. Cut the PVDF membrane to a size slightly bigger than the resolving SDS-PAGE gel. Put the sheet into a dish with methanol for 1 min on a rocker platform, and then place it in one of the dishes containing transfer buffer.

5. Put a wetted Scotch-Brite pad on one side of the gel holder and then two sheets of Whatman paper saturated with transfer buffer on top of the pad.

Protocol 1. *Continued*

6. After the end of SDS-PAGE run, carefully remove the upper stacking gel, because it may stick to the membrane. The lower resolving gel can be kept for a short time in a dish containing transfer buffer.

7. Place the resolving gel on the Whatman paper in the gel holder. Pour a few millilitres of transfer buffer on top of the gel.

8. Place a sheet of PVDF membrane (step **4**) on the gel. Roll over the membrane with a glass rod to remove air bubbles from between the gel and the membrane.

9. Place two sheets of Whatman paper pre-wetted with the transfer buffer on top of the membrane and finally a pre-wetted second Scotch-Brite pad on top of the Whatman sheets.

10. Close the holder and place it in the transfer tank remembering that the membrane should face the anode.

11. Blot overnight at 20 V, preferably in a cold-room.

2.2 Visualization of the blotted proteins

The use of protein stains on PVDF membranes allows for the quick assessment of blotting performance and for the location of protein bands which are to be used as immunogens. A number of stains can be used to detect proteins on PVDF blots. These include Coomassie Blue (8, 9), Amido Black (8–10), Ponceau S (2), India ink (8, 11), colloidal gold (8, 9), and fluorescent stains (12–14). We have not checked the compatibility of all the stains with the subsequent elution of proteins from the PVDF membrane. As a general rule the methods of staining which are reversible and do not lead to protein denaturation on the membrane are preferred (*Figure 1*). Two such methods, staining with aqueous solution of Amido Black and staining with Ponceau S in 1% acetic acid are described in *Protocols 2* and *3*. The sensitivity of these stains for protein detection on PVDF membranes is of the order of 1 μg for most proteins. When this detection level is not satisfactory, Coomassie Blue staining will give approximately a tenfold increase in sensitivity. In this case staining and destaining is performed in concentrated acetic acid/methanol which may affect subsequent protein elution. However, our experience shows that a considerable number of Coomassie Blue-stained proteins are effectively eluted when protein-bearing PVDF is treated wth SDS/Triton X-100 mixture (*Protocol 5*). An alternative to protein staining has been suggested (15) which eliminates the exposure of the PVDF membrane to staining and destaining solutions. This method requires some experience and should be used with caution. It is based on the use of visible light to detect protein bands on PVDF membrane immediately after transfer. When

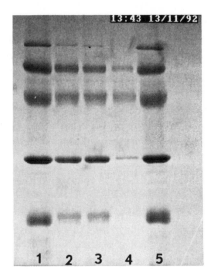

Figure 1. Effect of staining on the recovery of PVDF-bound proteins. A mixture of proteins (from top to bottom: phosphorylase b (3 μg), bovine serum albumin, ovalbumin, carbonic anhydrase, and soybean trypsin inhibitor (6 μg of each protein) was separated by SDS-PAGE, transferred to a PVDF membrane, stained and eluted with a mixture of 2% SDS and 1% Triton X-100. After precipitation of proteins with acetone, the mixture was applied again to SDS-PAGE gel to check the effect of the method of PVDF staining on the recovery of proteins. 1 and 5: Original mixture of proteins not subjected to any treatment. 2: Proteins eluted from the PVDF membrane stained with Ponceau S in 1% acetic acid. 3: Proteins eluted from the PVDF membrane stained with 0.01% Amido Black in water. 4: Proteins eluted from the PVDF memrane stained with Coomassie Blue in acetic acid/methanol.

illuminated with white light, protein bands appear as white, opaque areas surrounded by slightly translucent protein-free membrane. A protein to be eluted is marked with a pencil (taking care not to dry the membrane) and then the PVDF sheet is transferred to a dish with a buffer where it is kept until ready for elution.

Protocol 2. Reversible staining of PVDF blots with aqueous solutions of Amido Black

Materials and equipment

- a rocker platform
- glass vessels
- 0.01% Amido Black in water (depending on the supplier and batch of Amido Black, the sensitivity of protein detection with this reagent may

---

Protocol 2. *Continued*

vary; Amido Black purchased from Research Organics, Cleveland, OH, USA or Sigma Chemical Co., St Louis, MO, USA gives optimum results)

Method

1. After the transfer, remove the gel holder from the transfer apparatus, open the holder, and put the PVDF membrane into a glass vessel containing 200 ml of Amido Black solution. If staining is not performed immediately after transfer, store the membrane in the transfer buffer. Do not allow the membrane to dry.

2. Put the glass vessel on a rocker platform and stain the membrane for 10–15 min. After about 5 min of staining the protein bands should be visible.

3. If protein bands are not clearly visible, transfer the membrane to a second vessel with 200 ml of fresh solution of Amido Black.

4. Stain the membrane for another 10–15 min.

5. Mark the position of the protein which is to be used as an immunogen with a pencil.

6. Destain the membrane by a few consecutive washes with distilled water. The colour of protein bands gradually fades and finally disappears.

7. Keep the membrane in distilled water until the elution step.

Protocol 3. Reversible staining of PVDF membranes with Ponceau S

Materials and equipment

- a rocker platform
- glass vessel
- 0.5% Ponceau S in 1% acetic acid

Method

1. Immerse the PVDF membrane in a glass vessel containing 200 ml of Ponceau S solution.

2. Stain the membrane for 5–10 min on a rocker platform.

3. Remove the unbound stain by washing the membrane in distilled water for 2 min.

4. Mark the position of a protein band with a pencil.

5. Incubate the membrane in distilled water for additional 10 min (or longer) to completely destain the protein bands.

6. Do not dry the membrane. Keep it in distilled water until the elution step.

Protocol 4. Staining of PVDF blots with Coomassie Blue

Materials and equipment

- a rocker platform
- glass vessels
- 0.1% Coomassie Blue R-250 in an aqueous solution of 7% acetic acid (v/v) and 50% methanol (v/v)
- destaining solution—7% acetic acid (v/v) and 50% methanol (v/v) in water

Method

1. Immerse the PVDF membrane in 200 ml of Coomassie Blue solution.

2. Stain the membrane for 15 min on a rocker platform.

3. Remove the unbound stain from the membrane by two consecutive 10 min washes in 200 ml of destaining solution.

4. Transfer the membrane from the destaining solution to distilled water and keep it in water until ready for elution.

---

3. Elution of proteins from the PVDF membranes

3.1 General comments

Proteins transferred to PVDF membranes can be eluted by a variety of methods. None of these methods are quantitative for every protein tested, but recoveries as high as 70–80% have been reported. Probably the most thorough examination of the utility of various eluents for protein recovery from PVDF blots was carried out by Simpson *et al.* (*Table 1*, adapted from reference (6)). The authors presented the data for a number of radiolabelled and electroblotted proteins. Proteins were recovered from detergent containing eluates by inverse-gradient HPLC. The diversity of methods used to recover proteins from blots indicates that no single eluent is universal for elution of diverse proteins which may vary in size and their physical properties. However, for most of the proteins, use of the mixture of ionic and non-ionic detergents at pH > 9 will result in good recoveries.

Table 1. Average elution of electroblotted proteins from PVDF membranes by various eluents, arranged in order of elution efficiency

Eluent	Recovery (%)
2% SDS–1% Triton X-100–0.1% DTT	68.6
2% SDS–1% Nonidet P40–0.1% DTT	66.8
2% SDS–1% Nonidet P40	63.1
2% SDS–1% Triton X-100	63.1
2% SDS–1% Tween 20	59.5
2% SDS–1% Tween 20–0.1% DTT	59.0
2% SDS–1% Brij-35	54.6
2% SDS–1% Lubrol	54.0
70% 1-propanol–5% TFA	38.5
70% 1-propanol–5% TFA–0.1% DTT	37.1
20% acetonitrile–2% SDS	14.8

Data derived from (6), showing elution of ^{125}I-labelled proteins from a Coomassie Blue R-250 stained electroblot. Excised bands were passively eluted in 50 mM Tris–HCl buffer (pH 9.0) plus detergent as indicated in an Eppendorf tube with 2 × 100 μl eluent for 30 min at 25 °C. Elution efficiencies given are means of values derived for five different proteins.

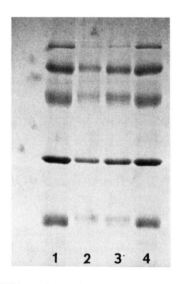

Figure 2. Recovery of PVDF-bound proteins eluted either by the mixture of ionic/non-ionic detergent or by GuHCl-based eluent. The same mixture of proteins as described in *Figure 1* was subjected to SDS-PAGE, transferred to a PVDF membrane, stained with 0.01% Amido Black in water and eluted either with 2% SDS/1% Triton X-100 or with 7 M GuHCl/0.5% lysophosphatidylcholine. Proteins were precipitated with acetone, in the former case, dialysed in the latter case, and then applied to an SDS-PAGE gel. 1 and 4: Original mixture of proteins not subjected to any treatment. 2: Proteins eluted from the PVDF membrane by 7 M GuHCl/0.5% lysophosphatidylcholine in 100 mM Tris–HCl, pH 8.0. 3: Proteins eluted from the PVDF membrane by 2% SDS/1% Triton X-100 in 50 mM Tris–HCl, pH 9.0.

196

Boguslaw Szewczyk and David R. Harper

3.2 Elution of proteins with detergent-based eluants

The elution system based on the use of a mixture of 2% SDS and 1% Triton X-100 (*Figure 2*) allows for a quick recovery of a polypeptide from a PVDF membrane. The method described in *Protocol 5* does not require any specialized equipment and the elution is performed at room temperature. We have used this method to obtain a variety of bacterial, viral, and eukaryotic polypeptides. It follows from our experience that practically all the protein bound to the PVDF membrane is released by the mixture of SDS and Triton X-100 provided that the pH of the eluant is basic (pH 9.0 or higher). However, the subsequent step of detergent removal may sometimes lead to a substantial loss of eluted proteins. The proteins are precipitated with acetone to render them free of SDS which causes adverse effects in immunized animals. Precipitation of proteins with organic solvents is affected by a number of factors (16). It occurs more readily when the pH is close to the pI of the protein. Hydrophobicity and size of a protein also influence its precipitation behaviour. Hydrophobic proteins are precipitated poorly by organic solvents, while a larger protein will precipitate at lower concentrations of organic solvent than a smaller protein with otherwise similar properties.

Protocol 5. Elution of proteins from PVDF membranes with a mixture of SDS and Triton X-100

Materials and equipment
- a microfuge
- a dry-ice bath
- a vortex shaker
- small dissecting scissors
- injection needles
- Eppendorf tubes
- disposable gloves
- eluent—2% SDS/1% Triton X-100 in 50 mM Tris–HCl, pH 9.0
- acetone

Method
1. Excise the band(s) of interest from a stained PVDF membrane using small dissecting scissors. Do not allow the excised piece of membrane to dry.

197

Protocol 5. *Continued*

2. Place the piece of membrane in an Eppendorf tube containing 0.2–0.5 ml of eluent per cm^2 of the membrane.

3. Mix well by vortexing the tube or centrifuge the tube at low revolutions (500–1000 $\times$ *g*) in a microfuge for 10–20 min.

4. Spin down the membrane in a microfuge at maximum revolutions for 2 min.

5. Transfer the supernatant to a new tube.

6. Add 0.2–0.5 ml of fresh eluent to the tube with the PVDF membrane.

7. Using a disposable needle, break up the crumpled PVDF membrane into a few pieces.

8. Mix it by vortexing or centrifuge at low revolutions in a microfuge for 5–10 min.

9. Spin down the membrane in a microfuge at maximum speed for 2 min.

10. Combine this supernatant with the supernatant from the first elution (step **5**).

11. Pierce the bottom of the tube containing the membrane with a hot needle.

12. Place ths tube on top of another open Eppendorf tube and cut off caps of both tubes.

13. Centrifuge at maximum speed for a few seconds to remove the rest of the eluent from the membrane.

14. Transfer the eluent from the lower tube to the tube containing combined supernatants (step **10**).

15. Centrifuge the combined supernatants at maximum speed for 5 min to remove last traces of PVDF membrane.

16. Collect the supernatant, divide it into appropriate number of tubes and add four volumes of cold acetone (−20 °C) to each tube.

17. Leave the tubes at dry-ice bath for 1 h or overnight at −20 °C.

18. Centrifuge the tubes in a microfuge at maximum speed for 10 min, preferably in a cold-room.

19. Carefully remove the supernatant from the tubes.

20. Wash the pellets twice with 0.5 ml of acetone.

21. Resuspend the pellets in a small volume of water or 20 mM Tris–HCl, pH 7.5.

22. Check the efficiency of the procedure by taking a part of the

suspension (mix well before dispensing) for SDS-PAGE. In calcu-
lating the amount to be taken for analysis assume about 50%
recovery.

23. Use the rest of the eluted protein for immunizations.

3.3 Elution of proteins with other eluents

In exceptional cases the yield of protein eluted from the PVDF membrane by
SDS/Triton X-100 mixture is not satisfactory. If the loss of protein can be
attributed to its solubility in 80% acetone, then the alternative method of
detergent removal described by Simpson *et al.* (6) can be tried. In this case,
proteins are recovered from the eluates using inverse-gradient HPLC.
However, it is often more practical to use another method of elution rather
than to check each consecutive experimental step for protein loss. Two
methods of elution can be recommended in cases of poor protein recovery by
the SDS/Triton X-100 method. The first method was described by Yuen *et al.*
(17). Proteins are eluted with a mixture of isopropyl alcohol and trifluoro-
acetic acid (TFA). This method is described in *Protocol 6*.

Protocol 6. Elution of proteins from a PVDF membrane with
isopropyl alcohol/TFA mixture

Materials and equipment

- a microfuge
- a Speed-Vac centrifuge
- a vortex shaker
- small dissecting scissors
- disposable gloves
- eluent—70% isopropyl alcohol/5% TFA

Method

1. Excise the protein-bearing band with small dissecting scissors.
2. Place the piece of membrane in an Eppendorf tube containing about
   0.2 ml of eluent.
3. Vortex and incubate at room temperature for 1 h.
4. Remove the membrane from the tube and transfer it to a new tube
   containing the same volume of eluent.
5. Vortex and again incubate the membrane for 1 h.

Protocol 6. *Continued*

6. Remove the membrane and combine the eluents.

7. Centrifuge the eluent in a microfuge at maximum speed for 5 min to remove traces of PVDF membrane.

8. Evaporate the supernatant in a Speed-Vac centrifuge to dryness.

9. Resuspend the eluted protein in a small volume of phosphate-buffered saline or other buffer compatible with future immunization.

Elution efficiences ranging from 25–50% are to be expected when the method described in *Protocol 6* is employed. Good recoveries of eluted proteins can be also obtained when an eluent containing high concentrations of guanidinium hydrochloride (GuHCl) is used (*Figure 2*). This eluent is composed of a mixture of 7 M GuHCl and 0.5% lysophosphatidylcholine (Sigma Catalogue No. L-5254) in 100 mM Tris–HCl, pH 7.5–8.0 (D. F. Summers, unpublished data). Most of the proteins tested by us are eluted completely from the PVDF membrane by this eluent. Here again, the final recovery of blotted proteins is very often dependent to a great extent on the further processing of protein solution in eluent. In case of GuHCl-based eluent two methods described in *Protocol 7* can be used to remove GuHCl: extensive dialysis or precipitation with ethanol. Dialysis is not recommended for small polypeptides as they may diffuse through pores of a dialysis membrane. When dialysing the concentrated GuHCl solution in a dialysis bag, it is important to leave some space in the bag as there is a significant increase in volume with the decrease of GuHCl concentration. The complete removal of GuHCl is a lengthy process which requires at least four to five changes of buffer.

GuHCl is soluble in ethanol which allows for the precipitation of proteins with this solvent. This alternative method of GuHCl removal requires; however, a very high concentrations of ethanol in the sample (over 90%) to assure the complete precipitation of proteins.

Protocol 7. Elution of proteins from a PVDF membrane with GuHCl/lysophosphatidylcholine mixture

Materials and equipment

- a microfuge
- a Speed-Vac centrifuge
- a vortex shaker
- a device for dialysis of small liquid volumes
- small dissecting scissors

- disposable gloves
- 7 M GuHCl in 100 mM Tris–HCl, pH 8.0
- lysophosphatidylcholine (Sigma L-5254)
- absolute ethanol

Methods
The eluent is prepared just before the elution by adding solid lyso-phosphatidylcholine to the buffered 7 M GuHCl (pH should be checked and, if necessary, adjusted before the addition). The final concentration of lysophosphatidylcholine should be equal to 0.5%. The initial steps of the elution are the same as described in *Protocol 5*, steps **1** to **15**. The removal of GuHCl can be achieved in two ways:

A. *Precipitation of proteins with ethanol*
1. Divide the supernatant (*Protocol 5*, step **15**) into small aliquots, about 50–100 μl per 1.5 ml Eppendorf tube.
2. Add enough cold absolute ethanol to the tubes to obtain at least 90% final ethanol concentration (preferably higher).
3. Leave the tubes at −20 °C overnight.
4. Centrifuge the tubes in a microfuge at maximum speed for 5 min.
5. Discard the supernatant.
6. Wash the pellet twice with absolute ethanol.
7. Finally, resuspend the pellet in a small volume of distilled water or a buffer compatible with injections into animals.
8. Check the recovery of protein by applying a part of the suspension to an SDS-PAGE gel.

B. *Dialysis*
1. Pour the supernatant (*Protocol 5*, step **15**) into a dialysis bag or into one of commercially available devices for dialysis of small volumes.
2. Dialyse against large volume of a buffer compatible with injections into animals, change the buffer at least four times.
3. Transfer the dialysed sample into Eppendorf tube(s).
4. If the volume of the sample is too large for injections, concentrate the sample by one of these two methods:
   (a) Evaporate the excess of water in a Speed-Vac centrifuge; if this method of concentration is used, then a buffer for the last change during dialysis should be either volatile or of low ionic strength.
   (b) If a Speed-Vac centrifuge is not available, precipitate protein(s)

Protocol 7. *Continued*

  with trichloroacetic acid (final TCA concentration around 10%),
  spin down the precipitate, wash it twice with very cold acetone,
  and resuspend in appropriate buffer.
5. Check the recovery by analysing part of the sample on an SDS-PAGE
   gel.

4. Immunization

Production of antibodies is not an exact science, and the procedure which
works for one immunogen may not work for another. Therefore, we do not
intend to survey here the vast array of methods for raising antibodies in
different species of animals. We confine ourselves to a short description of a
method for production of polyclonal antibodies used routinely by us when
immunizing rabbits with different PVDF-eluted polypeptides. This method is
described in *Protocol 8*; however, a few additional explanations and hints may
be helpful for those attempting to immunize animals for the first time:

(a) The amount of immunogen needed to stimulate a high level of antibodies
varies for different proteins, but generally 50–500 µg of protein per rabbit
is sufficient to induce the formation of high levels of antibody.

(b) For polypeptides of low molecular weight (below 10–15 kd), conjugation
to a carrier protein is recommended to elicit immunogenicity; keyhole
limpet haemocyanin (KLH) is an example of a carrier widely used for this
purpose which can be conjugated to a polypeptide by the glutaraldehyde
method (18).

(c) The immunogen for the first injection is often prepared in an adjuvant,
usually in Freund's complete adjuvant (FCA), which is a suspension of
heat-killed *mycobacteria* in mineral oil; subsequent immunizations are
given using Freund's incomplete adjuvant (FIA) which does not contain
bacteria.

(d) FCA causes ulceration resulting in considerable discomfort to the animal
if the whole dose of immunogen is administered in one spot on the
animal, which the use of multiple inoculations can avoid. However, FCA
can also cause systemic reactions. Alternative 'second generation'
adjuvants (such as Hunter's 'TiterMax' or the RIBI monophosphoryl
lipid systems) may be used to prevent this problem.

(e) The immunogen should be administered as a stable emulsion. If FCA is
used, this can be prepared either by passing the mixture of an adjuvant
and protein solution through two glass syringes connected with a double-
hub needle or by sonicating the mixture placed in an Eppendorf tube.

Preparation of other adjuvants should be in accordance with the manufacturer's instructions.

(f) A rabbit may be bled every week (10–15 ml of blood each time) provided that booster injections are administered every 6–8 weeks; when this schedule is followed large volume of antiserum can be collected from a single animal without unnecessary harm.

Protocol 8. Immunization of rabbits with PVDF-eluted proteins

Materials and equipment

- an ultrasonification apparatus (100 W minimum output) fitted with a titanium microprobe with a tip diameter around 3 mm
- syringes
- short thin needles (22-g or thinner) for injections
- short thick needles for bleeding
- sterile tubes for blood
- phosphate-buffered saline (PBS), pH 7.4, 8 g of NaCl, 0.2 g of KH_2PO_4, 2.8 g of $Na_2HPO_4.12 H_2O$ and 0.2 g of KCl, dissolved and made up to 1 litre in water
- an immunogen—PVDF-eluted protein
- adjuvants
- xylene
- ethanol
- sodium azide solution
- rabbits (no specified individual strain is required)

Method

1. Prepare a stable 1:1 (v/v) emulsion of 25–250 μg of a polypeptide in a buffer (preferably PBS) and the complete adjuvant. For FCA, this is done by subjecting the mixture of the above in an Eppendorf tube to a short ultrasonic treatment (three to four pulses for 10–20 sec each time). The tube should be placed on ice during sonication. Wait 1–2 min between consecutive ultrasonic treatments.

2. Place a small drop of the emulsion on the surface of cold water. The emulsion is stable if the drop stays on as a discrete globule.

3. Inject about 1 ml of this emulsion intradermally at multiple sites at the back of the rabbit (about 10 injection sites should be sufficient for FCA).

Protocol 8. *Continued*

4. A minimum of three weeks after the first injection immunize the animal subcutaneously, holding the skin between the thumb and forefinger. The emulsion is prepared in the same way and in the same quantity as before with the exception that, where FCA was used for the initial inoculation the incomplete adjuvant, FIA, is used.

5. Test bleed the rabbit from an ear vein about two weeks after the second injection. Swab the vein with xylene to dilate the vein before introducing the needle.

6. After collecting sufficient volume of blood, stem the blood flow by sustained pressure on the puncture site with a tissue. Remove xylene by washing the ear with an ample volume of ethanol.

7. Allow the blood to clot by keeping it at room temperature for 2 h and then at 4 °C overnight to allow the clot to shrink in size.

8. Detach the clot carefully from the sides of the tube and transfer the serum to a centrifuge tube.

9. Centrifuge the clot at 2500g for 10–15 min at 4 °C. Remove any supernatant carefully and combine with the serum of step **8**.

10. Centrifuge the pooled serum at 3000g for 10–15 min at 4 °C to remove intact blood cells.

11. Transfer the supernatant to a fresh tube. It should be straw-coloured, or pink if some haemolysis has taken place. Slight haemolysis does not affect antiserum performance in most assays.

12. Sodium azide (0.02% final concentration) may be added to the antiserum to inhibit bacterial growth. However, sodium azide is not inert. In particular, if methods employing horseradish peroxidase are used for the detection of antigen–antibody complexes then it is advisable to use thiomersal to prevent bacterial growth (sodium azide is a potent inhibitor of the peroxidase).

13. Aliquot and store the antiserum at −20 °C.

14. Check the antiserum titre. If it is not satisfactory, repeat the booster injection and proceed with subsequent steps of this protocol.

Acknowledgements

This work was supported in part by KBN grant 2229/4/91. We are very grateful to Grazyna Kochan and Zbigniew Pilat for their help in preparation of this manuscript.

Boguslaw Szewczyk and David R. Harper

References

1. Parekh, B. S., Mehta, H. B., West, M. D., and Montelaro, R. C. (1985). *Anal. Biochem.*, **148**, 87.
2. Montelaro, R. C. (1987). *Electrophoresis*, **8**, 432.
3. Anderson, P. J. (1985). *Anal. Biochem.*, **148**, 105.
4. Knudsen, K. A. (1985). *Anal. Biochem.*, **147**, 285.
5. Diano, M., Le Bivic, A., and Hirn, M. (1992). In *Methods in molecular biology*, Vol. 10, (ed. M. Manson), pp. 13–22. The Humana Press, Totowa, NJ.
6. Simpson, R. J., Ward, L. D., Reid, G. E., Batterham, M. P., and Moritz, R. (1989). *J. Chromatogr.*, **476**, 345.
7. Hames, B. D. (1981). In *Gel electrophoresis of proteins: a practical approach*, (ed. B. D. Hames and D. Rickwood), pp. 1–91. IRL Press, Oxford.
8. Gultekin, H. and Heermann, K. H. (1988). *Anal. Biochem.*, **172**, 320.
9. Christiansen, J. and Houen, G. (1992). *Electrophoresis*, **13**, 179.
10. Szewczyk, B. and Summers, D. F. (1988). *Anal. Biochem.*, **168**, 48.
11. Hughes, J. H., Mack, K., and Hamparian, V. V. (1988). *Anal. Biochem.*, **173**, 18.
12. Coull, J. M. and Pappin, D. J. C. (1990). *J. Protein Chem.*, **9**, 259.
13. Pappin, D. J. C., Coull, J. M., and Koester, H. (1990). *Anal. Biochem.*, **187**, 10.
14. Szewczyk, B. and Summers, D. F. (1992). In *Methods in molecular biology*, Vol. 10, (ed. M. Manson), pp. 261–6. The Humana Press, Totowa, NJ.
15. Walsh, M. J., McDougall, J., and Wittmann-Liebold, B. (1988). *Biochemistry*, **27**, 6867.
16. Harris, E. L. V., Andrews, B. A., and Asenjo, J. A. (1989). In *Protein purification methods: a practical approach*, (ed. E. L. V. Harris and S. Angal), pp. 125–74. IRL Press, Oxford.
17. Yuen, S. W., Chui, A. H., Wilson, K. J., and Yuan, P. M. (1989). *BioTechniques*, **7**, 74.
18. Hancock, D. C. and Evan, G. I. (1992). In *Methods in molecular biology*, Vol. 10, (ed. M. Manson), pp. 23–32. The Humana Press, Totowa, NJ.

16

Amino acid sequence analysis of blotted proteins

RICHARD G. COOK

1. Introduction

In the past 10 years, our ability to obtain amino acid sequence information on proteins and peptides has improved dramatically. The amount of protein required for sequencing has been decreased by approximately three logs— from 1 nmol to 1 pmol. The major reason for this increased sensitivity has been the development of automated gas and pulsed-liquid-phase sequencers with in-line HPLC detection systems. While the chemistry utilized in sequencing remains the classic Edman degradation (with slight modifications), the protein sequencer instrumentation has been vastly improved at several levels. These include:

(a) a compact table-top design that allows for a lower and more efficient usage of reagents and solvents

(b) ease of use through computer-controlled reagent/solvent delivery and data analysis software

(c) in-line HPLC systems that provide immediate analysis of the cleaved phenylthiohydantoin (PTH) amino acids

(d) the use of inert supports such as glass fibre filters and membranes for the immobilization of proteins to be sequenced

A major factor contributing to our ability to detect, isolate, and sequence picomole quantities of proteins is the use of proteins blotted to membranes. The techniques of SDS-PAGE and the transfer of proteins to membranes are routine and easy to perform our most laboratories. In many instances, this alleviates the need for conventional chromatography or HPLC as a final step in purification. As a result, biologically relevant proteins that several years ago would not be pursued due to low abundance can now be isolated, partial amino acid sequences determined, and eventually the gene encoding them cloned and sequenced.

The purpose of this chapter is to review current strategies and methods for the isolation and amino acid sequence analysis of proteins using gel electrophoresis and the transfer of proteins/peptides to membranes. A schematic representation of pathways used to generate samples for sequence analysis that are covered in this chapter are shown in *Figure 1*.

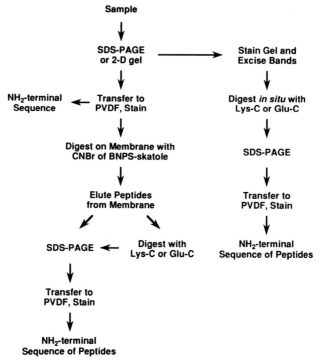

Figure 1. Schematic of pathways that can be used to prepare proteins and peptides for amino acid sequence analysis.

2. Preparation of the sample for sequencing

2.1 Gel electrophoresis

The isolation of proteins for sequencing from samples of limited heterogeneity is done most frequently using one-dimensional SDS-PAGE. However, if the sample is complex (for example whole cell lysate), then two-dimensional (2D) gels employing IEF in the first dimension and SDS-PAGE in the second dimension are generally utilized. In any gel electrophoresis procedure used to isolate proteins for sequencing and in the blotting and detection procedures discussed later, it is critical to use the following:

● high-quality deionized water
● high-purity acrylamide, bisacrylamide, SDS, buffer salts, etc.

• freshly prepared solutions that contain urea, if urea is required for solubilization

Impurities present in any reagents used in electrophoresis or in prior purification steps could lead to poor electrophoretic separations, artifactual blockage of amino termini of proteins, poor transfer and high backgrounds on blots, and high protein sequencing backgrounds due to contaminating free amino acids.

2.1.1 One-dimensional SDS-PAGE

There are several SDS-PAGE systems that have been successfully used in the isolation of proteins for sequence analysis. The three systems listed below are most frequently cited but do not represent the only systems that will work. No matter which gel system is used, there are precautions to be employed that will help to prevent amino terminal blockage and amino acid modification due to non-polymerized acrylamide monomer, reactive polymerization by-products, peroxides, and free radicals:

(a) use a separating gel that was cast 24 h or more prior to electrophoresis

(b) add sodium thioglycolate to the upper reservoir running buffer at a final concentration of 0.1 mM

(c) maximize the amount of protein loaded per lane without compromising resolution of the protein(s) of interest

(d) optional—pre-electrophorese the separating gel for 2–6 h in the presence of thioglycolate (0.1 mM).

i. Tris–glycine gels

This is the standard discontinuous gel system as described by Laemmli (1) and is used most frequently for the separation of proteins for sequencing. While this system may not be optimal for obtaining sequence on some proteins ((2), see below), we have not experienced any difficulties in sequencing proteins isolated on Laemmli gels if the above precautions are followed.

ii. Multiphasic zone electrophoresis (MZE) 3328.IV system

The MZE 3328.IV system was originally described by Jovin (3) and has been reported to be superior to Tris–glycine gels with respect to initial yields in protein sequencing (2). The MZE 3328.IV system operates at neutral pH, whereas the Laemmli Tris–glycine system operates at alkaline pH. It is thought that the alkaline pH may promote blockage of protein NH_2 termini through reaction with reactive species in the gels during electrophoresis and thus reduce the amount of protein that can be sequenced. The 3328.IV system is not difficult to set up and, based on the results reported by Moos *et al.* (2), it may be the gel electrophoresis system of choice.

iii. Tris–tricine gels

This system as described by Schägger and Von Jagow (4) is better suited for separating proteins and peptides with molecular mass less than 20 kd.

2.1.2 Two-dimensional gel electrophoresis

Although successful NH_2-terminal sequences can be obtained on proteins isolated on 2D (IEF:SDS-PAGE) gels, there is probably a greater likelihood of chemically blocking NH_2 termini due to the reagents involved in the IEF gels (see (5) for a review of 2D gels). Precautions which should be taken include the use of high-purity ampholytes and non-ionic detergents, and the use of freshly prepared urea. With time, solutions containing urea will generate cyanate ions which can react with and block amino termini. More frequently, if 2D gels are used, the proteins isolated are chemically or enzymatically digested to yield peptides for sequence analysis (6) (see Section 4).

2.2 Blotting procedures

Proteins separated by gel electrophoresis can be prepared for sequencing by electroelution and dialysis (7). While the elution step is generally efficient, the recovery of the protein from SDS and buffer salts by precipitation is often poor. A significant advance in sample preparation is the use of blotting procedures to transfer the proteins to membranes for sequence analysis or further manipulations such as digestion or elution. In 1987 Matsudaira (8) described electroblotting to polyvinylidene difluoride (PVDF) membranes and subsequent NH_2-terminal sequence analysis. PVDF membranes can be stained and loaded directly in the sequencer and have become the method of choice for sample preparation for sequence analysis.

Protocol 1. Electroblotting to PVDF membranes

Equipment

PVDF membranes can be purchased from several vendors including:

- Immobilon-P from Millipore Corp.
- Immobilon-PSQ from Millipore Corp.
- ProBlott from Applied Biosystems, Inc.
- PVDF transfer membrane from Bio-Rad Laboratories

The latter three membranes are 'second-generation' PVDF membranes. They have higher protein capacities and may provide sequencing analyses with better repetitive yields than the original Immobilon-P.

Method

1. Cut the membrane to approximately the same size as the gel. Wear gloves that have been rinsed well with deionized water at all times when handling the gels and the PVDF membranes.

2. Place the membrane in 100% methanol for a few seconds to wet it. Transfer to electrotransfer buffer and soak for 10–15 min. The following two transfer buffers are frequently used:

   - 10 mM CAPS (3-[cyclohexylamino]-1 propane sulphonic acid), pH 11 containing 10% methanol, 0.1 mM thioglycolate
   - 25 mM Tris, 192 mM glycine, pH 8.3 containing 10% methanol, 0.1 mM thioglycolate

   The CAPS buffer has the advantage in that one does not have to worry about amino containing contaminants (Tris, glycine) which interfere with sequencing. However, the Tris–glycine system can be used if the blots are rinsed well with deionized water after transfer and after staining and destaining.

3. After electrophoresis, soak the gel in transfer buffer for about 5 min. Place the PVDF membrane next to the gel taking care to remove all air bubbles between the gel and the membrane. In initial experiments, use a second sheet of PVDF to catch any proteins that might transfer through the first sheet. Place the gel–PVDF between filter paper and sponges soaked in transfer buffer in your blotting cassette.

4. Transfer times will vary depending on the molecular weight of the protein, the thickness of the gel, the electrotransfer buffer, and the power supply. Conditions should be optimized for the protein of interest, but below is a general guide for a protein less than 100 K in molecular weight transferred from a 0.5 mm thick gel:

   - CAPS buffer: 50–100 V (constant voltage) or 0.5 A (constant amperage) for 30 to 60 min
   - Tris–glycine buffer: 40 V (constant voltage) or 0.5–1.0 A (constant amperage) for 2–4 h

   Thicker gels or proteins larger than 100 K may require longer transfer times.

5. After transfer, the membrane(s) is removed and rinsed in deionized water (two to three changes over 10 min) to remove salt and contaminants. This is especially important if transfer was done in Tris–glycine. The blot is now ready for staining.

2.3 Protein detection

Proteins blotted to PVDF can be stained using a number of dyes including Coomassie Blue, Ponceau S, or Amido Black.

2.3.1 Coomassie Blue

The wet PVDF membrane is stained with shaking for 1–5 min in deionized water containing 0.1% Coomassie Blue, 50% methanol, 1–2% acetic acid. The membranes will take up the dye so staining times should be minimized to prevent a high degree of background staining. Destain with 50% methanol in deionized water, using several changes over 10–30 min, until the protein bands are visible over the background. The membrane is then rinsed with several changes of deionized water and air dried. The sensitivity of staining with Coomassie Blue on PVDF is 100–200 ng.

2.3.2 Ponceau S

This method is less sensitive than Coomassie Blue (about five to ten times less), but the staining is reversible. Stain the wet membrane with 0.2% Ponceau S, 1% acetic acid in deionized water for 1–5 min with shaking. Destaining is accomplished with deionized water. Be careful not to over-destain such that the protein band becomes invisible. Air dry.

2.3.3 Amido Black

This dye is about as sensitive as Coomassie Blue. Stain the wet membrane with 0.1% Amido Black, 1% acetic acid in 40% methanol, 60% deionized water, for 1–5 min. Destain with 50% methanol in deionized water until the band is easily visible over the background. Rinse the membrane with several changes (two to three) of deionized water over 10–15 min. Air dry.

2.3.4 General comments

For any of these staining procedures, minimal concentrations (1%) of acetic acid are advised because some proteins can be eluted from PVDF membranes with prolonged exposure to acid. Up to 5% acetic acid can be used for staining if needed. Coomassie Blue is used most frequently due to familiarity and sensitivity. However, some proteins may stain better with either of the other dyes. None of the dyes interferes with sequencing. The biggest problem encountered in sequencing is Tris and glycine from the gels and/or the transfer buffer. Thus, be sure to rinse the blots well with deionized water before and after staining. Following air drying, the bands of interest are excised with a clean razor or scalpel blade and placed with forceps in microcentrifuge tubes. Short-term storage at room temperature is acceptable; but, for long-term storage, −20 °C is advisable.

3. NH$_2$-terminal sequence analysis

Because proteins stain to different intensities, one is rarely certain how much protein is present in a band(s) on a blot. For proteins less than 50kd, if you can clearly detect a band above the background you probably have enough for sequencing. For larger proteins, then two to three bands may be needed. Two to three bands of 2 × 10 mm in size are about the maximum mass of PVDF that can be loaded in a standard sequencer cartridge or in the Blott Cartridge (Applied Biosystems, Inc.).

PVDF-blotted proteins can be analysed on Applied Biosystems, Inc. (gas- or pulsed-liquid-phase) and Beckman/Porton Instruments (gas-phase) protein sequencers. Using the Blott Cartridge (9), which is designed for PVDF samples, we have observed comparable sequencing efficiencies using gas or pulsed-liquid-phase cleavage chemistries on the Applied Biosystems, Inc. 473A instrument. However, other laboratories may have preferences regarding instrumentation and/or chemistries.

How much sequence information can one expect to get from an NH$_2$-terminal sequencing run on a protein? Numerous factors contribute to this, including the amount of protein that is sequencing (initial yield), the molecular weight of the protein, and the amino acids encountered during the sequence analysis. Present lower limits for amount are 1–2 pmol (for example 30–60 ng of a 30kd protein). Obtaining 20–25 residues on such a sample would be considered outstanding. In general, even with 50–100 pmol, it is rare to sequence past 20–25 residues on a large (more than 100kd) protein due to background noise generated by random cleavages of the peptide backbone during sequencing. On the other hand, extended sequences of more than 60 residues can be determined on as little as 50 pmol of a small (~ 15–20kd) protein or peptide.

Unfortunately, more than 50% of the proteins in nature have NH$_2$ termini that are blocked—acetylated, formylated, cyclized. Amino terminal blockage naturally occurs *in vivo* and nothing can be done to prevent it. Artifactual blockage generated during electrophoresis can be minimized by taking precautions as described in Section 2.1.1. For small amounts of protein (5–50 pmol) routinely isolated by gel electrophoresis and blots, there are no efficient methods for deblocking amino termini. Thus, if one wants sequence on a blocked protein or to obtain an additional internal peptide sequence, then digestion of the protein and peptide isolation is generally performed.

4. Generation of peptides for internal sequence analysis

There are numerous methods for digesting proteins and isolating peptides using blotting techniques, and a comprehensive survey of all the available protocols is not feasible for this chapter. In the following sections, I shall provide protocols that we have used successfully and which have general applications. In general, for these techniques, a minimum of 50–100 pmol of protein (starting material) are required.

4.1 Elution and cleavage of proteins immobilized on PVDF

Proteins that have been electroblotted to PVDF membranes can be eluted to varying degrees (10–12). In general, the larger the protein, the poorer the recovery. Thus, rather than attempting to elute proteins and then digesting, it is generally advantageous to fragment the protein with CNBr (11) or BNPs-skatole (13) on the membrane prior to elution. *Prior to attempting Protocol 2 on your sample, a practice run on a known protein of a similar molecular weight is strongly recommended.*

Protocol 2. CNBr digestion and elution of peptides from PVDF

1. Transfer the sample to Immobilon-P, stain, destain, and rinse (see *Protocol 1*). The other PVDF membranes listed in *Protocol 1* are acceptable but, in general, are more difficult to elute proteins and peptides from.

2. Excise the bands of interest with a razor or scalpel blade. Avoid including PVDF that does not contain protein. Cut the bands into approximately 1 × 1 mm pieces and place in a 1.5 ml microcentrifuge tube.

3. Dissolve approximately 10 mg of CNBr in 1 ml of 70% formic acid. Since CNBr is toxic, the best way to do this is to pre-weigh a microcentrifuge tube and then add a few crystals of CNBr to the tube in a fume hood (avoid using old CNBr that is yellow). Next, reweigh the tube to determine the amount of CNBr and then, in the hood, add 70% formic acid to give a final CNBr concentration of 10 mg/ml.

4. If the PVDF pieces are dry, add a few microlitres of methanol to wet them and then add 100–200 μl of the CNBr solution to the tube. All of the PVDF pieces must be completely submerged. Cap tightly and place in the dark in the fume hood for 16–24 h. Mix by vortexing occasionally.

5. Transfer the supernatant solution to another 1.5 ml microcentrifuge tube and dry in a Speec-Vac. Some peptides will have been released into the CNBr/formic acid solution; but, to recover as many peptides as possible, it is necessary to further extract the PVDF membrane. There are a variety of ways to extract peptides that remain on the

---

membranes. Unfortunately, there is no best way to accomplish this because each protein behaves differently. Listed below are three methods that will elute peptides from PVDF. If the peptides are to be separated by SDS-PAGE and blotted, then methods (a) and (c) or (b) and (c) can be used. If the peptides are to be subjected to further cleavage (*Protocol 4*), then only extraction procedure (a) or (b) are appropriate.

(a) This is a combination of methods described by Stone *et al.* (1) and Yuen *et al.* (11). Add 150 μl of 40% acetonitrile, 0.1% TFA to the PVDF pieces, vortex and incubate at 37 °C for 1–2 h; vortex occasionally. Transfer the supernatant to the tube containing the original supernatant and continue drying. Repeat this extraction step one more time with incubation at 50 °C for 1–2 h. Transfer the extract solution again to the original supernatant tube and continue drying. Because all peptides may not be extracted using the above procedure, a second series of extractions is advised. Add 150 μl of 70% isopropanol, 5% TFA to the PVDF pieces and incubate at room temperature for 1–2 h; vortex occasionally. Transfer the supernatant to the original extract tube and continue drying. Repeat this extraction step one more time and transfer this final extract to the original tube and continue drying until approximately 10 μl remain in the tube.

(b) An alternative method for extracting CNBr cleaved peptides from PVDF blots is to use DMSO as reported by Wong *et al.* (12). If method (a) fails to yield acceptable recoveries, then the DMSO procedure should be used. Following transfer of the CNBr cleavage solution to the microcentrifuge tube, add 150 μl of DMSO to the PVDF pieces and vortex at medium speed for 2 h. Remove the DMSO and transfer to the microcentrifuge tube containing the CNBr extract and continue drying. Repeat this DMSO extraction of the PVDF membrane pieces once again and transfer the solution to the microcentrifuge tube and continue drying until the sample is nearly dry (~ 10 μl).

(c) Following removal of the original cleavage supernatant or after either of the two extraction procedures above, residual peptides can be eluted with an SDS–Triton solubilizing solution (13, 14). Rinse the PVDF pieces with approximately 500 μl deionized water. Remove as much of the liquid as possible and discard. Add 40 μl of 50 mM Tris pH 9.0 containing 3% SDS, 1% Triton X-100, and 5% (v/v) 2-mercaptoethanol. Incubate at room temperature for 1–2 h with occasional vortexing. Next, add 10 μl of a 5 × solution containing 50% (v/v) glycerol and 0.25% (w/v) bromphenol blue and heat at 100 °C for 1–2 min. Remove the solubilizing buffer

Protocol 2. *Continued*

from the PVDF pieces and either transfer to another micro-centrifuge tube for storage or load on the gel. The pH of this solubilizing buffer is 9.0. This pH results in more efficient elution of residual peptides from the PVDF (13). Although the ionic strength and pH of this sample are different from those used in the gel systems described earlier, the sample will electrophorese adequately. However, it is advisable not to combine it with peptides extracted by method (a) or (b).

6. When the tube containing the original supernatant solution and the subsequent extracts is nearly (10–20 µl remaining) dry, add 100–200 µl of deionized water and redry to remove traces of CNBr, acid, and solvent.

7. The extracted peptides are now ready for separation by SDS-PAGE. Any of the gel systems listed in Section 2.1 can be used. A relatively high-percentage gel (15%) or gradient gel is recommended so that smaller peptides (10kd or less) can be resolved. The Tris–tricine system may be the best choice due to its better resolution of small peptides (4). Be sure to take all precautions listed in Section 2.1.1 to avoid NH_2-terminal blockage. Add 50 µl of the appropriate solubilizing buffer containing 2.5% 2-mercaptoethanol to the microcentrifuge tube containing the extracted peptides. Heat at 100 °C for 3–5 min and load on the gel.

8. Transfer to PVDF, stain, destain, and rinse the membrane (see *Protocol 1*). The peptides generated by CNBr digestion are now ready for sequence analysis.

As an alternative to CNBr, BNPS-skatole which cleaves at tryptophan residues can be used (13).

Protocol 3. BNPS-skatole cleavage and elution of peptides from PVDF

1. Perform steps one and two as described in *Protocol 2*.

2. Wet the PVDF pieces with a few microlitres of methanol and add 100 µl of 1 mg/ml BNPS-skatole in 75% acetic acid. Wrap the tube in aluminium foil and incubate at 47 °C for 1 h; vortex occasionally. Remove the liquid and transfer it to a clean tube. Rinse the PVDF pieces three to five times with 500 µl of deionized water to remove residual BNPS-skatole; discard these rinses.

3. As with the CNBr digestion, some peptides will be eluted during the cleavage. To maximize recoveries, extractions of the PVDF pieces should be performed as detailed in step **5** in *Protocol 2*.

4. Perform steps **6** through **8** as detailed in *Protocol 2*.

4.2 Enzymatic cleavage of CNBr peptides eluted from PVDF

For very large proteins or proteins with few methionines or tryptophans, the CNBr or BNPS-skatole cleavages alone may not be adequate because the peptides generated are too large, too few, or poorly resolved. If this is the case, then smaller fragments can be generated using enzymatic cleavage as detailed below.

Protocol 4. Enzymatic cleavage of PVDF-eluted peptides

1. Perform *Protocol 2* or *3* to step **6**.

2. To the microcentrifuge tube containing the eluted CNBr or BNPS-skatole peptides, add 50–100 μl of 100 mM NH_4HCO_3 containing 5% acetonitrile and 0.05% SDS. The acetonitrile and SDS help to solubilize the peptides. Spot 1 μl of the solution on pH paper; the pH should be approximately 8.0. If it is below 6.5, then redry in the Speed-Vac and resolubilize in the above solution.

3. There are several proteases that can be used, but two of the most frequent are Lys-C and Glu-C which cleave at lysine and glutamic acid, respectively. These sequencing grade enzymes can be purchased from Boehringer Mannheim Corp. Add enzyme to the sample at an enzyme:protein ratio of 1:20 (w:w). Assume you have at most 50% of the protein you originally loaded on the gel. No matter how little protein you have, do not try using less than 0.5 μg of enzyme. Along with your sample, set up a mock control which contains digest buffer and enzyme. This is to help you determine whether any of the bands you see on your subsequent blot are derived from the enzyme.

4. Place the tubes at 37 °C and allow to digest for 2–16 h. Longer incubation times will obviously yield more complete digests and thus smaller fragments. Since a time course is generally not practical (unless you have a generous supply of protein), partial digests using short digestion times of 2–4 h are recommended for initial experiments.

5. After incubation, freeze the samples and dry in a Speed-Vac or lyophilize.

Protocol 4. *Continued*

6. The digests are now ready for analysis by SDS-PAGE. The Tris–tricine system (see Section 2.1) using an approximate 16.5% gel (4) is recommended due to the anticipated lower molecular weight of the peptides. Again, be sure to take all precautions in running the gel as stated in Section 2.1.1.

7. Transfer to PVDF, stain, destain, etc., as detailed in *Protocol 1*.

4.3 Enzymatic digestion of proteins in gel slices

An alternative method for generating peptides for internal amino acid sequence analysis is to perform limited digests of proteins in gel slices. This technique was originally described by Cleveland *et al.* (15) and has been used successfully over the years to obtain peptides for sequence analysis (6).

Protocol 5. Cleavage of proteins in gel slices

1. Electrophorese your sample on SDS-PAGE or 2D gels, taking all precautions discussed in Sections 2.1.1 and 2.1.2.

2. Stain the gel with 0.5% Coomassie Blue in 10% acetic acid:30% isopropanol:60% deionized water (7). Stain for the minimal amount of time needed to observe the proteins of interest (10–20 min should be adequate).

3. Destain the gel with gentle rocking using 5% acetic acid:20% methanol:75% deionized water. Usually 1–2 h is sufficient.

4. Carefully excise the bands of interest (taking no excess gel) with a scalpel or razor blade and transfer to a microcentrifuge tube. As a control, excise an equivalent amount of gel from a section that does not contain protein and place in a second microcentrifuge tube. Rinse the slices three to four times with 1 ml of cold deionized water and then equilibrate in 1 ml of 0.125 M Tris, pH 6.8 for 10–15 min.

5. Any of the three SDS-PAGE systems listed in Section 2.1.1 can be used. This gel should be cast 24 h prior to use. Remove the gel slices from the microcentrifuge tube and cut into approximately 1 mm × 1 mm cubes. These pieces are then loaded into one to two wells in the stacking gel. The mass of the gel pieces will determine the size and number of wells to be used. However, remember that two to three lanes worth of peptide is about all that can be loaded in the sequencer following the blotting. Control gel pieces are loaded into adjacent wells.

6. To the wells add the enzyme in 0.125 M Tris (pH 6.8), containing 10% glycerol, 1% 2-mercaptoethanol, 0.01% bromphenol blue, and 0.1% SDS. Use enough buffer to completely cover the gel fragments (50–100 μl). Immediately prior to adding the buffer, add to it either the Lys-C or Glu-C enzyme such that the buffer added (50–100 μl) contains approximately 1/20 (w/w) the amount of protein in the well. Estimate the protein content based on the staining intensity with Coomassie Blue. Use an equivalent amount with the control gel pieces.

7. Allow the gel/protein/enzyme to incubate 10–15 min and then electrophorese the sample to the stacking/separating gel interface at 15–20 mA. Turn off the current and let the sample incubate for 30 min to accomplish digestion. As stated in Section 2.1.1, add the thioglycolate to the upper running buffer.

8. Restart the electrophoresis and run the dye front to the bottom of the gel.

9. Remove the gel and transfer to PVDF as outlined in *Protocol 1*.

5. Concluding remarks

In this chapter, I have provided some strategies and methods for obtaining amino acid sequence of proteins and peptides blotted onto membranes. The use of SDS-PAGE to separate proteins/peptides and PVDF membranes for transfer were the focus of this review because of their widespread use and protein sequencer compatibility, respectively. Other methodologies that can be used for obtaining proteins/peptides for sequence analysis include the use of nitrocellulose as the blotting matrix followed by enzymatic digestion and elution of peptides (16, 17) and the use of reverse-phase HPLC for the separation and isolation of peptides generated by digestion (10, 16, 17).

Acknowledgements

This work was supported by the Baylor College of Medicine Advanced Technology Laboratories and NIH grant, HD24064. I thank Eleanor Chapman for preparation of this manuscript.

References

1. Laemmli, U. K. (1970). *Nature*, **227**, 680.
2. Moos, M., Nguyen, N. Y., and Liu, T.-Y. (1988). *J. Biol. Chem.*, **263**, 6005.
3. Jovin, T. M. (1973). *Ann. NY Acad. Sci.*, **209**, 474.
4. Schägger, H. and Von Jagow, G. (1987). *Anal. Biochem.*, **166**, 368.

5. Dunbar, B. S. (1987). *Two-dimensional electrophoresis and immunological techniques*. Plenum, New York.
6. Sweatt, J. D., Kennedy, T. E., Wager-Smith, K., Gawinowicz, M. A., Barzilai, A., Karl, K. A., and Kandel, E. R. (1989). *Electrophoresis*, **10**, 152.
7. Hunkapiller, M. W., Lujan, E., Ostrander, F., and Hood, L. E. (1983). In *Methods in enzymology*, (ed. C. H. W. Hirs and S. N. Timasheff), Vol. 91, pp. 227–36. Academic, New York.
8. Matsudaira, P. (1987). *J. Biol. Chem.*, **262**, 10035.
9. Reim, D. F., Hembach, P., and Speicher, D. W. (1992). In *Techniques in protein chemistry III*, (ed. R. Hogue Angeletti), pp. 53–60. Academic, San Diego.
10. Stone, K. L., McNulty, D. E., Lo Presti, M. L., Crawford, J. M., De Angelis, R., and Williams, K. R. (1992). In *Techniques in protein chemistry III*, (ed. R. Hogue Angeletti), pp. 23–34. Academic, San Diego.
11. Yuen, S. W., Chui, A. H., Wilson, K. J., and Yuan, P. M. (1989). *BioTechniques*, **7**, 74.
12. Wong, S., Padua, A., and Henzel, W. J. (1992). In *Techniques in protein chemistry III*, (ed. R. Hogue Angeletti), pp. 3–9. Academic, San Diego.
13. Crimmins, D. L., McCourt, D. W., Thomas, R. S., Scott, M. G., Macke, K., and Schwartz, B. D. (1990). *Anal. Biochem.*, **187**, 27.
14. Szewczyk, B. and Summers, D. F. (1988). *Anal. Biochem.*, **168**, 48.
15. Cleveland, D. W., Fischer, S. G., Kirschner, M. W., and Laemmli, U. K. (1977). *J. Biol. Chem.*, **252**, 1102.
16. Aebersold, R., Patterson, S. D., and Hess, D. (1992). In *Techniques in protein chemistry III*, (ed. R. Hogue Angeletti), pp. 87–96. Academic, San Diego.
17. Aebersold, R., Leavitt, J., Saavedra, R. A., and Hood, L. E. (1987). *Proc. Natl. Acad. Sci., USA*, **84**, 6970.

17

Renaturative catalytic blotting of enzyme proteins*

JIA-SHI ZHU and GARY M. GRAY

1. Introduction

Unlike receptor proteins (see Chapter 14) which may recover appreciable ligand-binding activity after full denaturation and renaturation, the active sites of enzyme proteins are usually more fragile, presumably because their catalytic function requires a highly restricted conformation to facilitate both high-affinity binding and subsequent catalysis of their specific substrate. Many enzymes are large membrane-associated glycoproteins having a hydrophobic anchor and are rich in glycosylated domains. Traditional biochemical studies and the cDNA-derived amino acid sequences have provided considerable information about the primary and subunit structures of the enzyme proteins, but little is known of the native conformation of many membrane-associated enzyme proteins. To examine the native structure of enzyme proteins and their catalytic functions, we have developed a technique of renaturative catalytic blotting of enzyme proteins, which has enhanced examination of the native, oligomeric structures of intestinal brush border (BB) membrane-associated oligosaccharidase complexes. This has allowed appreciable insight into the relationship of the native, oligomeric structures of glycosidase proteins and their catalytic functions. This chapter introduces the renaturative catalytic blotting technique and its methodological extension in enzyme protein studies, primarily based on our study in intestinal BB membrane sucrase–α-dextrinase (1). The application of the technique to other enzyme protein studies will also be discussed.

2. Renaturative catalytic blotting

The renaturative catalytic blotting technique developed for the study of intestinal sucrase–α-dextrinase (1) is schematically illustrated in *Figure 1*.

---

* The work presented in this chapter is partially reprinted with permission from *Biochemistry*, 1991, 30, 10399–10408, © 1991 American Chemical Society.

Renaturative catalytic blotting of enzyme proteins

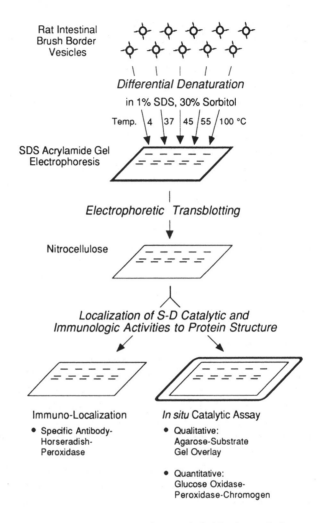

Rat Intestinal
Brush Border
Vesicles

Differential Denaturation

in 1% SDS, 30% Sorbitol

Temp. 4 37 45 55 100 °C

SDS Acrylamide Gel
Electrophoresis

Electrophoretic Transblotting

Nitrocellulose

*Localization of S-D Catalytic and
Immunologic Activities to Protein Structure*

Immuno-Localization

- Specific Antibody-
  Horseradish-
  Peroxidase

In situ Catalytic Assay

- Qualitative:
  Agarose-Substrate
  Gel Overlay

- Quantitative:
  Glucose Oxidase-
  Peroxidase-Chromogen

Figure 1. Schematic graph of the renaturative catalytic blotting technique.

This technique is composed of three major components:

(a) differential or sequential denaturation of intestinal BB proteins in SDS–sorbitol solution at selected temperatures

(b) SDS gel electrophoresis followed by electrophoretic transblotting to a nitrocellulose (NC) membrane sheet

(c) *In situ* localization of both immunoreactivity and catalytic activity of enzyme protein immobilized on the same NC membrane.

This section presents a step-by-step procedure for the qualitative analysis of BB sucrase–α-dextrinase (S–D) protein complex and correlation of its native protein structure with catalytic function. Section 3 details the quantitative application of the technique in the study of S–D complex.

For better understanding of the technique, a brief background of intestinal S–D will be provided. This enzyme, coded by a single gene, is an α-glycosidase oligomer which plays a key role in the final enterocyte surface digestion of oligosaccharide nutrients in preparation for the intestinal assimilation of released monosaccharides (2, 3). The enzyme complex anchors in the BB membrane via an N-terminal hydrophobic segement of the larger (~140 kd) α subunit (4), and the majority of the protein domains project into the intestinal lumen. Lacking a transmembrane domain, the smaller (~125 kd) β subunit remains non-covalently associated with its α partner on the luminal side of the BB membrane. Although S–D has been assumed to be a heterodimer of one α and one β subunit based on its analysis after solubilization of non-ionic detergents, an additional subunit, γ, has also been identified by many investigators (see (1) for review). Multiple-step trimming of the precursor forming unequal quantities of the subunits in BB membranes has also been observed (5). But the native structure and catalytic specificity of the S–D complex while it is a component of the enterocyte surface membrane had not been determined. We correlated the structural and catalytic activities of S–D in intact BB membranes after differential denaturation in SDS–sorbitol followed by maximal renaturation. This approach has allowed identification and comparison of immunoreactive and catalytically active macromolecular species by renaturative blotting in the same electrophoretic experiment (1). These experiments revealed that the S–D hybrid, rather than being a simple α–β dimer as previously assumed, exists primarily in two oligomeric forms consisting of combinations of the α, β, and γ subunits, strategically interrelated so that the sucrase catalytic site, a component of the larger α subunit, appears to sterically regulate the availability of the α-dextrinase catalytic site on the β subunit.

2.1 Differential denaturation of membrane protein and SDS electrophoresis transblotting

The following equipment and reagents are required:

- Mini-Protein II electrophoresis cell (Bio-Rad 165–2940) (7.5 × 5.5 × 0.15 cm gel)
- semi-dry electrophoretic transfer cell (Bio-Rad 170–3940)
- water bath incubators (37, 45, and 55 °C)
- SDS (Bio-Rad 161–0300), acrylamide (Bio-Rad 161–0103), BIS (Bio-Rad 161–0201), nitrocellulose membrane (Bio-Rad 162–0115), and protein standard for SDS electrophoresis (Bio-Rad 161–0309)

- BSA (Sigma A-7906), D-sorbitol (Sigma S-0900), DTT (Sigma D-0632), EDTA (Sigma E-5513), glycerol (Sigma G-8773), PMSF (Sigma P-7626), and Tris base (Sigma T-1503)
- [^{35}S]methionine (> 1000 Ci/mmol; Amersham SJ.1015)

Sample and solution:

- rat intestinal BB membrane vesicles, prepared as described by Ahnen *et al.* (6)
- PBS renaturation buffer—50 mM Na/K PO$_4$, 0.15 M NaCl, 0.5% BSA, 1 mM PMSF, pH 6.1
- SDS–sorbitol buffer—1% SDS, 30% sorbitol, 63 mM Tris, 10 mM DTT, 1.0 mM EDTA, 1.0 mM PMSF, 10% glycerol, pH 6.8
- TBS blocking buffer—25 mM Tris, 2% BSA, 0.15 M NaCl, pH 8.0

For maximal recovery of catalytic function of enzyme proteins, controlled differential denaturation of proteins must be applied to release the catalytic units in a form that can then be renatured for identification of both immunoreactivity and enzymatic activity. In preliminary experiments, the use of higher temperatures (75–100 °C) even for a few minutes produced irreversible denaturation of all enzyme activity. Pure, intact BB membrane vesicles were taken up directly in SDS–sorbitol buffer and incubated at various temperatures (4, 37, 45, or 55 °C) for 30 or 60 min, for comparison with the full denaturation produced by exposure to 100 °C for 5 min. Differentially denatured proteins were then analysed by SDS-polyacrylamide gel electrophoresis (SDS-PAGE), as described by Wyckoff *et al.* (7) with 6% polyacrylamide in the separation gel. A Bio-Rad mini-gel electrophoretic system was used at 4 °C to minimize the additional exposure of S–D protein to the denaturants. After *in vivo* intestinal labelling with [^{35}S]methionine, recovered radioactivity of the labelled BB proteins from acrylamide gels was 69–81% of the original starting material exposed to SDS–sorbitol, throughout the temperature range examined (see *Table 1*), with a coefficient of variation (CV) of 0.06. Molecular weights were determined by regression analysis of log–linear plots.

The BB proteins separated by SDS gel electrophoresis were electrophoretically transferred from the gel slab to a NC membrane at 4 °C by the Bio-Rad semi-dry electrotransblotter at 1.0–1.2 mA/cm^2 gel surface for 90 min or for a longer period depending upon the average molecular mass of the protein species (8, 9) (see Chapters 2–5 for more details). After transfer, the NC membrane was exposed to TBS blocking buffer at 4 °C for 1 h to ensure occupation of any residual protein binding sites. For maximal renaturation of the α-glycosidase proteins immobilized on the NC sheet, the residual denaturants were removed by washing twice with 40 ml of PBS renaturation

Table 1. Recovery of ^{35}S-labelled BB proteins and immunoreactive S–D protein after electrophoresis and blotting

Temperature	Time	Radioactivity[a]		Integral density of immunoblot[b]	
(°C)	(min)	f recovered	f of 4 °C	×10^{-3}	f of 4 °C
4	30	0.69	1.00	71	1.00
37	30	0.75	1.07	66	0.93
37	60	NA[c]	—	70	0.99
45	30	0.81	1.17	67	0.94
55	30	0.75	1.09	79	1.11
55	60	NA	—	81	1.14
100	5	0.81	1.17	17	0.24
		CV = 0.06		CV = 0.09[d]	

[a] An equal quantity of [^{35}S]methionine-labelled intact BB membranes was differentially exposed to SDS–sorbitol solution at the given temperature and time and subjected to SDS gel electrophoresis. After removal of the stacking gel, individual gel lanes were cut and the radioactivity was determined.
[b] An equal quantity of intact BB membranes was differentially denatured in SDS–sorbitol, subjected to gel electrophoresis, and transferred to a NC membrane sheet. S–D protein was detected by immunoblotting and individual lanes for each different denaturation condition were scanned by densitometry.
[c] NA, not assayed.
[d] Coefficient of variation (excluding 100 °C samples which displayed wide variation in immunoactivity loss).

buffer, and the NC membrane was stored at 4 °C in the same buffer until further examination.

The recovery of total immunoreactivity of S–D protein after differential denaturation and electrophoresis transblotting was also examined by probing the S–D protein immobilized on a NC membrane with a S–D polyvalent monospecific antibody and quantified by reflectance scanning of the immunoblot by a Hoefer densitometry system (see Section 2.2.2 for method). This analysis revealed a comparable immunological signal after pre-treatment with SDS–sorbitol at 4, 37, 45 and 55 °C with a CV of 0.09 (see *Table 1*). As might have been expected, there was considerable loss of the immunological S–D signal when BB membranes were fully denatured at 100 °C prior to electrophoresis, presumably because of persistence of denatured species of the enzyme.

2.2 *In situ* correlation of catalytic function with protein species

2.2.1 Identification of catalytically active protein species

The following equipment and reagents are required for this procedure:

- 37 °C incubator, temperature (55 °C) equilibrating water bath

- double-layer glass humidity container (23 × 23 × 7 cm round-corner square glass bowl and a 20 × 20 cm glass plate)
- GelBond film (FMC 53780), SeaPlaque low melting temperature agarose (FMC 50101)
- sucrose (Pfanstiehl S-117)
- 4-chloro-1-naphthol (Sigma C-8890), glucose oxidase (type V) (Sigma G-6891), isomaltose (Sigma I-7253), peroxidase (type II) (Sigma P-8250)
- agarose (Bio-Rad 162–0100)

together with the following solutions:

- PBS buffer—0.02 M Na/K PO_4, 0.15 M NaCl, pH 6.1
- peroxidase 6 mg/mL H_2O
- stock 4-chloro-1-naphthol solution–4 mg/ml methanol (freshly made)

In situ hydrolytic activities of the various S–D protein species immobilized on the NC membrane were identified by overlying the NC replica on the surface of 1.0% substrate/reagent-containing agarose gel (see *Figure 1*). The gel was prepared by modifying Filipe's method (10). Agarose 1.2% (w/v) was prepared in PBS buffer with 58 mM sucrose or 12 mM isomaltose. After the agarose was in a clear solution at 100 °C, the temperature of the gel solution was lowered in a 50–55 °C water bath. If lower temperatures are required for preservation of catalytic reagents, low melting temperature agarose (allowing cooling to 40–45 °C) can be substituted. After equilibration of the temperature of the gel solution, glucose oxidase (3.5 units/ml), peroxidase (25 mg/ml), and 4-chloro-1-naphthol solution were added and the gel solution was gently mixed (see *Protocol 1*). Certain glycosyl substrates at higher concentration, such as phlorizin at 2 mM, may inhibit glucose oxidase activity. If such substrates are to be used, the concentration must be decreased to less than 1 mM or the concentration of glucose oxidase can be increased two to three times. This agarose–substrate–reagent mixture was then overlaid on a GelBond support prepared with a thin layer (~0.3 cm) of plain agarose gel (1% agarose in water). This thin layer of the plain agarose gel prevents non-specific interactions of chromogen reagents with the GelBond matrix. The substrate/reagent-containing agarose gel was solidified at 22 °C for 5–10 min. After any remaining liquid buffer on the transblotted NC membrane was carefully taken off, the NC blot was settled on the agarose–substrate gel surface and incubated at 37 °C for 2–24 h (or longer) in a sealed humidified container to allow maximal development of a blue–purple colour. A control gel was prepared identically, except that sucrose or isomaltose substrate was not included in the gel. Because the colour accumulates mainly in the gel matrix and only traces adhere to the NC, the same NC membrane can be recovered and used for immunoblotting, as described below (see Section 2.2.2). Detailed protocols for preparing the substrate-containing agarose gel, for identifying catalytic active protein species on NC blot (*Protocol 1*) and for catalytic blotting (*Protocol 2*) are given below.

Protocol 1. Preparation of substrate (sucrose or isomaltose) containing agarose gel

1. Make 1% agarose in PBS buffer with 58 mM sucrose or 12 mM isomaltose.

2. Melt agarose gel solution:

	Melting	Equilibrating
regular agarose	100 °C	50–55 °C
low melting temperature agarose	70 °C	40–42 °C

3. Prepare a GelBond support, slightly larger than the NC membrane to be applied, with a thin layer (~0.3 cm) of plain agarose gel (1% agarose in water) on a level surface.

4. Gently mix the equilibrated agarose gel solution with reaction reagents:

   ● stock 4-chloro-1-naphthol solution (preheated to 50 °C): equilibrated agarose gel solution = 1:5

   ● glucose oxidase (3.5 units/ml agarose gel solution)

   ● peroxidase (25 units/ml agarose gel solution)

5. Carefully pour the agarose–substrate gel solution on the prepared GelBond.

6. Allow to solidify for 5–10 min at 22 °C for immediate use. If more than 10 min are required before proceeding to step **6** of *Protocol 2* (below), store the substrate gel in a sealed humidified container.

Protocol 2. Outline of renaturative catalytic blotting of enzyme proteins

1. Partially denature the BB proteins in SDS–sorbitol buffer (see Section 2.1).

2. Separate the proteins by SDS electrophoresis and electrophoretically transfer them onto a NC membrane sheet at 4 °C (see Section 2.1).

3. Block residual protein binding sites on the NC membrane with TBS blocking buffer at 4 °C (see Section 2.1).

Protocol 2. *Continued*

4. Wash off residual denaturants on the NC twice with 30 ml PBS renaturation buffer for 20 min at 4 °C (see Section 2.2) to maximally renature the active enzyme protein species.

5. Prepare substrate containing agarose gel (see *Protocol 1* for details).

6. Carefully take off any remaining liquid buffer on the NC replica and gently settle the sheet on the agarose–substrate gel surface.

7. Place the agarose gel–NC on the top layer of a double-layer humidity container with 1–2 ml water in the lower layer, being careful to prevent any water from contacting the gel–NC. Cover the container with clear plastic wrap.

8. Place the container in a 37 °C incubator.

9. Photograph the catalytic blots after proper colour development (sequential photography may be required; see Section 2.4 below for details).

10. Remove and use the same NC membrane for subsequent immuno-blotting (see Section 2.2.2 below for method).

2.2.2 Identification of immunoreactive protein species

Equipment required:

- GS-300 scanning densitometer (Hoefer Scientific Instruments GS-300) and GS-370 1-D data system (Hoefer Scientific Instruments GS-370)

After identification of catalytically active protein species, immunoreactive S–D on the NC membrane is then detected by immunoblotting (see Chapters 3–9 for more details) with a monospecific polyvalent rabbit anti-rat S–D antibody. Specifically bound antibody was localized by incubation with horseradish peroxidase conjugated goat anti-rabbit IgG antibody. Alkaline phosphotase labelled second antibody can be used in other systems but not in intestinal membrane analysis because of the presence of residual endogenous alkaline phosphatase under the renaturative conditions. The recovery of immunoreactivity after blotting determined by reflectance scanning of the photogram of the wet NC blot (see Section 2.4 for method for photographing) by the GS-300 scanning densitometer and integration by the GS-370 1-D data system revealed a comparable immune signal after pre-treatment at 4, 37, 45, and 55 °C with a CV of 0.09 (see *Table 1*). As might have been expected, there was considerable loss of the immunological S–D signal when BB membranes were completely denatured at 100 °C, probably because of some denaturation at higher temperatures.

2.2.3 Correlation of S–D immunoreactivity and catalytic activity during differential denaturation

By use of the renaturative catalytic blotting technique, appreciable renaturation of S–D species occurred after transferring from the electrophoretic gel to the NC replica followed by removing denaturants with the PBS renaturation buffer. This allowed precise localization of catalytic activity and immunoreactivity on the blots. Intact BB membrane vesicles were differentially denatured for 30 or 60 min at 4, 37, 45, and 55 °C, or for 5 min at 100 °C and analysed for S–D protein by immunoblot (see *Figure 2a*) and for activity by catalytic blot replicas for both sucrase (see *Figure 2b*) and α-dextrinase (see *Figure 2c*). The expected immunoreactive S and D species, designated as the α (140 kd), β (125 kd), and γ (110 kd) subunits according to their migration on the gel, were noted on the NC blot after full denaturation at 100 °C for 5 min (see *Figure 2a*, far right lane). Despite removal of the denaturants by the transblotting technique, no hydrolytic activity was recovered for any of these three subunits after treatment at 100 °C for 5 min (see *Figures 2b* and *2c*). In contrast, after exposure to SDS–sorbitol at low temperature (4 °C, 30 min), immunoreactive species were identified at 330, 260, 200, and 140 kd (see *Figure 2a*, 4 °C lane). Release of the 140 kd α, sucrase-containing unit after SDS–sorbitol exposure at 4 °C preceded that of the other monomeric subunits (see *Figure 2a*) and was associated with a loss of sucrase activity and a decrease of the normal S/D ratio of 1.0–1.2 to 0.82 (see *Table 2* below). Catalytic assay of the same blot revealed sucrase activity localized to the 330, 260, and 200 kd units (see *Figure 2b*), with the 260 kd species predominating. α-Dextrinase activity was associated with only the 330 and 260 kd species and predominated in the 330 kd moiety (see *Figure 2c*). Exposure to SDS–sorbitol at 37 °C (30 or 60 min) was associated with the loss of the discrete definition of the 330, 260, and 200 kd macromolecular species on the immunoblot and the appearance of a smaller immunoreactive species (170 kd; see *Figure 2a*). But, sucrase activity persisted in the 330, 260 and 200 kd units under these conditions (see *Figure 2b*) and α-dextrinase activity continued to be associated predominantly with the 330 kd unit (see *Figure 2c*). Exposure to 45 °C resulted in the appearance of a 125 kd unit (β) on the immunoblot (see *Figure 2a*); the corresponding catalytic blot showed reduction of sucrase activity with no qualitative change in the localization (see *Figure 2b*), but α-dextrinase activity increased and shifted (see *Figure 2c*) dramatically to lower molecular units (260 and 200 kd). Notably, this shift of the active α-dextrinase species was associated with the release of the inactive 125 kd β unit from the active oligomers (see *Figure 2a*, 45 °C lane). Incubation at even higher temperature (55 °C; 30 or 60 min) resulted in the complete loss of sucrase activity (see *Figure 2b*) and the concomitant persistence of α-dextrinase activity associated with the 330, 260, and 200 kd species; indeed, the α-dextrinase activity appeared to increase further after the 55 °C

Renaturative catalytic blotting of enzyme proteins

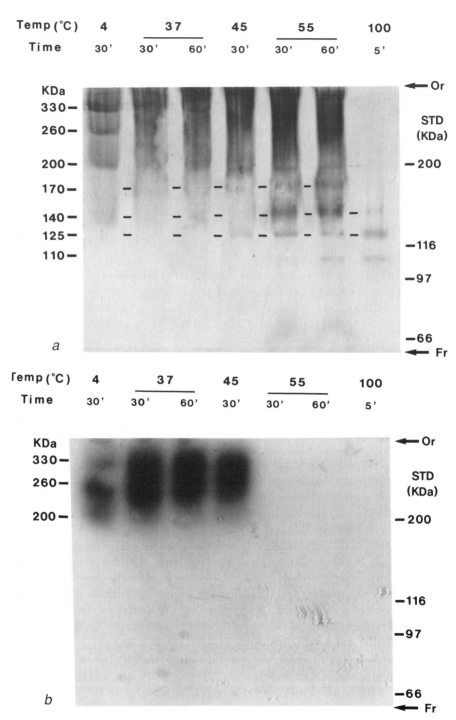

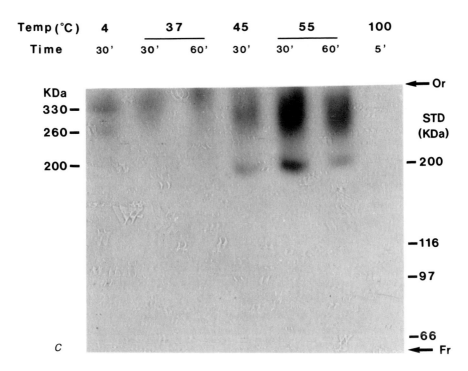

Temp (°C)	4		37		45		55		100
Time	30'	30'	60'		30'	30'	60'		5'

KDa
330—
260—
200—

STD
(KDa)

← Or

— 200

—116

—97

—66
← Fr

c

Figure 2. Immunoblotting and renaturative catalytic blotting of S–D species after differential denaturation. Equal quantities of intact BB membrane vesicles from the same preparation were exposed to SDS–sorbitol solubilization buffer at 4, 37, 45, and 55 °C (30 or 60 min) or at 100 °C (5 min), subjected to SDS electrophoresis, and transferred to a NC sheet. Immunoreactive S–D (*a*), detected by specific anti-S–D serum, was compared with *in situ* activities of sucrase (*b*) and α-dextrinase (*c*) by renaturative catalytic blotting. Apparent molecular masses of standard proteins are on the right and those for each S–D species on the left.

exposure (see *Figure 2c* and Section 3 below for quantitation). Although there appeared to be some loss of α-dextrinase activity associated with the longer 60 min exposure at 55 °C, the overall pattern of the catalytic blot was similar to that seen at 30 min. The complete loss of the sucrase activity by the exposure to 55 °C was associated with the emergence of a predominant 140 kd moiety and the appearance of additional inactive immune species at 110 kd (the γ species) and a diffuse band at 70 kd (*Figure 2a*).

After analysis by immunoblotting and catalytic blotting, the individual S–D protein species can be recovered from the SDS gel by electrophoretic elution or diffusion into 8 M urea, 0.06 M Tris, pH 6.8, and, after full denaturation at 100 °C for 5 min, analysed by urea–SDS electrophoresis (1, 11) to determine the subunits which comprise the active, renatured species. If the sample is only partially purified, then the subunits can be identified by immunoblotting (12). For detailed results using intestinal S–D, the reader is referred to (1).

2.3 Technical comments

Short exposure (~30 min) of proteins to SDS–sorbitol at low temperatures (4–55 °C) may not completely unfold the native conformation, thereby favouring subsequent renaturation and recovery of catalytic function. Under these partial denaturing conditions, however, the precise molecular masses of proteins can only be approximated because proteins may not be in the linear conformation required for migration as a strict function of mass on SDS gels. Yet in other experiments, not detailed here, these active α-glycosidase oligomers consistently migrated at the same estimated molecular mass on acrylamide gels of differing effective pore sizes (5.3, 5.6, 5.9, and 6.4% total acrylamide). Therefore, differences in charge alone are unlikely to account for the differences in migratory behaviour. Being separable on the basis of their relative resistance to movement through the gel interstices, these active oligomers are, at a minimum, conformationally distinct. The maintenance of some tertiary and/or quaternary structure under partial denaturation conditions is undoubtedly required for reformation of the active site, a necessity for *in situ* catalytic assay. Also, optimal conformation of the sucrase and α-dextrinase catalytic sites may required physical association of the α, β, and γ monomers, perhaps with one or more additional macromolecular units that may not be recognized by the S–D polyvalent antiserum after full denaturation. On the other hand, a relaxed and stable conformation of each individual subunit might result in migration as a much larger macromolecule than a random coil or a rod through the acrylamide interstices. Under the native structural arrangement, the subunits are strategically associated in proximity so that the sucrase-carrying unit, a component of the larger α subunit, appears to sterically regulate the functional availability of the α-dextrinase catalytic sites (1) (also see Section 3 below for quantitative analysis).

2.4 Photography of immunoblots and catalytic blots

The following equipment and reagents are required:

- electrophoresis duplicating paper (EDP) with amber light filter (Kodak 182–7831)
- three containers (for developer, fixer, and washing water) and plastic rubber-tip tongs
- dark-room with safety light and a height-adjustable 15 W daylight fluorescent light
- EDP/EDF photochemical (developer and fixer) (Kodak 807–7927)

232

together with the following solutions:

- Kodak EDP/EDF developer prepared according to manufacturer's menu
- Kodak EDP/EDF fixer prepared according to manufacturer's menu

During or after maximal colour development for immunoblotting or catalytic botting, the NC membrane attached to the agarose gel should be photographed while still wet. Although any photographic technique may be employed, translumination photography with a daylight fluorescent light passing through the wet NC sheet, allowing absorbance of the immune or catalytic signals through the entire depth of the NC membrane sheet and the agarose gel, is superior to reflectance photography. This is particularly important for quantitative analysis of total signal from either immunoblots (as shown in *Table 1*) or catalytic blots. If a photographic facility is not available, a Kodak electrophoresis duplicating (EDP) photographing system may be suitable, as illustrated in *Figure 3*. By simply adjusting the exposure time, even weak signals can be enhanced and the contrast optimized. For nitrocellulose illumination, a 15 W daylight fluorescent light is preferable to an incandescent lamp and should be placed at a distance of 50–70 cm, allowing the light to pass uniformly through the NC membrane–gel to the EDP photographic paper beneath. Typically when an amber light filter is used, the EDP paper needs 3–8 sec exposure. If a good contrast is suboptimal because of the short exposure time, a second amber filter film can be added. Alternatively, increasing the distance between the fluorescent light and EDP photographing paper or decreasing the light intensity may be helpful. Variation in light penetration of NC membranes can be avoided by placing the NC sheet between clear plastic sheets or in a clear plastic bag with careful removal of air bubbles. If the photograph proves to be suboptimal, additional incubation may augment the colour development; care should be taken to maintain the NC sheet in the exact template position to the substrate gel matrix.

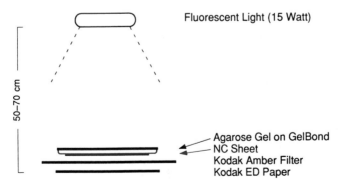

Figure 3. Schematic graph of Kodak electrophoresis duplicating (ED) photographing system.

3. Quantitative application of renaturative catalytic blotting: quantitation of renatured S–D on nitrocellulose blots

For this procedure the following equipment is required:

- 37 °C shaking incubator
- ^{125}I-labelled anti-rabbit IgG antibody (750–3000 Ci/mmol from donkey, Amersham IM.134) or [^{125}I]Protein A (> 30 Ci/mg, Amersham IM.112)

The following solutions are needed:

- PBS washing/storing buffer—50 mM Na/K PO_4, 0.1% BSA, 0.15 M NaCl, 1 mM PMSF, pH 6.1
- TBS washing buffer—25 mM Tris, 0.5% BSA, 0.15 M NaCl, pH 8.0

In addition to the qualitative analysis of native structure and functional correlates of S–D enzyme protein described above, the renaturative catalytic blotting can also be modified for quantitative assay of activity of enzyme proteins immobilized on NC membranes (1). After the partially dentured proteins are separated on the SDS gel and transferred to a NC membrane sheet, residual protein binding sites were blocked with TBS blocking buffer (see Section 2.1), and individual lanes or particular protein species were excised, washed, and stored at 4 °C in PBS renaturation buffer (see Section 2.1). Sucrase and α-dextrinase activities of the immobilized species on the NC membrane strips were determined in test tubes (13 × 100 mm glass tube), as previously described (2, 13), except that the reaction volume was increased to 200 or 300 μl, to ensure continuous contact with the NC strip during incubation in a 37 °C shaking incubator. The SDS gel electrophoresis was terminated when the dye front had migrated only far enough (~2 cm) into the separating gel to allow separation of the protein species. Typically, the NC replica was cut to 2.5 (width) × 0.7 (length) cm strips for a ten-lane SDS gel electrophoresis experiment. At the end of the incubation, the reaction solution was transferred to a second tube for detection of released glucose product. Activity was expressed as nanomoles of substrate hydroloysed per min (mU) per immobilized sample (mU/strip). The NC strips were washed three times with 5 ml PBS renaturation buffer and stored in the buffer at 4 °C for subsequent assay. Repeated assays of fresh or stored NC strips for sucrase and α-dextrinase over a period of one month revealed reproducible values (CV = 0.045).

The total immunoreactive protein can also be quantified on NC strips by solid-phase radioimmunoassay (12). Similar to the protocol for immuno-blotting as described earlier in Chapter 3, the NC strips, blocked with TBS blocking buffer after catalytic blotting, were exposed to primary rabbit anti-

S–D antibody at 22 °C for 10 h. After extensive washes with PBS washing buffer, the strips were incubated with ^{125}I-labelled second antibody or [^{125}I]protein A directed to the specifically bound rabbit anti-S–D antibody; they were then washed with 5 ml TBS washing buffer at least three times for 1–2 h on a shaker, and the radioactivity determined in a gamma counter. When desired, the specific catalytic activity on each NC strip can be normalized to total immunoreactivity of the enzyme protein (12).

Equal quantities of the purified intact BB membrane vesicles (13 mU sucrase each) were pretreated in SDS–sorbitol (see Section 2.1) for 30 min at 4, 37, 45, or 55 °C and subjected to SDS electrophoresis. The separated BB proteins were then transferred to a NC membrane sheet. After the blocking of any residual protein binding sites on the NC sheet at 4 °C (see Section 2.2), individual lanes were excised, and the catalytic activities for sucrase and α-dextrinase were quantified on the NC strips. Notably, after SDS–sorbitol treatment at 4 °C for 30 min, recovery of the sucrase and α-dextrinase activities was over 35% of that originally assayed in BB membrane starting material as shown in *Table 2*. The dramatic changes in the activities of the two saccharidase components of S–D occurred in response to the prior SDS–sorbitol exposure at various temperatures. While appreciable activity was recovered after incubation at 37 °C, sucrase was decreased somewhat by exposure to SDS–sorbitol at 45 °C and inactivated completely at 55 °C. In marked contrast, α-dextrinase reciprocally increased to nearly four times the activity present in the 4 °C control sample. As a result, the S/D activity ratio declined from 0.82 at 4 °C to 0.16 at 45 °C.

Because repeated assays of sucrase and α-dextrinase immobilized onto fresh or stored NC strips over a period of one month revealed reproducible catalytic values (CV = 0.045), kinetic analyses for sucrase and α-dextrinase were performed on the strips over a ten-fold range of substrate concentrations at 37 °C (1), and kinetic parameters (K_m) were computed from Eadie–Hofstee plots (14). This analysis revealed a stable K_m for either sucrase or α-dextrinase after prior exposure to SDS–sorbitol at 4 or 45 °C and SDS

Table 2. Recovery of S–D activity after exposure of brush borders to 1% SDS–30% sorbitol[a]

Temperature	Sucrase		α-Dextrinase		
(°C)	mU	f of 4 °C	mU	f of 4 °C	S/D ratio
4	4.6	1.0	5.6	1.0	0.82
37	5.5	1.2	8.8	1.6	0.61
45	2.6	0.6	16	2.8	0.16
55	0	0	22	3.9	0

[a] After exposure to 1% SDS–30% sorbitol for 30 min at the temperatures shown, equal quantities (13 mU sucrase) or purified, intact BB membrane vesicles were subjected to SDS electrophoresis on a 6% gel and transblotted to a NC sheet. Individual lanes were excised out and sucrase and α-dextrinase activities were quantified.

electrophoresis (1). In marked contrast, there was a dramatic tripling of the V_{max} for α-dextrinase in response to the SDS–sorbitol exposure at 45 °C, while the V_{max} for sucrase declined only slightly (−27%). Because the changes in V_{max} occurred without an apparent change in the affinity of either active site for its substrate (as estimated from the constant K_m value), the conformation of the catalytic sites did not appear to change significantly. The excellent reproducibility of these assays for the immobilized enzyme suggests that other enzymes from various tissue could be analysed in a similar way.

4. General application of renaturative catalytic blotting

Clearly, the renaturative catalytic blotting technique has served as a powerful tool in our reserch for intestinal BB sucrase–α-dextrinase. It allowed examination of the native, oligomeric structure of this complex α-glycosidase protein and correlation of its structure and catalytic functions. In order to apply the technique to studies of other enzyme proteins, two factors need to be examined:

(a) Partial denaturation of enzyme protein: Many enzymes are known to be very sensitive to the denaturants normally used in SDS-PAGE at 100 °C, although some, notably proteases, may maintain some activity after conventional denaturing treatment (15, 16). Partial denaturation at low temperature may be crucial for renaturation after SDS electrophoresis (1, 12, 17), although the recovery of activity for the individual enzyme may vary. Notably, even under minimal conditions of denaturation, some enzymes may become unstable after maximal renaturation, probably due to incomplete recovery of the essential conformation in the domain of the catalytic site. On the other hand, addition of a substrate analogue or antagonist in the denaturing reaction may afford some protection, thereby favouring maximal renaturation after transblotting. As shown in our study, sorbitol, a monosaccharide alcohol routinely used in gradient centrifugation for BB membrane purification, has some structural similarities to the glucose units in saccharide substrates and might have played an important role in the renaturation of the glucosidases. In another study, addition of ATP protected active H/K-ATPase during mild SDS treatment, allowing full recovery of the enzymatic activity (18). Pre-treatment of proteases with their inhibitor(s) prior to SDS electrophoresis also displayed a protective effect on the active sites (19, 20).

(b) *In situ* identification of renatured enzyme on NC blot: *In situ* identification of catalytic activity is possible for many enzymes, especially since commonly used histochemistry protocols could be easily modified for the catalytic blotting technique (10). A low melting temperature agarose could be chosen if necessary to preserve reagents or substrate in the catalytic reaction in the gel. Alternatively, co-polymerization of substrate and acrylamide prior to SDS electrophoresis has been also used to study proteases (21). Catalytic reactions in solution without any gel support have also been employed (17, 22, 23). In such instances, preparation gel support can be eliminated, but immunoblotting for specific protein species after the catalytic identification may not be possible unless a non-chromogen method (for example radiolabelled antibody) is used. The versatile methodology of catalytic identification provides many technical options for studying renatured active enzymes. Thus, the renaturative catalytic blotting technique may be particularly useful for analysis of structural and functional correlates of both soluble and membrane-associated enzymes.

5. Conclusion

The renaturative catalytic blotting technique, especially when coupled with immunoblotting in the same experiment, is a powerful research tool for the exploration of the native structure of enzyme proteins and facilitates the correlation of their structure with their catalytic function. This technique can be expected to have wide application. The information generated from correlative catalytic and immune blotting can provide additional insight incremental to that derived from knowledge of the subunit structure and the primary amino acid sequence.

Acknowledgements

This work was supported by grants from the National Institutes of Health (DK 11270 and DK 35033) and a Digestive Disease Center Grant (DK 38707). Dr Zhu was supported by fellowship from Pharmacia Inc. and by DDK-Pilot/Feasibility Award from Grant DK 38707–04. The authors are grateful for suggestions about the use of the histochemical and transblotting technique by Kenneth A. Conklin and Lawrence A. Scheving.

References

1. Zhu, J.-S., Conklin, K. A., Scheving, L. A., Smith, A. J., and Gray, G. M. (1991). *Biochemistry*, **30**, 10399.
2. Conklin, K. A., Yamashiro, K. M., and Gray, G. M. (1975). *J. Biol. Chem.*, **250**, 5735.
3. Semenza, G. (1981). In *Carbohydrate metabolism and its disorders*, (ed. R. J. Randle, D. F. Steiner, and W. J. Whelan), Vol. 3, pp. 425–79. Academic, London.

4. Spiess, M., Brunner, J., and Semenza, G. (1982). *J. Biol. Chem.*, **257**, 2370.
5. Shapiro, G. L., Bulow, S. D., Conklin, K. A., Scheving, L. A., and Gray, G. M. (1991). *Am. J. Physiol.*, **261**, G847.
6. Ahnen, D. J., Santiago, N. A., Cézard, J. P., and Gray, G. M. (1982). *J. Biol. Chem.*, **257**, 12129.
7. Wyckoff, M., Rodhard, D., and Chrambach, A. (1977). *Anal. Biochem.*, **78**, 459.
8. Gershoni, J. and Palade, G. E. (1983). *Anal. Biochem.*, **131**, 1.
9. Towbin, H., Staehelin, T., and Gordon, J. (1979). *Proc. Natl. Acad. Sci., USA*, **76**, 4350.
10. Filipe, M. I. (1987). In *Histochemistry in pathologic diagnosis*, (ed. S. S. Spicer), pp. 353–88. Marcel Dekker, New York.
11. Delacourte, A., Dousti, M., and Loucheux-Lefebvre, M. H. (1982). *Biochim. Biophys. Acta*, **709**, 99.
12. Zhu, J.-S. (1993). *PhD. Dissertation*, Stanford University.
13. Dahlqvist, A. (1968). *Anal. Biochem.*, **22**, 99.
14. Wong, J. T.-F. (ed.) (1975). *Kinetics of enzyme mechanisms*, pp. 5–9. Academic, New York.
15. Lee, S. G., Kalyan, N., Wilhelm, J., Hum, W. T., Rappaport, R., Cheng, S. M., Dheer, S., Urbano, C., Hartzell, R. W., and Ronchetti-Blume, M. (1988). *J. Biol. Chem.*, **263**, 2917.
16. Tans, G., Janssen-Claessen, T., and Rosing, J. (1989). *Thrombosis and Haemostasis*, **61**, 386.
17. Jahagirdar, A. P. and Seligy, V. L. (1992). *Anal. Biochem.*, **202**, 96.
18. Yeh, L. A., Cosgrove, P., and Holt, W. F. (1990). *Membr. Biochem.*, **9**, 129.
19. Clarke, G. A., Proctor, G. B., Garrett, J. R., and Smith, R. E. (1990). *Appl. Theor. Electrophor.*, **1**, 201.
20. Sweadner, K. J. (1991). *Anal. Biochem.*, **194**, 130.
21. Neale, K.A. and Alderete, J. F. (1990). *Infection and Immunity*, **58**, 157.
22. Furlong, C. E., Richter, R. J., Chapline, C., and Crabb, J. W. (1991). *Biochemistry*, **30**, 10133.
23. Kurosawa, N. and Ogita, Z. (1989). *Electrophoresis*, **10**, 189.

Index

Index

Index